A-Level Year 1 & AS
Biology
Exam Board: OCR A

Let's face it, Biology is a tough subject. You'll need to get to grips with a lot of difficult concepts, and have plenty of practical skills up your lab-coat sleeve.

But don't worry — this brilliant CGP book covers everything you'll need for the new OCR A courses. It's packed with clear explanations, exam practice, advice on maths skills and practical investigations... and much more!

It even includes a free Online Edition to read on your PC, Mac or tablet.

How to get your free Online Edition

Go to **cgpbooks.co.uk/extras** and enter this code...

0403 3225 1576 8112

This code will only work once. If someone has used this book before you, they may have already claimed the Online Edition.

Contents

Introduction

How to use this book   i

How Science Works

The Scientific Process   1

Module 1

Development of Practical Skills

1. Planning an Experiment   5
2. Carrying Out an Experiment   9
3. Processing Data   11
4. Presenting Data   17
5. Drawing Conclusions and Evaluating   23
Exam-style Questions   29

Module 2

Section 1: Cell Structure

1. Cells and Organelles   30
2. Organelles Working Together   36
3. Prokaryotic Cells   38
4. How Microscopes Work   39
5. Using Microscopes   44
Exam-style Questions   49

Section 2: Biological Molecules

1. Water   51
2. Macromolecules and Polymers   54
3. Carbohydrates   55
4. Lipids   58
5. Proteins   61

6. Inorganic Ions   66
7. Biochemical Tests for Molecules   68
8. Separating Molecules   74
Exam-style Questions   78

Section 3: Nucleotides and Nucleic Acids

1. Nucleotides   80
2. Polynucleotides and DNA   83
3. DNA replication   86
4. Genes and Protein Synthesis   88
5. Transcription and Translation   91
Exam-style Questions   95

Section 4: Enzymes

1. Action of Enzymes   97
2. Factors Affecting Enzyme Activity   101
3. Enzyme-Controlled Reactions   104
4. Cofactors and Enzyme Inhibition   108
Exam-style Questions   114

Section 5: Biological Membranes

1. Cell Membranes — The Basics   116
2. Cell Membranes and Signalling   122
3. Diffusion and Osmosis   124
4. Facilitated Diffusion and Active Transport   131
Exam-style Questions   137

Section 6: Cell Division and Cellular Organisation

1. The Cell Cycle and Mitosis   139
2. Sexual Reproduction and Meiosis   143
3. Stem Cells and Differentiation   147
4. Tissues, Organs and Systems   152
Exam-style Questions   156

Module 3

Section 1: Exchange and Transport

1. Specialised Exchange Systems — 158
2. Gas Exchange in Mammals — 163
3. Ventilation in Mammals — 166
4. Gas Exchange in Fish and Insects — 169
5. Dissecting Gas Exchange Systems — 172
Exam-style Questions — 175

Section 2: Transport in Animals

1. Circulatory Systems — 177
2. Blood Vessels — 180
3. Heart Basics — 183
4. Electrical Activity of The Heart — 187
5. Haemoglobin — 191
Exam-style Questions — 196

Section 3: Transport in Plants

1. Xylem and Phloem — 198
2. Water Transport — 203
3. Transpiration — 206
4. Translocation — 210
Exam-style Questions — 214

Module 4

Section 1: Disease and the Immune System

1. Pathogens and Communicable Diseases — 216
2. Defence Against Pathogens — 219
3. The Immune System — 222
4. Antibodies — 226
5. Primary and Secondary Immune Responses — 228
6. Immunity and Vaccinations — 230
7. Antibiotics and Other Medicines — 234
Exam-style Questions — 238

Section 2: Biodiversity

1. Investigating Biodiversity — 240
2. Genetic Diversity — 246
3. Factors Affecting Biodiversity — 248
4. Biodiversity and Conservation — 251
Exam-style Questions — 258

Section 3: Classification and Evolution

1. Classification Basics — 260
2. The Evolution of Classification Systems — 264
3. Variation — 267
4. Investigating Variation — 270
5. Adaptations — 276
6. The Theory of Evolution — 279
7. More on Evolution — 282
Exam-style Questions — 285

Exam Help

EXAM HELP

1. The Exams — 287
2. Command Words — 288
3. Time Management — 288

Reference

Answers — 289
Glossary — 320
Acknowledgements — 328
Index — 330

How to use this book

Learning Objectives

- These tell you exactly what you need to learn, or be able to do, for the exam.
- There's a specification reference at the bottom that links to the OCR A specification.

How Science Works

- You need to know about How Science Works. There's a section on it at the front of the book.
- How Science Works is also covered throughout the book wherever you see this symbol.

Examples

These are here to help you understand the theory.

---

6. The Theory of Evolution

Evolution is the slow and continual change of organisms from one generation to the next. Darwin and Wallace came up with a neat little theory to explain it.

Darwin's contribution

Scientists use theories to attempt to explain their observations — Charles Darwin was no exception. Darwin made four key observations about the world around him.

Darwin's observations:

1. Organisms produce more offspring than survive.
2. There's variation in the characteristics of members of the same species.
3. Some of these characteristics can be passed on from one generation to the next.
4. Individuals that are best adapted to their environment are more likely to survive.

Natural selection

Darwin wrote the **theory of evolution by natural selection** to explain his observations. His theory was that:

- Individuals within a population show variation in their phenotypes (their characteristics).
- Selection pressures (environmental factors such as predation, disease and competition) create a struggle for survival.
- Individuals with better adaptations (characteristics that give a selective advantage, e.g. being able to run away from predators faster) are more likely to survive and have reproductive success — in other words, they reproduce and pass on their advantageous adaptations to their offspring.
- Over time, the proportion of the population possessing the advantageous adaptations increases.
- Over generations this leads to evolution as the favourable adaptations become more common in the population.

We now know that genes determine many of an organism's characteristics and that individuals show variations in their phenotypes partly as a result of genetic variation, i.e. the different alleles they have. When an organism with advantageous characteristics reproduces, the alleles that determine those characteristics may be passed on to its offspring.

Example — peppered moths

- Peppered moths show variation in colour — there are light ones (with alleles for light colour) and dark ones (with alleles for dark colour).
- Before the 1800s there were more light moths than dark moths.
- During the 1800s, pollution had blackened many of the trees that the moths lived on.
- Dark coloured moths were now better adapted to this environment — they were better camouflaged from predators, so would be more likely to survive, reproduce and pass on the alleles for their dark colouring to their offspring.
- During this time the number of dark moths increased and the alleles for dark colour became more common in the population.

Learning Objectives:

- Know the contribution of Darwin and Wallace in formulating the theory of evolution by natural selection.
- Understand the mechanism by which natural selection can affect the characteristics of a population over time and appreciate that genetic variation, selection pressure and reproductive success (or failure) results in an increased proportion of the population possessing the advantageous characteristic(s).
- Know the evidence for the theory of evolution by natural selection, including fossil, DNA and molecular evidence.

Specification Reference 4.2.2

Tip: The opposite is also true — organisms without advantageous adaptations are less likely to survive and reproduce.

Tip: When Darwin published his theory in 1859, he didn't know about genes and alleles.

Figure 1: Two colours of peppered moth on tree bark.

Module 4: Section 3 Classification and Evolution **279**

Practical Activity Groups

If you're doing the A-level Biology course you'll need to show you've mastered some key practical skills in your Practical Endorsement. Information on the skills you need and opportunities to apply them are marked up throughout the book.

Exam Tips

There are tips throughout the book to help with all sorts of things to do with answering exam questions.

Tips

These are here to help you understand the theory.

Investigating diffusion

You can investigate diffusion using model cells — these are materials that are used to represent real cells. Agar jelly is commonly used as a model cell because it has a similar consistency to the cytoplasm of a real cell.

PRACTICAL ACTIVITY GROUP 8

Phenolphthalein is a chemical that can be used to investigate diffusion. It's a pH indicator — it's pink in alkaline solutions and colourless in acidic solutions. If you place cubes of agar jelly containing phenolphthalein and an alkali, such as sodium hydroxide, in an acidic solution and leave them for a while they'll eventually turn colourless as the acid diffuses into the agar jelly and neutralises the sodium hydroxide.

The following three examples show you how you can use agar jelly and phenolphthalein to investigate factors that affect the rate of diffusion:

Example 1 — Concentration gradient

1. First, make up some agar jelly with phenolphthalein and dilute sodium hydroxide. This will make the jelly a lovely shade of pink.
2. Prepare 5 test tubes containing hydrochloric acid (HCl) in increasing concentrations, e.g. 0.2 M, 0.4 M, 0.6 M, 0.8 M, 1 M.
3. Using a scalpel, cut out 5 equal-sized cubes from the agar jelly.
4. Put one of the cubes into the first test tube and use a stopwatch to time how long it takes for the cube to turn colourless.
5. Then do the same for the rest of the test tubes of HCl using a new cube each time.

Dilute acid

The acid diffuses into the agar cube

Agar cube containing phenolphthalein

Colourless agar cube

Figure 2: Using agar jelly cubes, phenolphthalein and acid to investigate diffusion.

You would expect the cube in the highest concentration of HCl to go colourless fastest, because the concentration gradient is the greatest (see previous page).

Example 2 — Surface area

Prepare the agar jelly as in Example 1. Then cut it into different sized cubes and work out their surface area to volume ratio (see page 158). Time how long it takes each cube to go colourless when placed in the same concentration of HCl. You would expect the cube with the largest surface area to volume ratio to go colourless fastest.

Example 3 — Temperature

Prepare the agar jelly as in Example 1 and cut into equal-sized cubes. Then prepare several boiling tubes containing the same concentration of HCl (and put the boiling tubes into water baths at different temperatures). When the HCl in each tube has reached the desired temperature, put a cube of the agar jelly into it and time how long it takes the cube to go colourless. You would expect the cube in the highest temperature to go colourless fastest.

Tip: Before you start your experiment, make sure you do a risk assessment and identify any hazards. You should wear safety goggles and a lab coat when working with acids.

Exam Tip

There are other ways to investigate diffusion in model cells. For example, a different substance could be used as the model cell (e.g. Visking tubing or gelatine cubes) and different pH indicators could be used (e.g. cresol red). Don't worry if you get a question in the exam that uses a different method or different equipment to what's used here — just apply what you know about diffusion to the context you're given.

Tip: Don't forget to repeat your experiment at least three times and calculate the mean of your results. This helps to reduce the effect of random errors, making your results more precise (see page 6).

Tip: Remember you only change the variable you are investigating — all the other variables should be kept constant (see page 5).

Tip: Don't increase the temperature above 65 °C or the agar jelly will start to melt.

Module 2: Section 5 Biological Membranes **125**

i

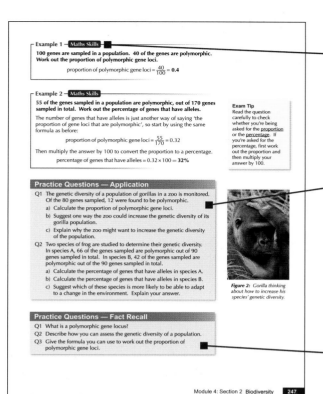

Maths Skills

There's a range of maths skills you could be expected to apply in your exams. Examples that show these maths skills in action are marked up like this.

Practice Questions — Application

- Annoyingly, the examiners expect you to be able to apply your knowledge to new situations — these questions are here to give you plenty of practice at doing this.
- All the answers are in the back of the book (including any calculation workings).

Practice Questions — Fact Recall

- There are a lot of facts you need to learn — these questions are here to test that you know them.
- All the answers are in the back of the book.

Exam-style Questions

- Practising exam-style questions is really important — you'll find some at the end of each section.
- They're the same style as the ones you'll get in the real exams — some will test your knowledge and understanding and some will test that you can apply your knowledge.
- All the answers are in the back of the book, along with a mark scheme to show you how you get the marks.

Exam Help

There's a section at the back of the book stuffed full of things to help with your exams.

Glossary

There's a glossary at the back of the book full of useful words — perfect for looking up key words and their meanings.

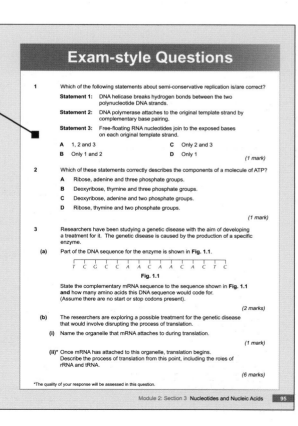

Published by CGP

Editors:
Charlotte Burrows, Rachel Kordan, Christopher Lindle, Christopher McGarry, Sarah Pattison, Claire Plowman,
Rachael Rogers, Camilla Simson and Hayley Thompson.

Contributors:
Sophie Anderson, Gloria Barnett, James Foster, Paddy Gannon and Adrian Schmit.

ISBN: 978 1 78294 320 4

With thanks to Joe Brazier, Janet Cruse-Sawyer, Katherine Faudemer, Megan Pollard, Glenn Rogers,
Jonathan Rowley and Karen Wells for the proofreading.
With thanks to Laura Jakubowski for the copyright research.

Printed by Elanders Ltd, Newcastle upon Tyne.
Clipart from Corel®

The Scientific Process

Science tries to explain how and why things happen. It's all about seeking and gaining knowledge about the world around us. Scientists do this by asking questions and suggesting answers and then testing them, to see if they're correct — this is the scientific process.

Developing theories

A **theory** is a possible explanation for something. Theories usually come about when scientists observe something and wonder why or how it happens. Scientists also sometimes form a **model** too — a simplified picture of what's physically going on.

Tip: A theory is only scientific if it can be tested.

Examples

- Darwin came up with his theory of evolution by natural selection after observing wildlife (e.g. finches) and fossils during a trip around South America and the Galapagos Islands.

- The theory that smoking causes lung cancer was developed after it was observed that many people who contracted lung cancer also smoked.

- John Snow came up with the theory that cholera is transmitted in water, rather than air, after observing lots of cases of cholera clustered around a water pump.

- Edward Jenner came up with the idea that being infected with cowpox protected you from getting smallpox after observing that milkmaids didn't get smallpox.

Figure 1: *Drawings of finches that Darwin made in the Galapagos Islands.*

Testing theories

The next step is to make a **prediction** or **hypothesis** — a specific testable statement, based on the theory, about what will happen in a test situation. Then an experiment or study is carried out to provide evidence that will support the prediction (or help to disprove it). If it's disproved it's back to the drawing board — the theory is modified or a completely new one is developed.

Tip: The results of one experiment can't prove that a theory is true — they can only suggest that it's true. They can however disprove a theory — show that it's wrong.

Examples

- Louis Pasteur designed an experiment to test his idea that 'germs' in the air caused disease and decomposition. He boiled two flasks of broth, both of which were left open to the air. One of the flasks had a curved neck (see Figure 2) to trap any airborne bacteria so they couldn't get into the broth. The broth in the flask with the curved neck stayed fresh, whereas the other broth went off. This provided evidence to support his theory. (After more evidence like this modern microbiology was born.)

- Edward Jenner tested his idea that getting cowpox protected people from getting smallpox by infecting a boy with cowpox, then exposing him to smallpox. The boy didn't get smallpox, which provided evidence to support his theory. (Eventually this led to the development of a smallpox vaccine.)

Figure 2: *Pasteur's experiment — the flask with the curved neck stayed fresh.*

Communicating results

The results are then published — scientists need to let others know about their work. Scientists publish their results in **scientific journals**. These are just like normal magazines, only they contain scientific reports (called papers) instead of the latest celebrity gossip.

Tip: Some well known biological journals are Nature, The Lancet and the British Medical Journal.

Scientific reports are similar to the lab write-ups you do in school. And just as a lab write-up is reviewed (marked) by your teacher, reports in scientific journals undergo **peer review** before they're published. The report is sent out to peers — other scientists who are experts in the same area. They examine the data and results, and if they think that the conclusion is reasonable it's published. This makes sure that work published in scientific journals is of a good standard.

Tip: Scientific findings are also communicated at conferences around the world.

But peer review can't guarantee the science is correct — other scientists still need to reproduce it. Sometimes mistakes are made and flawed work is published. Peer review isn't perfect but it's probably the best way for scientists to self-regulate their work and to publish quality reports.

Validating theories

Other scientists read the published theories and results, and try to test the theory themselves in order to validate it (back it up). This involves:

Tip: Even negative results are communicated — knowing that something is wrong improves scientific knowledge.

- Repeating the exact same experiments.
- Using the theory to make new predictions and then testing them with new experiments.

Examples

- In 1998 a study was published that linked the MMR vaccine to autism (a developmental disorder). Other scientists then conducted different studies to try to find the same link, but their results didn't back up (validate) the theory.
- In the 1940s a study was published linking smoking and lung cancer. After this many more studies were conducted all over the world that validated the conclusion of the first study.

Tip: Once an experimental method is found that gives good evidence it becomes a protocol — an accepted method to test that particular thing that all scientists can use.

How do theories evolve?

If multiple experiments show a theory to be incorrect then scientists either have to modify the theory or develop a new one, and start the testing again. If all the experiments in all the world provide good evidence to back a theory up, the theory is thought of as scientific 'fact' (for now) — see Figure 3. But it will never become totally indisputable fact. Scientific breakthroughs or advances could provide new ways to question and test the theory, which could lead to new evidence that conflicts with the current evidence. Then the testing starts all over again... And this, my friend, is the tentative nature of scientific knowledge — it's always changing and evolving.

Tip: Sometimes data from one experiment can be the starting point for developing a new theory.

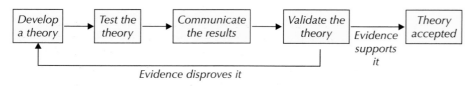

Figure 3: Flow diagram summarising the scientific process.

Figure 4: *Redi's experiment — the meat in the sealed flask (that flies couldn't enter) didn't produce maggots.*

Example

For many years, many people (including scientists) believed in spontaneous generation — the theory that life can arise from non-living organic matter. This theory was supported by observations such as maggots arising from rotting meat, and sterilised broth becoming cloudy with bacteria.
Over time, the theory was disproved by scientists such as Francesco Redi, whose experiments showed that maggots only arose from meat if flies laid their eggs on it (see Figure 4), and Louis Pasteur, whose experiment with a curved-neck flask (see page 1) showed that there were bacteria in the air that could cause decomposition.

Collecting evidence

1. Evidence from lab experiments

Results from controlled experiments in laboratories are great. A lab is the easiest place to control **variables** (quantities that have the potential to change) so that they're all kept constant (except for the one you're investigating). This means you can draw meaningful conclusions.

Tip: Module 1 (p. 5-29) is all about designing and carrying out experiments.

Example

If you're investigating how pH affects enzyme activity, you need to keep everything but the pH of the solution constant. This means controlling things like the temperature of the solution, the concentration of the substrate, etc. Otherwise there's no way of knowing if it's the change in pH that's affecting the rate, or some other changing variable.

2. Designing studies

There are things you can't investigate in a lab — you have to do a study instead. You still need to try and make the study as controlled as possible to make it valid. But in reality it's very hard to control all the variables that might be having an effect. You can do things to help, but you can't easily rule out every possibility.

Tip: There's more about variables and drawing conclusions from lab experiments on pages 5 and 23.

Examples

- You can't investigate whether stress causes heart attacks in the lab, so you have to do a study. You could compare the number of heart attacks suffered by a group of people with a high amount of stress to the number suffered by a group with a low amount of stress. But there are always differences between groups of people. The best you can do is to have a well-designed study using matched groups — choose two equally-sized groups of people (those who have quite stressful jobs and those who don't) who are as similar as possible (same mix of ages, same mix of diets etc.) apart from the amount of stress they suffer. But you still can't rule out every possibility.

- It's also tricky to investigate whether adding fertiliser to farmland causes an increase in algal growth in nearby rivers, in the lab. You'd have to do a study on a river that's next to a fertilised field. However, there are variables other than the amount of fertiliser which may have an effect on the amount of algae, such as water temperature and amount of sunlight. You can't easily rule out every possibility. In this case, using a **negative control** too, e.g. a river next to an unfertilised field, can be a useful method for accounting for the effects of variables beyond your control — the results for the negative control could be used as a comparison, so any difference in the results could be attributed to the fertiliser.

Tip: In fieldwork, the effect of variables beyond your control can be reduced by methods such as random sampling (see p. 241).

Tip: There's more about negative controls on page 6.

Science and decision making

Scientific knowledge is used by society (that's you, me and everyone else) to make decisions — about the way we live, what we eat, what we drive, etc. All sections of society use scientific evidence to make decisions, e.g. politicians use it to devise policies and individuals use science to make decisions about their own lives.

Examples

- The maximum amount of salt people are advised to eat per day was reduced in government guidelines in 2004, due to the results of a study which showed that reducing salt intake could significantly reduce heart disease.

- Leaded petrol in cars was phased out in many countries after it was found to cause air pollution that damaged the brain.

Factors affecting decision making

Other factors can influence decisions about science or the way science is used:

Economic factors

Society has to consider the cost of implementing changes based on scientific conclusions. Sometimes it decides the cost outweighs the benefits.

Example

The NHS can't afford the most expensive drugs without sacrificing something else. Sometimes they decide to use a less effective, but less expensive drug, despite evidence showing there's a more effective one.

Social factors

Decisions affect people's lives — sometimes people don't want to follow advice, or are strongly against some recommendations.

Examples

- Scientists may suggest banning smoking and alcohol to prevent health problems, but shouldn't we be able to choose whether we want to smoke and drink or not?

- Scientists may be able to cure many diseases using stem cells, but some people are strongly against the idea of embryonic stem cell research.

Environmental factors

Some scientific research and breakthroughs might affect the environment. Not everyone thinks the benefits are worth the possible environmental damage.

Examples

- Scientists believe unexplored regions like remote parts of rainforests might contain untapped drug resources. But some people think we shouldn't exploit these regions because any interesting finds may lead to deforestation and reduced biodiversity in these areas.

- Scientists have developed genetically modified (GM) crops (e.g. with frost resistance, or high nutrient content), but some people think the possible environmental harm they could do outweighs their benefits.

Figure 5: *Man protesting against the production of genetically modified organisms (GMOs).*

1. Planning an Experiment

You have to do practical work in class as part of your course. You'll be asked about it in exams too, so you need to know how to plan the perfect experiment.

Testing a theory

Before you start planning an experiment, you need to be clear about what you're trying to find out. You should start off by making a **prediction** or **hypothesis** — see page 1. You then need to plan a good experiment that will provide evidence to support the prediction — or help disprove it.

Getting good results

A good experiment is one that will give results that are:

- **Precise** — precise results don't vary much from the mean. Precision is reduced by **random error**.
- **Repeatable and reproducible** — repeatable means that if the same person repeats the experiment using the same methods and equipment, they will get the same results. Reproducible means that if someone different does the experiment, using a slightly different method or piece of equipment, the results will still be the same.
- **Valid** — valid results answer the original question. To get valid results you need to control all the variables (see below) to make sure you're only testing the thing you want to.
- **Accurate** — accurate results are really close to the true answer.

Here are some things you need to consider when designing a good experiment:

1. Variables

Variables are quantities that have the potential to change, e.g. temperature, pH. In an experiment you usually change one variable and measure its effect on another variable.

- The variable that you change is called the **independent variable**.
- The variable that you measure is called the **dependent variable**.

All the other variables should be controlled — when you're investigating a variable you need to keep everything else that could affect it constant. This means you can be sure that only your independent variable is affecting the thing you're measuring (the dependent variable).

┌─ **Example** ─────────────────────────

For an investigation into how temperature affects an enzyme's activity:

- Temperature is the independent variable.
- Enzyme activity is the dependent variable.
- pH, volume, substrate concentration and enzyme concentration should all stay the same (and the quantities should be recorded to allow someone else to reproduce the experiment).

Learning Objectives:

- Know how to design experiments, including how to solve problems set in a practical context.
- Be able to evaluate whether an experimental method is appropriate to meet the expected outcomes.
- Be able to identify variables that must be controlled, where appropriate.
- Be able to select suitable apparatus, equipment and techniques for carrying out an experiment.

Specification Reference 1.1.1

Tip: If you're studying a sample of a population (p. 241), a larger sample size will increase the accuracy of your results.

Exam Tip
Examiners love getting you to suggest improvements to methods — e.g. how a method could be improved to make the results more precise, so make sure you know how to design a good experiment.

Tip: There's more on how enzymes work on pages 97-103.

2. Controls

Negative controls are used to check that only the independent variable is affecting the dependent variable. Negative controls aren't expected to have any effect on the experiment.

> **Example**
>
> When investigating how temperature affects an enzyme's activity, you should measure a negative control at each temperature you're investigating. The controls should contain everything used except the enzyme. No enzyme activity should be seen with these controls.

Positive controls can also be used. They should show what a positive result of the experiment should look like, to check that it is possible.

> **Example**
>
> If the product of an enzyme-catalysed reaction changes the colour of an indicator solution, a positive control for an experiment using this reaction would be a solution of the product and indicator, showing the colour change.

In studies, **control groups** are used. The subjects in the study are split into two groups — the experimental group and the control group. The control group is treated in exactly the same way as the experimental group, except for the factor you're investigating.

> **Example**
>
> If you were investigating the effect of margarine containing omega-3 fish oils on heart disease, you'd have two groups — an experimental group that would be given margarine containing omega-3 fish oils, and a control group that would be given margarine without fish oils. This is done so that you can tell any reduction in heart disease is due to the fish oil, not some other substance in the margarine.

When testing new drugs to see if they work, control groups should always be used. The control group is treated in exactly the same way as the experimental group, except they're given a **placebo** instead of the drug.

3. Repeats

Taking several repeat measurements and calculating the mean can reduce the effect of random error on your experiment, making your results more precise. Doing repeats and getting similar results each time also shows that your data is repeatable. This makes it more likely that the same results could be reproduced by another scientist in an independent experiment.

> **Example**
>
> For an investigation into how temperature affects enzyme activity, the experiment should be repeated at least three times at each temperature used. A mean result should be calculated for each temperature (see page 11).

Repeating measurements also reduces the likelihood that the results are due to chance — see below.

4. Sample Size

Sample size is the number of samples in the investigation, e.g. the number of people in a drug trial. As with carrying out repeats, having a large sample size reduces the likelihood that the results are due to chance (e.g. if you get the same result twice it might be because of chance, but if you get it 100 times it's much more likely that it's not due to chance).

Exam Tip
If you get an exam question asking why a control is important in a particular experiment, make sure your answer is specific to that experiment (not just generally about why controls are good).

Tip: In a study with human participants, you should try to keep the variables of all the participants the same, e.g. they should all be the same age, sex, etc.

Tip: A placebo is a dummy pill or injection that looks exactly like the real drug, but doesn't contain the drug. It's used to make sure that people don't improve just because they think they're being treated.

Tip: Precise results are sometimes referred to as reliable results.

Tip: Scientists can use statistical tests to figure out if a result is likely to be due to chance or not. See page 16 for more.

Taking accurate measurements

When you're planning an experiment you need to decide what it is you're going to measure and how often you're going to take measurements.

Example

If you're investigating the rate of respiration, you could either measure the volume of oxygen used over time or the volume of carbon dioxide produced over time. You could take measurements at 30 second or 60 second intervals, for example.

Then you need to choose the most appropriate apparatus, equipment and techniques for the experiment.

The measuring apparatus you use has to be sensitive enough to measure the changes you're looking for. For example, if you need to measure changes of 1 cm³ you need to use a measuring cylinder that can measure in 1 cm³ increments. It'd be no good trying with one that only measures 10 cm³ increments — it wouldn't be sensitive enough. And if you need to measure small changes in pH, a pH meter (which can measure pH to several decimal places) would be more sensitive than indicator paper.

The equipment and apparatus you choose has to be appropriate for the function it needs to perform.

Example

If you are studying the nuclei of cells under the microscope you need to stain them with a dye that stains nuclei, e.g. methylene blue. It would be no good staining them with eosin, as this doesn't stain the nuclei.

The technique you use has to be the most appropriate one for your experiment. E.g. if you want to make a series of solutions for a calibration curve, you'd usually use a serial dilution technique (see p. 71).

Figure 1: *pH meters can be used to measure small changes in pH.*

Tip: There's more about choosing the correct technique on page 9.

Risk assessments

In order to work safely, you need to carry out a risk assessment for your experiment. To do this, you need to identify:

- All the dangers in the experiment, for example any hazardous chemicals, microorganisms or naked flames.

- Who is at risk from these dangers — this could be you and your lab partner, but it could also be anyone who is in the same room or building.

- What can be done to reduce the risk. You should wear a lab coat and goggles as a standard precaution, but you may need to take other safety precautions, such as carrying out your experiment in a fume cupboard.

Ethical issues

You also need to consider any ethical issues in your experiment.

Example

If you're using living animals (e.g. insects) you must treat them with respect. This means handling them carefully and keeping them away from harmful chemicals, extreme heat sources and other things that might cause them physical discomfort.

Figure 2: *Chemicals marked with hazard warning signs.*

Tip: A potometer is a piece of apparatus used to estimate transpiration rate by measuring a plant's water uptake. There's loads more about transpiration rate on pages 206-207.

Q1 A student wants to investigate the effect of light intensity on transpiration rate. She sets up a potometer as shown below.

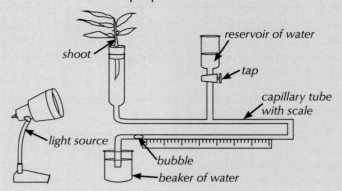

The student first measures the distance the bubble moves along the tube in ten minutes when the light source is 0 cm away from the shoot (i.e. right next to it). She then repeats the experiment with the light source 30 cm away from the shoot, then again with the light source 60 cm away.

a) Name the independent variable in this investigation.

b) Name two variables in this investigation that the student should keep the same.

c) Give one thing the student could do to make to her results more precise.

Tip: You can read all about how to measure the rate of an enzyme-controlled reaction on pages 104-105.

Q2 A student wants to investigate the effect of substrate concentration on the activity of the enzyme catalase, which catalyses the breakdown of hydrogen peroxide into oxygen and water. His experiment involves mixing catalase and hydrogen peroxide in a sealed boiling tube with a delivery tube attached.

a) Suggest an appropriate piece of equipment for measuring how much gas has been given off by the reaction.

b) Suggest a negative control for this experiment.

Practice Questions — Fact Recall

Q1 What does it mean if your results are repeatable?

Q2 What are valid results?

Q3 What is a dependent variable?

Q4 What does a negative control show?

Q5 What does a positive control show?

Q6 What three things should you consider when carrying out a risk assessment?

2. Carrying Out an Experiment

As part of your AS or A-level in Biology, you're expected to carry out Practical Activity Groups (PAGs) and be familiar with the techniques and apparatus involved in each one. You could be asked about the skills you've learnt in your exams.

Using the correct apparatus and techniques

Examiners could ask you about a whole range of different apparatus and techniques. Make sure you know how to use all the instruments and equipment you've come across in class and can carry out all the techniques too. Here are some examples of equipment you should be able to use:

> **Examples**
>
> **Graduated pipettes**
> These have a scale so you can measure specific volumes. Make sure you read the volume from the bottom of the meniscus (the curved upper surface of the liquid) when it's at eye level — see Figure 1.
>
> **Water baths**
> Make sure you allow time for water baths to heat up before starting your experiment. Don't forget that your solutions will need time to get to the same temperature as the water before you start the experiment too.
>
> **Data loggers**
> Decide what you are measuring and what type of data logger you will need, e.g. temperature, pH. Connect an external sensor to the data logger if you need to. Decide how often you want the data logger to take readings depending on the length of the process that you are measuring.

Make sure you perform all techniques carefully and that any apparatus is set up correctly — this will help to minimise errors which would affect your results.

Using appropriate units

Make sure you're measuring things using appropriate units — to choose the correct units to use, you might have to think about how you're going to analyse them later.

> **Example**
>
> If you're measuring time, it might be better to use seconds rather than minutes — when you come to processing your results, it'll be easier to work with a result of 73 seconds than a result of 1.217 minutes.

Also, make sure you record your units properly, e.g. if you're measuring the length of something and accidently write cm instead of mm, any calculations you do will be affected and your conclusions may be wrong.

Recording data

As you get your results, you need to record them. It's a good idea to draw a **table** to record the results of your experiment in. When you draw a table, make sure you include enough rows and columns to record all of the data you need to. You might also need to include a column for processing your data (e.g. working out the mean — see page 11). Make sure each column has a heading so you know what's going to be recorded where. The units should be in the column heading, not the table itself — see Figure 2 on the next page.

Learning Objectives:

- Know how to use a wide range of practical apparatus and techniques correctly.
- Be able to select appropriate units for measurements.
- Be able to present observations and data in an appropriate format.
- Be able to identify anomalies in experimental measurements.

Specification References 1.1.2, 1.1.4

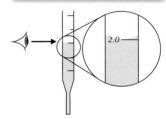

Figure 1: *Measuring volume using the bottom of the meniscus.*

Tip: A data logger (or data recorder) is an electronic device that can record data over time using a sensor. They can sometimes be connected to a computer.

Figure 2: *Table showing the number of different species and the length of hedgerows found on three farms.*

Farm	Length of hedgerows (km)	Number of species
1	49	21
2	90	28
3	155	30

data → heading → units → column
row →

Using frequency tables

A **frequency table** is just a table that shows how many of each value there are. They usually have three columns. The first column just gives the values or names of the different pieces of data. The second column shows a mark for each piece of data — this is the **tally**. The third column is the **frequency**, which you get by adding up the tally marks.

You can draw a frequency table for data you've already collected, or to record the data straight into.

Example ── **Maths Skills**

To record the number of individuals of different species of bird observed in a garden:

1. Draw a table with three columns. Give the columns the headings 'species', 'tally' and 'frequency'.

2. Record the data by drawing a tally mark in the right row to represent each piece of data.

3. Add up the tally marks in each row when you've finished recording your data. This is the frequency.

species	tally	frequency
sparrow	卌 II	7
blue tit	IIII	4
goldfinch	II	2
blackbird	卌 卌	10

Anomalous results

When you look at all the data in your table, you may notice that you have a result that doesn't seem to fit in with the rest at all. These results are called **anomalous results**.

You should investigate anomalous results — if you can work out what happened (e.g. you measured something totally wrong) you can ignore them when processing your results. However, you can't just exclude a value just because you don't like the look of it.

Practice Questions — Fact Recall

Q1 The diagram on the right shows a pipette with graduations to mark every 0.1 cm^3. What volume of water is shown to be in the pipette?

Q2 If your experiment uses a water bath, why should you wait a while after switching it on before carrying out the experiment?

Q3 What is a frequency table?

Q4 What is an anomalous result?

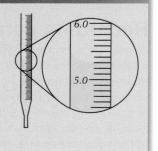

3. Processing Data

Processing data means taking raw data and doing some calculations with it, to make it more useful. This is where your maths skills really come in.

Summarising your data

Once you've collected all your data, it's useful to summarise it using a few handy-to-use figures — like the mean and the range.

Mean and range

When you've done repeats of an experiment you should always calculate a **mean** (a type of average). To do this add together all the data values and divide by the total number of values in the sample.

You might also need to calculate the **range** (how spread out the data is). To do this find the largest data value and subtract the smallest data value from it. You shouldn't include anomalous results when calculating the mean or the range.

┌─ **Example** ──**Maths Skills**────────────────────────────

Compare the mean result and range for test tubes A and B in the table on the right.

Test tube	Repeat (g)		
	1	2	3
A	27.8	37.0	32.2
B	47.5	50.2	45.3

To calculate the means:

- Add up the three data values for A, then divide by three.
  *A: (27.8 + 37.0 + 32.2) ÷ 3 = 97.0 ÷ 3 = **32.3 g***

- Do the same for B.
  *B: (47.5 + 50.2 + 45.3) ÷ 3 = 143.0 ÷ 3 = **47.7 g***

  B has the higher mean.

To find the range of results for each test tube, subtract the smallest result from the largest result.
*A: 37.0 − 27.8 = **9.2 g***   *B: 50.2 − 45.3 = **4.9 g***   **B has the smaller range.**

You might be asked to work out the mean rate from a table in your exam. To do this, just divide the amount of change by the difference in time.

┌─ **Example** ──**Maths Skills**────────────────────────────

The table on the right shows the number of cases of disease X for four different years.

Calculate the average increase in number of cases per year between 1992 and 2004.

Year	Number of cases
1992	127
1998	212
2004	247

- Work out the increase in the number of cases between 1992 and 2004.
  247 − 127 = 120

- Work out the difference in the number of years.
  2004 − 1992 = 12

- Divide the increase in number of cases by the difference in years.
  120 ÷ 12 = 10

  So the average increase in number of cases per year is **10**.

Learning Objectives:
- Be able to process, analyse and interpret qualitative and quantitative experimental results, including reaching valid conclusions where appropriate.
- Be able to use appropriate mathematical skills for analysis of quantitative data.
- Understand the appropriate use of significant figures.

Specification Reference 1.1.3

Exam Tip
At least 10% of your AS Biology marks will come from assessment of maths skills in the exam.

Tip: Averages and range values have the same units as the data used in the calculation.

Tip: When people talk about an <u>average</u>, they are usually referring to the <u>mean value</u>.

Standard deviation

Standard deviation can be more useful than the range because it tells you how values are spread about the mean rather than just the total spread of data. A small standard deviation means the repeated results are all similar and close to the mean, i.e. they are precise. There's more on standard deviation on p. 271.

Median and mode

Like the mean, the **median** and **mode** are both types of average.

To calculate the median, put all your data in numerical order. The median is the middle value in this list. If you have an even number of values, the median is halfway between the middle two values.

To calculate the mode, count how many times each value comes up. The mode is the number that appears most often. A set of data might not have a mode — or it might have more than one.

Tip: If all the values in your data are different, there won't be a mode at all.

Example — Maths Skills

The number of days survived without watering was recorded for a species of drought-resistant plant. The results were as follows:

| 26 | 24 | 29 | 24 | 22 | 26 | 25 | 27 | 24 | 21 | 22 | 27 |

Calculate the median and mode of these results.

1. Put the data in numerical order:

    21   22   22   24   24   24   25   26   26   27   27   29

2. Find the middle value (the median):

    *There are 12 values, so the median is between the 6th and 7th numbers. The 6th number is 24 and the 7th number is 25, so the median is **24.5**.*

3. Count how many times each value comes up to find the mode:

    *24 comes up three times. None of the other numbers come up more than twice. So the mode is **24**.*

Tip: To find the value halfway between two numbers, add the two numbers together and then divide by two. E.g. 24 + 25 = 49, 49 ÷ 2 = 24.5.

Practice Questions — Application

Q1 The maximum volume of air breathed out was measured for ten people using a spirometer. The results are listed below.

$3.9 \, dm^3$ $3.5 \, dm^3$ $3.1 \, dm^3$ $3.9 \, dm^3$ $3.4 \, dm^3$
$3.5 \, dm^3$ $3.7 \, dm^3$ $3.9 \, dm^3$ $4.2 \, dm^3$ $3.2 \, dm^3$

   a) What is the range of these results?

   b) Calculate the median and mode of these results.

Tip: When analysing results, you need to watch out for any that are anomalous (see page 10).

Q2 The Benedict's test was used on three different glucose solutions and the absorbance of each solution was measured using a colorimeter. The results are shown in the table on the right.

| | Absorbance (arbitrary units) | | |
Solution	1	2	3
A	0.81	0.84	0.82
B	0.54	0.55	0.11
C	0.12	0.12	0.15

Calculate the mean absorbance for each solution.

Tip: There's more about the Benedict's test and using colorimetry to measure the absorbance of the solution on pages 71-72.

Q3 The number of individuals of a species in a forest was recorded in three different years. The results are shown in the table on the right. What was the mean decrease in number of individuals per year between 1995 and 2015?

Year	Number
1995	292
2005	169
2015	105

12   Module 1: Development of Practical Skills

Calculating percentages

Calculating **percentages** helps you to compare amounts from samples of
different sizes. To give the amount X as a percentage of sample Y, you need to
divide X by Y, then multiply by 100.

> ┌─ **Example** — **Maths Skills**
>
> **A tissue sample containing 50 cells is viewed under the microscope. 22
> are undergoing mitosis. What percentage of cells are undergoing mitosis?**
> 1. Divide 22 by 50: $22 \div 50 = 0.44$
> 2. Multiply by 100: $0.44 \times 100 = \mathbf{44\%}$

Calculating percentage change

Calculating **percentage change** helps to quantify how much something has
changed, e.g. the percentage of plants that were killed with a herbicide in a
particular year compared to the previous year.
To calculate it you use this equation:

$$\text{Percentage change} = \frac{\text{final value} - \text{original value}}{\text{original value}} \times 100$$

A positive value indicates an increase and a negative value indicates a decrease.

> ┌─ **Example** — **Maths Skills**
>
> Three sets of potato chips were weighed, then each set was placed in a
> solution containing a different concentration of sucrose. After 24 hours
> the chips were removed from the solution, patted dry and weighed again.
> **Calculate the percentage change in mass for the chips in each solution.**
>
> | Concentration of sucrose (M) | 0.0 | 0.2 | 0.4 |
> |---|---|---|---|
> | Mass before (g) | 7.7 | 9.8 | 8.6 |
> | Mass after (g) | 9.4 | 10.2 | 7.1 |
>
> Potato chips in 0.0 M sucrose solution:
> $$\textit{Percentage change} = \frac{(9.4 - 7.7)}{7.7} \times 100 = \frac{1.7}{7.7} \times 100 = \mathbf{22\%}$$
>
> Potato chips in 0.2 M sucrose solution:
> $$\textit{Percentage change} = \frac{(10.2 - 9.8)}{9.8} \times 100 = \frac{0.4}{9.8} \times 100 = \mathbf{4.1\%}$$
>
> Potato chips in 0.4 M sucrose solution:
> $$\textit{Percentage change} = \frac{(7.1 - 8.6)}{8.6} \times 100 = \frac{-1.5}{8.6} \times 100 = \mathbf{-17\%}$$

Using ratios

Ratios can be used to compare lots of different types of quantities.
For example, an organism with a surface area to volume ratio of 2 : 1 would
theoretically have a surface area twice as large as its volume.

Ratios are usually most useful in their simplest (smallest) form.
To simplify a ratio, divide each side by the same number. It's in its simplest
form when there's nothing left you can divide by. To get a ratio of X : Y in the
form X : 1, divide both sides by Y.

Exam Tip
Rather that having to
calculate a percentage,
sometimes you might
just have to give your
answer as a fraction
i.e. X/Y. To simplify
a fraction, divide the
top and bottom of the
fraction by the same
number. To get the
fraction as simple as
possible, you might have
to do this more than
once.

Exam Tip
The examiners just love
getting you to calculate
percentage changes,
including percentage
increases and decreases,
so make sure you learn
this formula.

Tip: Percentage change
can be either positive
or negative, depending
on whether the value
has gone up or down.
However, percentage
increase and percentage
decrease are both
written as positive
numbers because the
direction of the change
has already been taken
into account.

Tip: There's more about genetic polymorphism on page 246.

Tip: If you're not sure what number to divide by to simplify a ratio, start by trying to divide both sides by a small number, e.g. 2 or 3, then check to see if you can simplify your answer further. E.g. you could simplify 28 : 36 by dividing each side by 2 to get 14 : 18. But you could simplify it further by dividing by 2 again to get 7 : 9. You can't simplify the ratio any further, so it's in its simplest form.

Tip: For ratio questions like Q2b here, remember to give your answer in its simplest form.

Tip: You may also want to round measurements to a certain number of significant figures when you're recording your data, e.g. if you're using a data logger that records data to several decimal places.

Tip: When rounding a number, if the next digit after the last significant figure you're using is <u>less than 5</u> you should round it <u>down</u>, and if it's <u>5 or more</u> you should <u>round it up</u>.

Examples — Maths Skills

- To simplify the ratio 28 : 36, divide both sides by 4. You get **7 : 9**.
- To write the ratio 28 : 36 in the form of X : 1, just divide both sides by 36:
$$28 \div 36 = 0.78 \qquad 36 \div 36 = 1$$
So the ratio is **0.78 : 1**.
- The method still works when one or both sides are less than one — so to write the ratio 2.7 : 0.45 in the form of X : 1, just divide both sides by 0.45:
$$2.7 \div 0.45 = 6 \qquad 0.45 \div 0.45 = 1$$
The ratio is **6 : 1**.

Practice Questions — Application

Q1 In a sample of 65 genes in a population, 36 genes were found to be polymorphic. What percentage of the genes in the sample were polymorphic?

Q2 A study investigated the number of people admitted for a chest infection in three different hospitals between 2004 and 2008.
The table on the right shows some of the results of the study.

Hospital	Number of cases per 1000 patients		
	2004	2006	2008
A	22	24	29
B	14	16	19
C	25	28	31

   a) Which hospital had the largest percentage increase in the number of people admitted for chest infections between 2004 and 2008?

   b) Use the values in the table to calculate the ratio of cases in Hospital A : Hospital B in 2006.

Rounding to significant figures

The first **significant figure** of a number is the first digit that isn't a zero. The second, third and fourth significant figures follow on immediately after the first (even if they're zeros). When you're processing your data you may well want to round any really long numbers to a certain number of significant figures.

Example

0.6874976 rounds to **0.69** to **2 s.f.** and to **0.687** to **3 s.f.**

When you're doing calculations using measurements given to a certain number of significant figures, you should give your answer to the lowest number of significant figures that was used in the calculation.

Example — Maths Skills

For the calculation: $1.2 \div 1.85 = 0.648648648...$

1.2 is given to 2 significant figures. 1.85 is given to 3 significant figures.
So the answer should be given to 2 significant figures.
Round the final significant figure (0.6<u>4</u>8...) up to 5: $1.2 \div 1.85 = \textbf{0.65}$

The lowest number of significant figures in the calculation is used because the fewer digits a measurement has, the less accurate it is. Your answer can only be as accurate as the least accurate measurement in the calculation.

Writing numbers in standard form

When you're processing data you might also want to change very big or very small numbers that have lots of zeros into something more manageable — this is called standard form.

Examples

1 000 000 can be written 1×10^6. 0.017 can be written 1.7×10^{-2}.

To do this you just need to move the decimal point left or right. The number of places the decimal point moves is then represented by a power of 10 — this is positive for big numbers, and negative for numbers smaller than one.

Example — **Maths Skills**

To write 16 500 in standard form:

1. Move the decimal point to give the smallest number you can between 1 and 10.

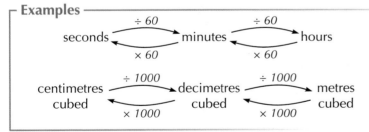

$$16\ 500 \longrightarrow 1.6500$$

2. Count the number of places the decimal point has moved.

   The decimal point has moved four places to the left.

3. Write that number as the power of ten. If the decimal point has moved to the left, the power is positive. If the decimal point has moved to the right, the power is negative.

$$16\ 500 = \boldsymbol{1.65 \times 10^4}$$

Tip: When you're writing a measurement in standard form, make sure you keep the same number of significant figures. E.g. $0.00400\ cm^3 = 4.00 \times 10^{-3}\ cm^3$. This'll make sure that you don't lose any accuracy.

Tip: Double check you've got it right by doing the multiplication — you should end up with the number you started with. So for this example, you'd check $1.65 \times 10^4 = 16\ 500$.

Converting between units

When processing your data, you need to have all the data in the correct units. Make sure you can convert between common units of time, length and volume.

Examples

$$\text{seconds} \underset{\times\ 60}{\overset{\div\ 60}{\rightleftarrows}} \text{minutes} \underset{\times\ 60}{\overset{\div\ 60}{\rightleftarrows}} \text{hours}$$

$$\underset{\substack{\text{centimetres} \\ \text{cubed}}}{} \underset{\times\ 1000}{\overset{\div\ 1000}{\rightleftarrows}} \underset{\substack{\text{decimetres} \\ \text{cubed}}}{} \underset{\times\ 1000}{\overset{\div\ 1000}{\rightleftarrows}} \underset{\substack{\text{metres} \\ \text{cubed}}}{}$$

Tip: One decimetre cubed ($1\ dm^3$) is the same as one litre (1 L).

Examples — **Maths Skills**

1. **The total lung capacity of a patient is 5430 cm³. What is the patient's lung capacity in dm³?**

   There are 1000 cm³ in one dm³, so you need to divide by 1000:
   5430 cm³ ÷ 1000 = **5.430 dm³**

2. **The volume of oxygen produced over time was measured for an enzyme-controlled reaction. The initial rate of reaction was found to be 8.4 cm³ min⁻¹. What is this rate in cm³ s⁻¹?**

   8.4 cm³ min⁻¹ means 8.4 cm³ oxygen was produced per minute. You want to find out the volume produced per second. There are 60 seconds in one minute, so you need to divide the volume by 60:
   8.4 cm³ min⁻¹ ÷ 60 = **0.14 cm³ s⁻¹**

Tip: Make sure your answer makes sense — if you're converting from a small unit (e.g. cm³) to a larger unit (e.g. dm³) you need to <u>divide</u> the value, so your answer should be <u>smaller</u> than the number you started with.

Statistical tests

Statistical tests are used to analyse data mathematically. They can be used to analyse quantitative (numerical) or qualitative (non-numerical) results. You can be more confident in your **conclusions** (see page 26) if they're based on results that have been analysed using a statistical test.

If you're planning on analysing your data using a statistical test, you first need to come up with a **null hypothesis** — this is a special type of hypothesis that states there is no significant difference (or correlation) between the things you're investigating. You then collect data to try to disprove the null hypothesis before analysing it statistically. There's more on null hypotheses on page 274.

Student's t-test

You can use the Student's t-test when you have two sets of data that you want to compare, e.g. whether males and females performed well in the same test. It tests whether there is a significant difference in the means of the two data sets.

The value obtained is compared to a critical value, which helps you decide how likely it is that the results or 'differences in the means' were due to chance. If the value obtained from the t-test is greater than the critical value at a probability (or **P value**) of 5% or less (≤ 0.05), then you can be 95% confident that the difference is significant and not due to chance. This is called a **95% confidence limit** — which is good enough for most biologists to reject the null hypothesis.

Chi-squared test

You can use the Chi-squared test when you have categorical (grouped) data and you want to know whether your observed results are statistically different from your expected results. You compare your result to a critical value — if it's larger than the critical value at $P = 0.05$, you can be 95% certain it's significant.

Spearman's rank correlation coefficient

Spearman's rank correlation coefficient allows you to work out the degree to which two sets of data are correlated (see page 23 for more on correlation). It is given as a value between 1 and -1. A value of 1 indicates a strong positive correlation, 0 means there is no correlation and -1 is a strong negative correlation. You can then compare your result to a critical value to find out whether or not the correlation is significant. See pages 273-275 for more on how to use the Spearman's rank correlation coefficient.

Tip: Qualitative data is <u>descriptive</u> — there's more about it on the next page.

Tip: Quantitative results can be <u>discrete</u> or <u>continuous</u> data (see pages 17-19).

Tip: < means 'less than', << means 'much less than', > means 'greater than', >> means 'much greater than', $\leq$ means 'less than or equal to' and $\geq$ means 'greater than or equal to'.

Tip: If the result of your statistical test is greater than the critical value at a P value of less than 2% (< 0.02), or even 1%, you can be even more confident that the difference is significant.

Exam Tip
When you're talking about the results of a statistical test and using the 95% confidence limit, make sure you refer to the probability as less than 0.05 or 5%, <u>not</u> 0.05%.

Exam Tip
In the exams, you could be asked to calculate the result of a statistical test and interpret it.

Practice Questions — Application

Q1 Write 0.0045 in standard form.

Q2 Give the answers to the following calculations to the correct number of significant figures:
   a) 4.53×3.142 b) $0.315 \div 0.025$

Q3 A student was investigating the effect of light intensity on plant growth. He measured the heights of seedlings grown under a lamp and the heights of seedlings grown in a cupboard, then used the Student's t-test to compare the heights of the two groups. The value obtained was greater than the critical value at $P = 0.05$. What does this tell you about the student's results?

4. Presenting Data

Presenting your data can make it easier for you to understand your results and spot any trends. There are several different ways to do it though, and you need to be able to choose the best way for the data you've got.

Qualitative and discrete data

Qualitative data is non-numerical data, e.g. blood group, hair colour.
Discrete data is numerical data that can only take certain values in a range, e.g. shoe size, number of patients. You can use **bar charts** or **pie charts** to present these types of data.

┌─ **Example** ─ **Maths Skills** ─────────────────────

The table shows the results of a survey into people's blood groups.

Blood group	Number of people
A	9
B	8
AB	2
O	17

To draw a bar chart from it:

1. **Space out each category evenly on the x-axis.**
   The blood groups are the categories so they go on the x-axis. Space each category out evenly. The bars for different categories shouldn't touch each other.

2. **Choose a sensible scale for your y-axis.**
   The number of people (the thing that was measured in this survey) goes on the y-axis. The highest number of people is 17, so an axis running from 0 to 20 would work nicely.

3. **Draw a bar for each category.**

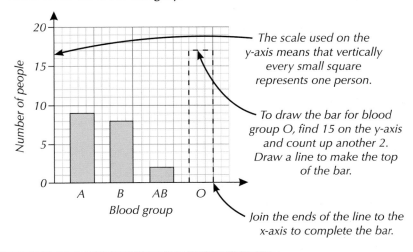

The scale used on the y-axis means that vertically every small square represents one person.

To draw the bar for blood group O, find 15 on the y-axis and count up another 2. Draw a line to make the top of the bar.

Join the ends of the line to the x-axis to complete the bar.

Learning Objectives:
- Be able to plot suitable graphs from experimental results, including selecting and labelling axes with appropriate scales, quantities and units.
- Understand how to interpret graphs of experimental results.
- Be able to measure gradients and intercepts of graphs.
  Specification Reference 1.1.3

Tip: Qualitative data can also be called categorical data — all the data can be sorted into categories and values between categories don't exist.

Exam Tip
If you are asked to draw a graph or chart in your exam, don't forget to label the axes (including the quantity and units), choose a sensible scale and make sure that it covers at least half the graph paper.

Tip: Graph paper tends to be divided vertically and horizontally into groups of 10 squares. So axes that go up in 1s, 2s, 5s or 10s make data a lot easier to plot.

Tip: You can choose the width of the bars — just make sure they're all the same.

Tip: This bar chart shows that most people in the survey had blood group O.

Continuous data

Continuous data is data that can take any value in a range, e.g. height or weight. You can use **line graphs** or **histograms** to present this type of data.

Line graphs

Line graphs often show how a variable changes over time. The data on both axes is continuous.

Tip: The graph on the right is a line graph. Line graphs look a bit like scattergrams (see next page), but the points on line graphs are joined together.

Tip: The line graph on the right shows that the volume increases over time but the rate of increase is slowing down. There's more about rate on page 20.

┌─ **Example** ─────────────────

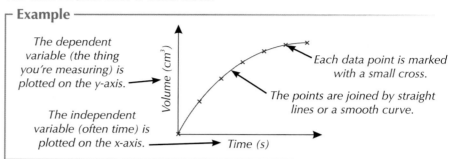

The dependent variable (the thing you're measuring) is plotted on the y-axis.

Each data point is marked with a small cross.

The points are joined by straight lines or a smooth curve.

The independent variable (often time) is plotted on the x-axis.

Histograms

Histograms are a useful way of displaying frequency data when the independent variable is continuous. They may look like bar charts, but it's the area of the bars that represents the frequency (rather than the height). The height of each bar is called the **frequency density**.

Tip: Don't be fooled by the height of the bars in a histogram — the tallest bar doesn't always belong to the class with the greatest frequency.

┌─ **Example** ─────────────────

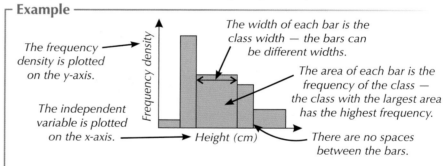

The frequency density is plotted on the y-axis.

The width of each bar is the class width — the bars can be different widths.

The area of each bar is the frequency of the class — the class with the largest area has the highest frequency.

The independent variable is plotted on the x-axis.

There are no spaces between the bars.

Tip: If all the class widths are the same, you can just plot the frequency on the y-axis.

You calculate the frequency density using this formula:

frequency density = frequency ÷ class width

┌─ **Example** ── **Maths Skills** ───────

Tip: The continuous data here has been split into classes. $0 \leq x < 5$ means the data in the class is more than or equal to 0 and less than 5.

The table on the right shows the results of a study into variation in pea plant height. The heights of the plants were grouped into four classes.

Height of pea plant (cm)	Frequency
$0 \leq x < 5$	5
$5 \leq x < 10$	14
$10 \leq x < 15$	11
$15 \leq x < 30$	3

1. To draw a histogram of the data, you first need to work out the width of each class. Write the class width in a new column.

Class width
$5 - 0 = 5$
$10 - 5 = 5$
$15 - 10 = 5$
$30 - 15 = 15$

2. Use the formula on the previous page to calculate the frequency density for each class and write it in another new column.

Frequency density
5 ÷ 5 = **1**
14 ÷ 5 = **2.8**
11 ÷ 5 = **2.2**
3 ÷ 15 = **0.2**

Tip: You might have to round the frequency density — if so, choose a sensible number of decimal places that will be possible to plot using your graph's scale.

3. Work out a suitable scale for each axis, then plot the histogram. It should look something like this:

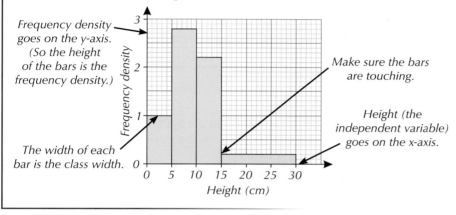

Frequency density goes on the y-axis. (So the height of the bars is the frequency density.)

Make sure the bars are touching.

Height (the independent variable) goes on the x-axis.

The width of each bar is the class width.

Tip: You can calculate the frequency of a class from a histogram by rearranging the formula: frequency = frequency density × class width.

Tip: The width of the whole histogram shows the range of results (how spread out they are).

Scattergrams

When you want to show how two variables are related (or correlated, see page 23) you can use a **scattergram**. Both variables must be numbers.

Tip: Scattergrams can also be called scatter graphs, or scatter diagrams.

Example

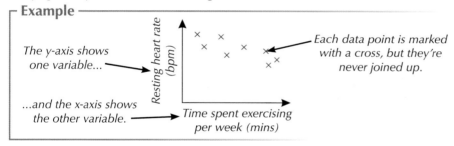

The y-axis shows one variable...

Each data point is marked with a cross, but they're never joined up.

...and the x-axis shows the other variable.

Tip: Data that's made up of numbers is called quantitative data.

You can draw a **line** (or curve) **of best fit** on a scattergram to help show the trend in your results. To do so, draw the line through or as near to as many points as possible, ignoring any anomalous results.

Tip: You should never join the points together on a scattergram.

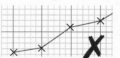

A line of best fit shows a <u>trend</u> rather than changes between data points.

Example

The number of organisms of one species on a rocky beach was recorded at different distances from the shore. The graph below shows the results, including a line of best fit.

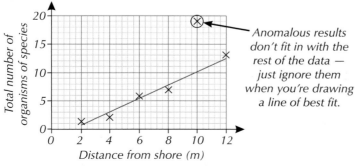

Anomalous results don't fit in with the rest of the data — just ignore them when you're drawing a line of best fit.

Tip: A trend shown by a scattergram is called a <u>correlation</u>. The graph on the left shows a positive correlation — as the distance from the shore increases, the total number of organisms of one species increases. There's more about correlation and what it means on page 23.

Finding the rate from a graph

Rate is a measure of how much something is changing over time. Calculating a rate can be useful when analysing your data, e.g. you might want to the find the rate of a reaction. You can find the rate from a graph that shows a variable changing over time by finding the **gradient** (how steep it is):

Tip: Linear graphs are graphs with a straight line.

Linear graphs

For a linear graph you can calculate the rate by finding the gradient of the line, using the equation:

$$\text{Gradient} = \frac{\text{Change in } y}{\text{Change in } x}$$

Tip: When using this equation to find a rate, x should always be the time.

Change in y is the change in value on the y-axis and **change in x** is the change in value on the x-axis.

The equation of a straight line can always be written in the form $y = mx + c$, where m is the gradient and c is the y-intercept (this is the value of y when the line crosses the y-axis).

┌ Example ─ [Maths Skills]

To find the rate at which oxygen is produced in the graph on the right:

1. Pick two points on the line that are easy to read and a good distance apart.

2. Draw a vertical line down from one point and a horizontal line across from the other to make a triangle.

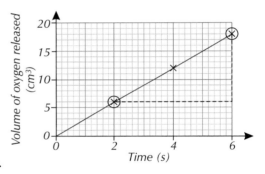

Tip: The graph on the right is a straight line graph in which one variable increases in proportion with the other. The symbol for 'proportional to' is '∝'. Here, you can say that volume of oxygen released ∝ time.

3. Use the scales on the axes to work out the length of each line. The vertical side of the triangle is the change in y and the horizontal side of the triangle is the change in x.

Tip: When drawing a triangle to calculate a gradient like this, the hypotenuse of the triangle should be at least half as long as the line of the graph itself.

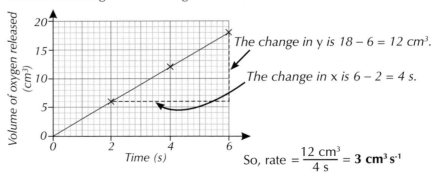

The change in y is $18 - 6 = 12$ cm³.

The change in x is $6 - 2 = 4$ s.

So, rate $= \dfrac{12 \text{ cm}^3}{4 \text{ s}} = \textbf{3 cm}^3\,\textbf{s}^{-1}$

Tip: The units for the gradient are the units for y divided by the units for x. Remember, cm³ s⁻¹ means the same as cm³/s (centimetres cubed per second).

To find the equation of the line you need the gradient (which is the same as the rate) and the y-intercept (where the line crosses the y-axis).

The gradient is 3 and the line crosses the y-axis where y is 0.

So the equation for the line is $y = 3x + 0$.

Since $c = 0$, the equation can be written as just $y = 3x$.

Knowing the equation of the line allows you to estimate results not plotted on the graph:

Example — Maths Skills

For the reaction shown in the graph on the right, estimate the volume of oxygen released after 20 seconds.

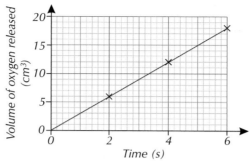

The equation for the line is $y = 3x$ (see previous page), where y is the volume of oxygen released (in cm³) and x is the time (in seconds).

To find the value of y when x is 20 s, just replace x with 20 in the equation.

$$y = 3 \times 20 = \mathbf{60 \ cm^3}$$

Tip: This is an estimate because you are assuming that the relationship between the two variables doesn't change after six seconds (so as time increases, the volume of oxygen released keeps increasing at the same rate).

Curved graphs

For a curved (non-linear) graph you can find the rate by drawing a **tangent**. A tangent is a straight line that touches a single point on the curve.

Example — Maths Skills

To find the rate of reaction when time = 30 seconds on the graph below:

1. Position a ruler on the graph at the point on the curve where you want to know the rate (so on this graph, find the point on the curve where $x = 30$).

2. Angle the ruler so there is equal space between the ruler and the curve on either side of the point.

Tip: Look at the gaps on either side of the point — keep wiggling the ruler about until the two gaps look about the same size.

3. Draw a line along the ruler to make the tangent.
    Extend the line right across the graph — it'll help to make your gradient calculation easier as you'll have more points to choose from.

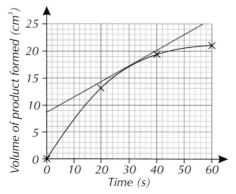

Tip: Always use a sharp pencil when drawing a tangent to draw a neat line — you'll need to read points off the line in the next step, so make sure the line's nice and clear.

4. To find the rate, calculate the gradient of the tangent in the same way you would calculate the gradient of a straight line graph (see p. 20).

(see p. 20)

Tip: Remember, gradient = change in y ÷ change in x.

Tip: Remember, the gradient of a tangent only tells you the rate at that particular point on the graph.

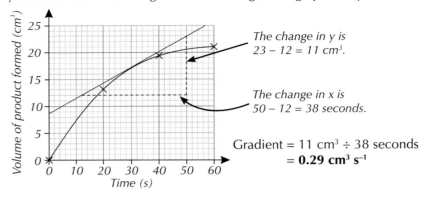

The change in y is $23 - 12 = 11$ cm³.

The change in x is $50 - 12 = 38$ seconds.

Gradient = 11 cm³ ÷ 38 seconds
= **0.29 cm³ s⁻¹**

Practice Questions — Application

Q1 A scientist is investigating the variation in wingspan in a species of bird. The results are shown in the table on the right.

What type of graph should the scientist use to display this data? Explain your answer.

Wingspan (cm)	Frequency
$14 \leq x < 16$	2
$16 \leq x < 18$	5
$18 \leq x < 20$	9
$20 \leq x < 22$	4

Q2 A group of students was investigating the effect of temperature on the respiration rate of locusts. Their results are shown in the graph below.

Tip: Respiration rate can be investigated by measuring volume of O_2 used or the volume of CO_2 produced.

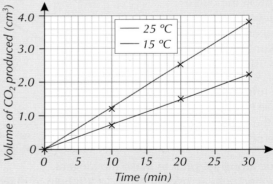

a) What is the rate of CO_2 production at 25 °C?

b) Assuming that the respiration rate remains constant, how much CO_2 will have been produced during the experiment at 15 °C after 50 minutes?

Q3 The concentration of product produced during an enzyme-controlled reaction was measured over time. The table below shows the results.

Plot a suitable graph for the data in the table.

Time (s)	0	10	20	30	40	50	60
Product concentration ($\mu mol/dm^3$)	0	6.1	10.3	12.5	13.6	14.1	14.2

5. Drawing Conclusions and Evaluating

You need to be able to draw conclusions from your results and evaluate them. You also need to be able to draw conclusions from other people's data and evaluate them — which is what you're likely to be asked to do in your exams.

Drawing conclusions from data

Conclusions need to be **valid**. A conclusion can only be considered as valid if it answers the original question.

Correlations and causal relationships

You can often draw conclusions by looking at the relationship (**correlation**) between two variables:

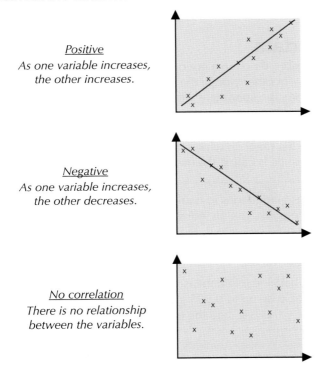

Positive
As one variable increases, the other increases.

Negative
As one variable increases, the other decreases.

No correlation
There is no relationship between the variables.

You have to be very careful when drawing conclusions from data like this because a correlation between two variables doesn't always mean that a change in one variable causes a change in the other (the correlation could be due to chance or there could be a third variable having an effect).

If there's a relationship between two variables and a change in one variable does cause a change in the other it's called a **causal relationship**. It can be concluded that a correlation is a causal relationship if every other variable that could possibly affect the result is controlled.

Drawing specific conclusions

When you're making a conclusion you can't make broad generalisations from data — you have to be very specific. You can only conclude what the results show and no more.

Learning Objectives:

- Understand how to evaluate results and draw conclusions.
- Understand precision and accuracy of measurements and data, including margins of error, percentage errors and uncertainties in apparatus.
- Be able to identify the limitations in experimental procedures.
- Be able to refine experimental design by suggesting improvements to the procedures and apparatus.

Specification Reference 1.1.4

Tip: The closer the points are to the line of best fit, the stronger the correlation. You can calculate a correlation coefficient (see p. 16) to get a numerical value for how strong the correlation is.

Tip: In reality, concluding that a correlation is a causal relationship is very hard to do — correlations are generally accepted to be causal relationships if lots of studies have found the same thing, and scientists have figured out exactly how one factor causes the other.

Figure 1 shows the results from a study into the effect of penicillin dosage on the duration of fever in men.

What you can conclude from these results:
The only conclusion you can draw is that there's a negative correlation between penicillin dosage and duration of fever in men (as the dosage of penicillin increases, the duration of fever in men decreases).

What you <u>can't</u> conclude from these results:
You can't conclude that this is true for any other antibiotic, any other symptom or even for female patients — the results could be completely different. Without more information and the results from more studies, you can't conclude that the increasing penicillin dosage has caused the reduction in duration of fever either.

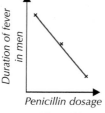

Figure 1: The relationship between penicillin dosage and the duration of fever in men.

Exam Tip
Being able to recognise correlations and causal relationships comes up a lot in Biology. It's really important that you learn how to do this and understand the difference between the two.

Uncertainty in data

When you draw a conclusion, it's often a good idea to talk about the uncertainty in your data — in other words, the amount of error there might be. The results you get from an experiment won't be completely perfect — there'll always be a degree of uncertainty in your readings or measurements due to limits in the sensitivity of the apparatus you're using.

A ± sign tells you the range in which the true value lies (to within a certain probability). The range is called the **margin of error**.

Tip: A reading is when you make a judgement about one value, e.g. when you read a value off a mass balance. A measurement is when you judge two values and find the difference, e.g. when you measure length with a ruler.

Examples

- A 10 cm³ pipette has graduations to mark every 0.1 cm³. If you measure a volume using the pipette, you are measuring to the nearest 0.1 cm³ — the real volume could be up to 0.05 cm³ less or 0.05 cm³ more. The uncertainty value of the pipette is ± 0.05 cm³, and so its margin of error is 0.1 cm³ (see Figure 2).

- An electronic mass balance might measure to the nearest 0.01 g, but the real mass could be up to 0.005 g smaller or larger. It has an uncertainty value of ± 0.005 g, and the margin of error is 0.01 g.

If you're combining readings or measurements, you'll need to combine their uncertainties:

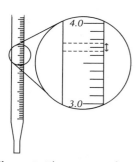

Figure 2: The margin of error for a reading of 3.7 cm³ using a 10 cm³ pipette.

Example — Maths Skills

In a serial dilution, 5 cm³ of glucose solution is transferred using a pipette that measures to the nearest 0.5 cm³. It is added to 10 cm³ water that was measured in a graduated cylinder with graduations to mark every 1 cm³.

The uncertainty in the pipette is ± 0.25 cm³.
The uncertainty in the graduated cylinder is ± 0.5 cm³.
So the total uncertainty will be 0.25 cm³ + 0.5 cm³ = **± 0.75 cm³**.

Tip: If the total uncertainty of combined errors is ± 0.75 cm³, the margin of error will be 2 × 0.75 = 1.5 cm³. This is the same as adding the two separate margins of error together.

Calculating percentage error

If you know the uncertainty value of your measurements, you can calculate the percentage error using this formula:

$$\text{percentage error} = \frac{\text{uncertainty}}{\text{reading}} \times 100$$

50 cm³ of HCl is measured with an uncertainty value of ± 0.05 cm³. What is the percentage error?

$$\frac{0.05}{50} \times 100 = \textbf{0.1\%}$$

Tip: The percentage error is the error as a <u>percentage</u> of the measured value, so you can use it to compare the uncertainty of two readings or measurements (see below).

Minimising errors in data

One obvious way to reduce errors in your measurements is to buy the most sensitive equipment available. In real life there's not much you can do about this one — you're stuck with whatever your school or college has got. But there are other ways to lower the uncertainty in experiments.

Example — Measuring a greater amount of something

So using a 500 cm³ cylinder to measure 100 cm³ of liquid will give you a percentage error of: $\frac{2.5}{100} \times 100 = \textbf{2.5\%}$

But if you measure 200 cm³ in the same cylinder, the percentage error is: $\frac{2.5}{200} \times 100 = \textbf{1.25\%}$

Hey presto — you've just halved the uncertainty.

Tip: You can also minimise errors by using a <u>larger sample size</u>, as this reduces the chance of getting a freak result — see page 6.

Evaluating results

When you evaluate your results, you need to think about whether they were repeatable and reproducible and whether they were valid.

Repeatability

- Did you take enough repeat readings or measurements?
- Would you do more repeats if you were to do the experiment again?
- Do you get similar data each time you carried out a repeat measurement?

If you didn't do any repeats, or enough repeats, you can't be sure your data is repeatable. Your repeated results need to be similar too. If you repeated a measurement three times and got a completely different result each time, your results aren't repeatable (or precise).

Reproducibility

Have you compared your results with other people's results and if so, were they similar? If not, you can't be sure your data is reproducible.

Validity

- Does your data answer the question you set out to investigate?
- Were all the variables controlled?

If you didn't control all the variables, you haven't answered the original question and your data isn't valid.

Example

You could only conclude from your results that the rate of activity of an enzyme is fastest at a particular temperature (see page 101) if you controlled all the other variables that could have affected enzyme activity in your experiment, e.g. pH, enzyme concentration, etc.

Exam Tip
If you're given data or a method to evaluate in the exam, you should be asking similar questions, e.g. were all the variables controlled? And if not, how should they have been controlled?

Tip: Think about whether other scientists could gain data showing the same relationships that are shown in your data.

Tip: If you don't control all other variables in your experiment, you can't tell if any trend in your results is linked to just the independent variable.

Evaluating methods

When you evaluate your method, you need to think about how you could improve your experiment if you did it again. Here are some things to consider:

- Is there anything you could have done to make your results more precise or accurate?

- Were there any limitations in your method, e.g. should you have taken measurements more frequently?

- Was your sample size large enough?

- Were there any sources of error in your experiment?

- Could you have used more sensitive apparatus or equipment?

Tip: This is where you take the uncertainty of your measurements (see page 24) into account. Think about the size of the margin of error, and whether you could have reduced the uncertainty.

Having confidence in your conclusion

Once you've evaluated your results and method, you can decide how much confidence you have in your conclusion. For example, if your results are repeatable, reproducible and valid and they back up your conclusion then you can have a high degree of confidence in your conclusion.

You can also consider these points if you're asked to evaluate a conclusion in the exam.

Exam Tip
Data questions are fairly common in the exams. You might be given a conclusion for the data and asked to evaluate it — this just means you have to give reasons why it is (or isn't) a valid conclusion. You could also be asked how far data supports a conclusion — it requires a similar type of answer.

Example

A study examined the effect of farm hedgerow length on the number of species in a given area. The number of species present during a single week on 12 farms was counted by placing ground-level traps. All the farms were a similar area. The traps were left out every day, at 6 am for two hours and once again at 6 pm for two hours. The results are shown in Figure 3:

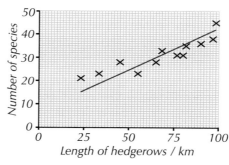

Figure 3: Scattergram to show relationship between number of species and length of hedgerows.

A journalist who read this study concluded that longer hedgerows cause the number of species in a given area to increase. Does the data support this conclusion? Explain your answer.

Yes — The data in the graph supports the conclusion as it shows that as the length of hedgerows increases, the number of species increases — the length of the hedgerows has a positive correlation with the number of species in that area.

No — You can't conclude that the increasing length of the hedgerows caused the increase in the number of species. Other factors may have been involved, for example, the number of predators in an area may have decreased or the farmers may have used less pesticide there.

Also, the study is quite small — they only used 12 farms. The trend shown by the data may not appear if 50 or 100 farms were studied, or if the farms were studied for a longer period of time.

The results are also limited by the method of trapping. Traps were placed on the ground, so species like birds weren't included, and they weren't left overnight, so nocturnal animals wouldn't get counted, etc. This could have affected the results.

Importantly, you're not told if all the other variables were controlled, e.g. you don't know if all the farms had a similar type of land, similar weather, the same crops growing, etc. This means you don't know how valid the study is — you can't be sure that the factor being investigated (hedgerows) is the only one affecting the thing being measured (number of species).

Overall — The limits of the study mean that the journalist's conclusion isn't well supported.

Tip: The method used to collect the data can bias the results. Bias is when someone intentionally or unintentionally favours a particular result — in the example on the left, the method of trapping gives results that are biased towards ground-dwelling species.

Practice Questions — Application

Q1 a) What is the uncertainty of a pipette that has graduations every 0.5 cm³?

   b) What is the percentage error of a measurement of 6.0 cm³ water made with the pipette in part a)?

Q2 A scientist was investigating the effect of temperature on the activity of enzyme X. She timed how long it took for 5 cm³ of product to be produced by enzyme X at 10 °C, keeping all variables other than temperature constant. The scientist repeated the experiment at 20 °C, 30 °C, 40 °C, 50 °C and 60 °C, then used the results to calculate a rate of reaction for each temperature. The results of the investigation are shown in Figure 4.

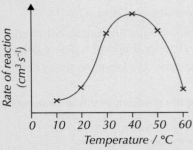

Figure 4: Graph to show the effect of temperature on the rate of an enzyme-controlled reaction.

   a) A science magazine came to the following conclusion from this data:

   "Enzyme X works best at 40 °C."

   Does the data support this conclusion? Explain your answer.

   b) Give one way in which the method for this experiment could be improved to provide more precise results.

   c) The scientist is also interested in the effect of temperature on the activity of enzyme Z. Could she use the results of the experiment above to predict the effect of temperature on enzyme Z? Explain your answer.

Section Summary

Make sure you know...

- The definitions of the terms precise, repeatable, reproducible, valid and accurate, when referring to experimental results.

- How to plan a good experiment and evaluate whether a method is appropriate to meet an expected outcome, including the consideration of variables (the independent variable, the dependent variable, and variables that need to be controlled), controls (positive controls, negative controls and control groups), repeats and sample size.

- How to select equipment that is of the right size, scale and sensitivity for an experiment.

- How to select the most appropriate technique(s) to use for an experiment.

- How to carry out a risk assessment for an experiment and identify any ethical issues.

- How to use lots of different techniques and equipment.

- How to choose the most appropriate units for your measurements.

- How to record results into a table of data, including frequency tables.

- How to identify anomalous results in data.

- How to process, analyse and interpret results, including:
  - How to calculate a mean, median, mode and range from a data set.
  - What standard deviation is.
  - How to calculate a percentage and percentage change.
  - How to write two values as a ratio, in the form X : Y or X : 1.
  - How to correctly use significant figures and standard form when processing data.
  - How to convert between units.
  - What the Student's t-test, chi-squared test and Spearman's rank correlation coefficient are used for and what the results of these tests can tell you about data.

- What qualitative and quantitative (discrete and continuous) data is.

- The different types of graphs you can use to display results (including bar charts, histograms, line graphs and scattergrams), and which type to use for different types of data.

- How to plot a graph, including selecting suitable axes and labelling them with appropriate scales, quantities and units.

- How to find the rate from a graph by calculating the gradient of a line or tangent.

- How to find the equation of a straight line graph.

- That two variables may have a positive, a negative or no correlation.

- That correlation between variables doesn't always mean that they have a causal relationship (where a change in one causes a change in the other).

- How to draw conclusions that are supported by data.

- What uncertainty in an experiment is and how to calculate the margin of error and percentage error of a measurement.

- How to minimise errors in experiments.

- How to evaluate results (including being able to identify repeatable, reproducible and precise results), identify the limitations in an experiment and suggest ways in which an experiment could be improved.

- How to evaluate how well a conclusion is supported by a set of results.

Q1   Which of the following has the largest percentage error?

    A   50 g measured to the nearest 1 g.

    B   5.0 g measured to the nearest 0.1 g.

    C   10 g measured to the nearest 0.2 g.

    D   15 g measured to the nearest 0.5 g.

(1 mark)

Q2   The effect of temperature on diffusion rate in cells was investigated, using agar jelly as a model of cell cytoplasm. Pink agar jelly, prepared with phenolphthalein and dilute sodium hydroxide, was cut into four equal-sized cubes. Each cube was placed into a test tube of hydrochloric acid at a different temperature and the time taken for the cube to become colourless was recorded. The experiment was repeated three times at each temperature. **Table 2.1** shows the results.

Temperature (°C)	Time taken for cube to become colourless (s)			
	Repeat 1	Repeat 2	Repeat 3	Mean
10	728	414	425	420
20	343	330	351	341
30	240	231	228	233
40	187	166	172	175

Table 2.1

(a) (i)   Give two benefits of repeating the experiment at each temperature.

(2 marks)

  (ii)   Draw a graph of these results, including a line of best fit.

(3 marks)

(b)   Describe any correlation shown by the graph.

(1 mark)

(c)   Write a conclusion for this investigation, based on the results shown by the graph.

(2 marks)

(d)   Hydrochloric acid is an irritant and can cause damage if it comes into contact with skin or eyes. Suggest two ways that the risk from hydrochloric acid could be reduced in this investigation.

(2 marks)

(e)   A student wants to repeat this experiment. Suggest two pieces of additional information that could be added to the method above, so that these results are more likely to be reproducible.

(2 marks)

Learning Objectives:

- Be able to understand the ultrastructure of eukaryotic cells and the functions of the different cellular components.
- Be able to describe the functions of the following cellular components:
  - plasma membrane
  - cell wall
  - nucleus
  - nuclear envelope
  - nucleolus
  - lysosomes
  - ribosomes
  - rough and smooth endoplasmic reticulum (ER)
  - Golgi apparatus
  - mitochondria
  - chloroplasts
  - centrioles
  - cilia
  - flagella.

  Specification Reference 2.1.1

Tip: The term 'cells' was first coined by Robert Hooke in the 17th century. Understanding what goes on inside cells is a key concept in biology because all living organisms are made up of them. Improvements in light microscopy and the development of electron microscopes (see p. 41) have been key to the advancement of our knowledge of the structure and function of cells.

1. Cells and Organelles

No doubt you learnt about cell structure at GCSE, but there's a lot more to it at AS — as you're about to find out...

Prokaryotes and eukaryotes

There are two main types of organism — eukaryotes and prokaryotes. Prokaryotic organisms are **prokaryotic cells** (i.e. they're single-celled organisms) and eukaryotic organisms are made up of **eukaryotic cells**. Both types of cells contain **organelles** (see below). Eukaryotic cells are complex and include all animal and plant cells. Prokaryotic cells are smaller and simpler, e.g. bacteria. There's more on prokaryotic cells on page 38.

Organelles

Organelles are parts of cells. Each one has a specific function. If you examine a cell through an electron microscope (see page 41) you can see its organelles and the internal structure of most of them — this is known as the **cell ultrastructure**. Everything you need to know about eukaryotic cell organelles is covered over the next few pages.

Animal and plant cells

Animal and plant cells are both eukaryotic. Eukaryotic cells are generally a bit more complicated than prokaryotic cells and have more organelles. You've probably been looking at animal and plant cell diagrams for years, so hopefully you'll be familiar with some of the bits and pieces...

Animal cells

Figure 1 shows the organelles found in a typical animal cell. You can compare these to the ones found in a typical plant cell on the next page.

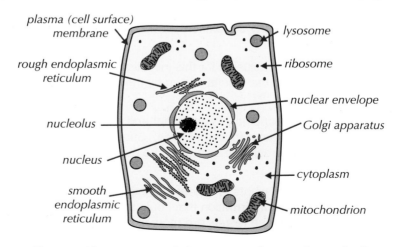

Figure 1: *The structure and ultrastructure of a typical animal cell.*

Plant cells

Plant cells have all the same organelles as animal cells, but with a few added extras:

- a cell wall with plasmodesmata ('channels' for exchanging substances between adjacent cells),

- a vacuole (compartment that contains cell sap),

- and of course good old chloroplasts (the organelles involved in photosynthesis).

These organelles are all shown in Figure 2.

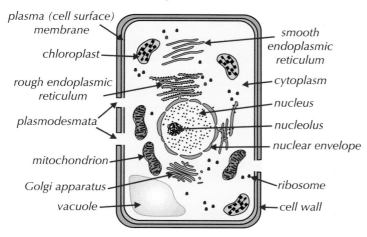

plasma (cell surface) membrane
chloroplast
rough endoplasmic reticulum
plasmodesmata
mitochondrion
Golgi apparatus
vacuole
smooth endoplasmic reticulum
cytoplasm
nucleus
nucleolus
nuclear envelope
ribosome
cell wall

Figure 2: *The structure and ultrastructure of a typical plant cell.*

Functions of organelles

This table contains a big list of organelles — you need to know the structure and function of them all. Sorry. Most organelles are surrounded by membranes, which sometimes causes confusion — don't make the mistake of thinking that a diagram of an organelle is a diagram of a whole cell. They're not cells — they're parts of cells.

Plasma membrane (Also called the cell surface membrane)

Description
The membrane found on the surface of animal cells and just inside the cell wall of plant cells and prokaryotic cells.
It's made mainly of lipids and protein.

Function
Regulates the movement of substances into and out of the cell. It also has receptor molecules on it, which allow it to respond to chemicals like hormones.

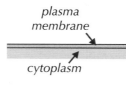

plasma membrane
cytoplasm

Cell wall

Description
A rigid structure that surrounds plant cells. It's made mainly of the carbohydrate cellulose.

Function
Supports plant cells.

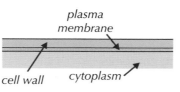

plasma membrane
cell wall   *cytoplasm*

Exam Tip
As well as being able to interpret diagrams of cells like Figure 1 and Figure 2, you're also expected to be able to interpret photos of cells and their organelles, taken through different types of microscopes. (These are called micrographs or photomicrographs.)

Tip: There are lots of different types of plant and animal cells and they won't all look exactly like the ones shown here or contain exactly the same organelles (e.g. not all plant cells contain chloroplasts). Make sure you know all the distinguishing features for each cell type.

Tip: There's more on the structure and function of the plasma membrane on pages 116-118.

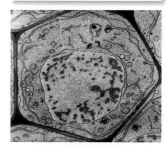

Figure 3: *An electron micrograph of a plant cell. The cell walls appear red/brown.*

Tip: In addition to plants, other organisms (e.g. fungi and bacteria) can have cell walls too but they aren't made of cellulose — see p. 38.

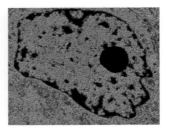

Figure 4: An electron micrograph of a nucleus, showing the nucleolus, nuclear envelope and nuclear pores.

Tip: There's more on DNA and RNA on pages 80-81.

Tip: Organelles in electron micrographs won't always look exactly the same as the ones shown here, e.g. they may vary in size and shape and they can be viewed from different angles, which can affect their appearance.

Nucleus

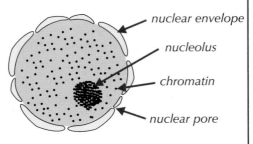

Description

A large organelle surrounded by a nuclear envelope (double membrane), which contains many pores. The nucleus contains chromatin (which is made from DNA and proteins) and often a structure called the nucleolus.

Function

The nucleus controls the cell's activities (by controlling the transcription of DNA — see p. 91). DNA contains instructions to make proteins — see page 88. The pores allow substances (e.g. RNA) to move between the nucleus and the cytoplasm. The nucleolus makes ribosomes (see below).

Lysosome

Description

A round organelle surrounded by a membrane, with no clear internal structure.

Function

Contains digestive enzymes. These are kept separate from the cytoplasm by the surrounding membrane, and can be used to digest invading cells or to break down worn out components of the cell.

Ribosome

Description

A very small organelle that either floats free in the cytoplasm or is attached to the rough endoplasmic reticulum. It's made up of proteins and RNA (see page 81). It's not surrounded by a membrane.

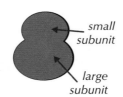

Function

The site where proteins are made.

Rough endoplasmic reticulum (RER)

Description

A system of membranes enclosing a fluid-filled space. The surface is covered with ribosomes.

Function

Folds and processes proteins that have been made at the ribosomes.

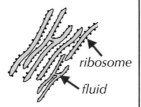

Smooth endoplasmic reticulum (SER)

Description

Similar to rough endoplasmic reticulum, but with no ribosomes.

Function

Synthesises and processes lipids.

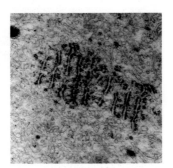

Figure 5: An electron micrograph showing SER (red-brown) and RER (blue).

Vesicle

Description

A small fluid-filled sac in the cytoplasm, surrounded by a membrane.

Function

Transports substances in and out of the cell (via the plasma membrane) and between organelles. Some are formed by the Golgi apparatus or the endoplasmic reticulum, while others are formed at the cell surface.

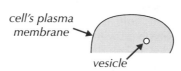

Golgi apparatus

Description

A group of fluid-filled, membrane-bound, flattened sacs. Vesicles are often seen at the edges of the sacs.

Function

It processes and packages new lipids and proteins. It also makes lysosomes.

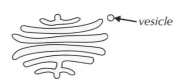

Mitochondrion

Description

It's usually oval-shaped. It has a double membrane — the inner one is folded to form structures called cristae. Inside is the matrix, which contains enzymes involved in respiration.

Function

The site of aerobic respiration, where ATP is produced. Mitochondria are found in large numbers in cells that are very active and require a lot of energy.

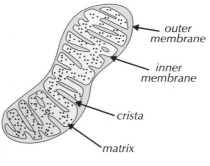

Chloroplast

Description

A small, flattened structure found in plant cells. It's surrounded by a double membrane, and also has membranes inside called thylakoid membranes. These membranes are stacked up in some parts of the chloroplast to form grana. Grana are linked together by lamellae — thin, flat pieces of thylakoid membrane.

Function

The site where photosynthesis takes place. Some parts of photosynthesis happen in the grana, and other parts happen in the stroma (a thick fluid found in chloroplasts).

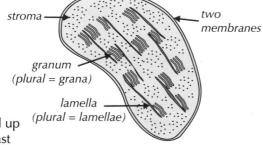

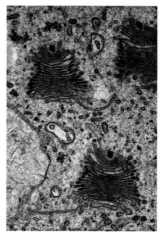

Figure 6: *An electron micrograph of Golgi apparatus.*

Exam Tip
Never say mitochondria produce energy in the exam — they produce ATP or release energy (energy can't be made).

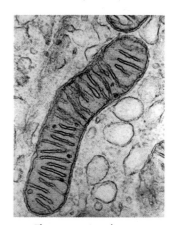

Figure 7: *An electron micrograph of a mitochondrion.*

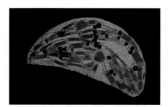

Figure 8: *An electron micrograph of a chloroplast.*

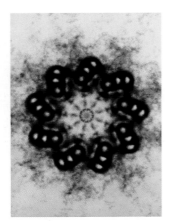

Figure 9: An electron micrograph of centrioles in a tumour cell.

Tip: Cilia in the trachea (windpipe) are used to sweep dust and dirt out of the lungs — see page 163.

Tip: The only example of a flagellum found in humans is the 'tail' of a sperm cell.

Tip: The formation of microtubules inside flagella and cilia is known as the '9 + 2' formation because there are nine pairs of microtubules surrounding two central microtubules.

Tip: 'Cilium' and 'flagellum' are singular. The plural versions are 'cilia' and 'flagella'.

Tip: You can find out more about electron micrographs on pages 41-42.

Centriole

Description
Small, hollow cylinders, made of microtubules (tiny protein cylinders). Found in animal cells, but only some plant cells.

Function
Involved with the separation of chromosomes during cell division (see page 140).

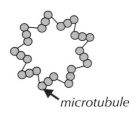
microtubule

Cilia

Description
Small, hair-like structures found on the surface membrane of some animal cells. In cross-section, they have an outer membrane and a ring of nine pairs of protein microtubules inside, with a single pair of microtubules in the middle.

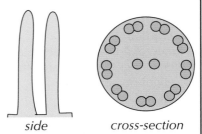
side   *cross-section*

Function
The microtubules allow the cilia to move. This movement is used by the cell to move substances along the cell surface.

Flagellum

Description
Flagella on eukaryotic cells are like cilia but longer. They stick out from the cell surface and are surrounded by the plasma membrane. Inside they're like cilia too — two microtubules in the centre and nine pairs around the edge.

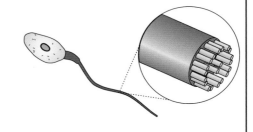

Function
The microtubules contract to make the flagellum move. Flagella are used like outboard motors to propel cells forward (e.g. when a sperm cell swims).

Practice Questions — Application

Q1 Identify the organelle(s) labelled 'A' in the following electron micrographs. Give the function of each organelle.

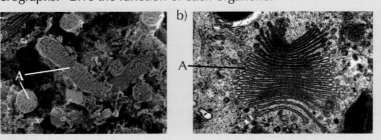
a)   b)

c)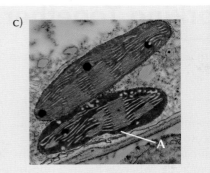

d)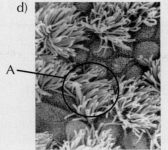

Exam Tip
Electron micrographs in the exam are often in black and white (see p. 42), so don't be thrown seeing them like this.

Q2 The images below each show a different type of cell.

a) Name organelle X in Image A.

b) Name organelle Y in Image B.

c) Which of the images is a plant cell? Explain your answer.

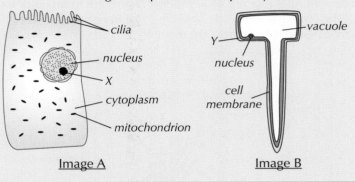

Image A   Image B

Practice Questions — Fact Recall

Q1 Name the organelles labelled A-H on the plant cell below.

Q2 Name three organelles that can be found in plant cells, but not in animal cells.

Q3 Describe the functions of the nucleus.

Q4 Give one function of a lysosome.

Q5 Describe how the structure of the rough endoplasmic reticulum is different from the smooth endoplasmic reticulum.

Q6 What is the function of the smooth endoplasmic reticulum?

Q7 Which organelle is responsible for making lysosomes?

Q8 Name the organelle responsible for the separation of chromosomes during cell division.

Q9 Draw a labelled cross-section of a cilium.

Exam Tip
Remember you could be asked about the structure and function of any of the organelles in the table on pages 31-34, so make sure you learn them all.

2. Organelles Working Together

There are loads of organelles, each with an important role. But it's when they work together that they start to become really impressive.

Protein production

Figure 1 shows the variety of organelles involved in protein production. Each one has a different role. Proteins are made at the ribosomes — the ribosomes on the rough endoplasmic reticulum (RER) make proteins that are excreted or attached to the cell membrane, whereas the free ribosomes in the cytoplasm make proteins that stay in the cytoplasm.

New proteins produced at the RER are folded and processed (e.g. sugar chains are added) in the RER. Then they're transported from the RER to the Golgi apparatus in vesicles. At the Golgi apparatus, the proteins may undergo further processing (e.g. sugar chains are trimmed or more are added). The proteins enter more vesicles to be transported around the cell. E.g. glycoproteins (found in mucus) move to the cell surface and are secreted.

Tip: Protein production in prokaryotes is slightly different as they don't have the same organelles as eukaryotes.

Tip: Proteins may be stored at the rough endoplasmic reticulum until they are needed by the Golgi apparatus.

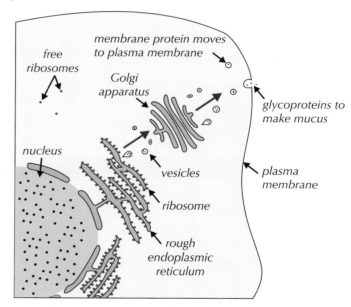

Figure 1: *Protein production in a eukaryotic cell.*

The cytoskeleton

The organelles in cells are surrounded by the cytoplasm. The cytoplasm is more than just a solution of chemicals though — it's got a network of protein threads running through it. These protein threads are called the cytoskeleton. In eukaryotic cells the protein threads are arranged as **microfilaments** (very thin protein strands) and **microtubules** (tiny protein cylinders). These are shown in Figure 2 and Figure 4 (on the next page).

The cytoskeleton has four main functions:

1. The microtubules and microfilaments support the cell's organelles, keeping them in position.

2. They also help to strengthen the cell and maintain its shape.

3. As well as this, they're responsible for the transport of organelles and materials within the cell.

Figure 2: *A fluorescent light micrograph of two cells and their cytoskeleton. The microfilaments appear purple, microtubules are shown in yellow and the nuclei are green.*

Examples

- The movement of chromosomes when they separate during cell division depends on contraction of microtubules in the spindle (see page 140 for more on cell division).
- The movement of vesicles around the cell relies on cytoskeletal proteins.

Tip: A cytoskeleton is found in prokaryotes as well as eukaryotes, but the prokaryotic cytoskeleton contains different proteins.

4. The proteins of the cytoskeleton can also cause the cell to move.

Example

The movement of cilia and flagella is caused by the cytoskeletal protein filaments that run through them. So in the case of single cells that have a flagellum (e.g. sperm cells), the cytoskeleton propels the whole cell.

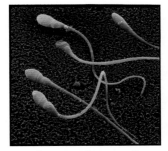

Figure 3: Sperm cells are propelled by their cytoskeleton.

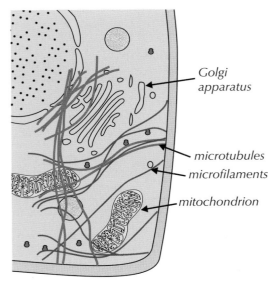

Golgi apparatus

microtubules

microfilaments

mitochondrion

Figure 4: Diagram showing part of a eukaryotic cell and its cytoplasm.

Tip: The assembly of microtubules and microfilaments, and the movement of materials along them, requires energy from respiration. So microtubules and microfilaments can be prevented from functioning using respiratory inhibitors.

Practice Questions — Application

Recent research has shown abnormalities in the Golgi apparatus in some brain cells in Alzheimer's sufferers. The Golgi apparatus in some cells were visualised as small, round, disconnected elements.

Q1 How would the appearance of normal Golgi apparatus differ to the abnormal ones described above?

Q2 Suggest what effect these altered Golgi apparatus might have on protein production.

Q3 Structural abnormalities have also been seen in the cytoskeleton of brain cells in some Alzheimer's sufferers. Suggest how abnormalities in the cytoskeleton may affect protein production.

Practice Questions — Fact Recall

Q1 Describe the role of the ribosomes and RER in protein production.

Q2 Describe the main functions of the cytoskeleton.

3. Prokaryotic Cells

Learning Objective:

- Be able to describe the similarities and differences in the structure and ultrastructure of prokaryotic and eukaryotic cells.

Specification Reference 2.1.1

Prokaryotic cells are different from eukaryotic cells.

Prokaryotes vs eukaryotes

The table below summaries the differences between prokaryotic and eukaryotic cells:

Prokaryotic cells	Eukaryotic cells
Extremely small cells (less than 2 µm diameter)	Larger cells (about 10-100 µm diameter)
DNA is circular	DNA is linear
No nucleus — DNA free in cytoplasm	Nucleus present — DNA is inside nucleus
Cell wall made of a polysaccharide, but not cellulose or chitin	No cell wall (in animals), cellulose cell wall (in plants) or chitin cell wall (in fungi)
Few organelles and no membrane-bound organelles, e.g. no mitochondria	Many organelles — mitochondria and other membrane-bound organelles present
Flagella (when present) made of the protein flagellin, arranged in a helix	Flagella (when present) made of microtubules arranged in a '9 + 2' formation
Small ribosomes (20 nm or less)	Larger ribosomes (over 20 nm)
Examples: *E. coli* bacterium, *Salmonella* bacterium	**Examples:** Human liver cell, yeast, amoeba

Tip: A micrometre (µm) is one millionth of a metre, or 0.001 mm.

Tip: When DNA is linear it has two distinct ends (imagine a long strand of DNA). Circular DNA on the other hand loops round and connects to itself to form a complete ring.

Tip: Prokaryotes are always single-celled organisms, but eukaryotes can be single-celled or multicellular.

Bacterial cells

Prokaryotes like bacteria are roughly a tenth the size of eukaryotic cells. This means that normal microscopes aren't really powerful enough to look at their internal structure. Figure 2 below shows a bacterial cell as seen under an electron microscope (see page 41).

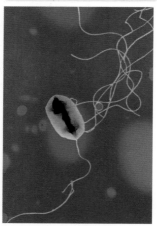

Figure 1: A prokaryotic cell. The long strands extending from the cell are flagella.

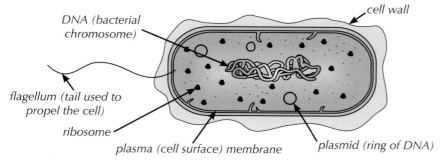

Figure 2: A bacterial cell — an example of a prokaryote.

DNA (bacterial chromosome)

cell wall

flagellum (tail used to propel the cell)

ribosome

plasma (cell surface) membrane

plasmid (ring of DNA)

Tip: Flagella and plasmids aren't always present in prokaryotic cells.

Practice Questions — Fact Recall

Q1 Give three differences between prokaryotes and eukaryotes.

Q2 Give one similarity between prokaryotic and eukaryotic cells.

4. How Microscopes Work

Investigating cells involves donning a lab coat and digging out your microscope.

Magnification and resolution of microscopes

We all know that microscopes produce a magnified image of a sample, but resolution is just as important...

Magnification

Magnification is how much bigger the image is than the specimen (the sample you're looking at). It's calculated using the formula shown on the right.

$$\text{magnification} = \frac{\text{image size}}{\text{object size}}$$

In the exam, you might be told the actual and magnified size of an object and then be asked to calculate the magnification. You can do this by using the formula above. You might also have to rearrange the formula to work out the image size or the object size.

┌─ **Examples** ─ **Maths Skills** ─────────────────────────

Calculating magnification

If you have a magnified image that's 5 mm wide and your specimen is 0.05 mm wide the magnification is:

$$\text{magnification} = \frac{\text{image size}}{\text{object size}} = \frac{5}{0.05} = \times \,\mathbf{100}$$

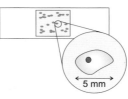

← 5 mm →

Calculating image size

If your specimen is 0.1 mm wide and the magnification of the microscope is × 20, then the image size is:

$$\text{image size} = \text{magnification} \times \text{object size} = 20 \times 0.1 = \mathbf{2\ mm}$$

Calculating object size

If you have a magnified image that's 5 mm wide and the magnification is × 50, then the object size is:

$$\text{object size} = \frac{\text{image size}}{\text{magnification}} = \frac{5}{50} = \mathbf{0.1\ mm}$$

└───

When you're calculating magnification you need to make sure that all lengths are in the same unit, e.g. all in millimetres. When dealing with microscopes these units can get pretty tiny. The table below shows common units:

To convert
× 1000
× 1000

Unit	How many millimetres it is:
Millimetre (mm)	1 mm
Micrometre (µm)	0.001 mm
Nanometre (nm)	0.000001 mm

To convert
÷ 1000
÷ 1000

The table shows that millimetres are three orders of magnitude (10^3 or 1000 times) bigger than micrometres, which are three orders of magnitude bigger than nanometres.

┌─ **Example** ─ **Maths Skills** ─────────────────────────

To convert from a smaller unit to a bigger unit you divide by 1000.
So to convert 6 micrometres to millimetres you divide 6 by 1000
= 0.006 mm. To go from a bigger unit to a smaller unit you times by 1000.

└───

Exam Tip
If you find rearranging formulas hard you can use a formula triangle to help:

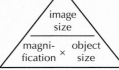

Just put your finger over the one you want and read off the formula. E.g. the formula to work out object size is image size ÷ magnification.

Resolution

Resolution is how detailed the image is. More specifically, it's how well a microscope distinguishes between two points that are close together. If a microscope lens can't separate two objects, then increasing the magnification won't help.

Example

When you look at a car in the dark that's a long way away you see the two headlights as one light. This is because your eyes can't distinguish between the two points at that distance — your eyes produce a low resolution image. When the car gets a bit closer you can see both headlights — a higher resolution image.

Practice Questions — Application

Q1 Image A shows a cartilage cell under a × 3150 microscope.

a) What is the diameter of the nucleus (labelled A) in millimetres?

b) What is the diameter of the cell (labelled B) in millimetres?

Image A

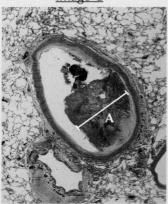

Q2 A researcher is examining some ribosomes under a microscope. Ribosomes are around 0.00002 mm long. Calculate the size of the image when viewed through a × 40 microscope. Give your answer in millimetres.

Image B

Q3 Rhinovirus particles are around 0.023 µm in diameter. They appear 0.035 mm under a microscope. What is the magnification of the microscope?

Q4 Image B shows some bacteria. It was taken using a × 7000 microscope. How long is the bacterium labelled A, in micrometres?

Q5 Image C shows a blood clot (labelled A) in an artery. The clot is 2 mm in diameter.

a) What is the magnification of the microscope?

b) The diameter of the artery is 3 mm. If the same specimen was examined under a × 50 microscope, what would the diameter of the artery in the image be?

Image C

Q6 A mitochondrion is 10 µm long. In a microscope image it is 10 mm. What is the magnification of the microscope?

Types of microscope

Light microscopes

They use light (no surprises there). They have a lower resolution than electron microscopes. They have a maximum resolution of about 0.2 micrometres (μm). So they're usually used to look at whole cells or tissues. The maximum useful magnification of a light microscope is about × 1500.

Laser scanning confocal microscopes

These are a special type of light microscope that use laser beams (intense beams of light) to scan a specimen that's usually tagged with fluorescent dyes.

A laser beam is focused through a lens which is aimed at a beam splitter. This splits the beam and some of the light is directed to the specimen. When the laser hits the dyes it causes them to give off fluorescent light. This light is then focused through a pinhole onto a detector. The detector is hooked up to a computer, which generates an image. The pinhole means that any out-of-focus light is blocked, so these microscopes produce a much clearer image than a normal light microscope.

These microscopes can be used to look at objects at different depths in thick specimens. Multiple images produced by the microscope can be combined by the computer to generate 3D images of a specimen.

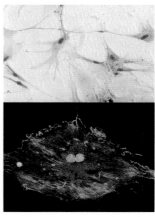

Figure 1: Lung cells seen under a light microscope (top) and a laser scanning confocal microscope (bottom).

Figure 2: The internal workings of a laser scanning confocal microscope. The image shows the laser beam (red) being focused onto the beam splitter.

Electron microscopes

Electron microscopes use electrons instead of light to form an image. They have a higher resolution than light microscopes so give more detailed images.

Types of electron microscope

There are two types of electron microscope:

Transmission electron microscope (TEM)

TEMs use electromagnets to focus a beam of electrons, which is then transmitted through the specimen to produce 2D images. Denser parts of the specimen absorb more electrons, which makes them look darker on the image you end up with.

TEMs are good because they provide high resolution images, so they can be used to look at very small organelles, e.g. ribosomes. They can also be used to look at the internal structures of organelles in detail. But specimens viewed on TEMs need to be quite thinly sliced. The angle at which specimens are cut can affect how they appear (see Figure 3).

Scanning electron microscope (SEM)

SEMs scan a beam of electrons across the specimen. This knocks off electrons from the specimen, which are gathered in a cathode ray tube to form an image. The images produced show the surface of the specimen and can be 3D but they give lower resolution images than TEMs.

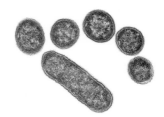

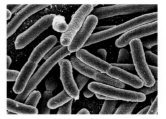

Figure 3: A TEM image (top), and SEM image (bottom) of E. coli bacteria. The E. coli in the TEM have been cut at different angles.

Interpretation of electron micrographs

You need to be able to interpret the micrographs that are produced by both transmission and scanning electron microscopes. The micrographs produced from transmission and scanning electron microscopes are different — this is due to how they are produced (see previous page).

(see previous page)

Tip: For more about the structure and function of mitochondria take a look back at page 33.

Tip: Figures 4 and 5 show the difference in resolution between TEM and SEM micrographs. Figure 4 has been produced by a TEM and has a much higher resolution (it's much clearer and you can see more fine detail) than the SEM micrograph in Figure 5.

Tip: Have a look at the electron micrographs in this section. Try and work out if they've been produced using a TEM or a SEM.

Tip: Adding colour to electron micrographs can make it easier to distinguish between different structures (e.g. you could make red blood cells appear red). There are examples of coloured micrographs on pages 31-35).

Tip: TEMs have the highest resolution because they can distinguish between the smallest objects (or objects that are only 0.0002 μm apart).

Examples

A transmission electron micrograph shows a cross section through a sample. The micrograph in Figure 4 shows internal structures of a mitochondrion — it's like you've taken a slice through the mitochondrion.

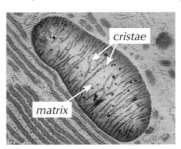

Figure 4: A transmission electron micrograph of a mitochondrion.

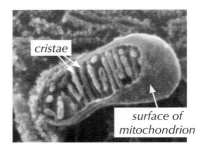

Figure 5: A scanning electron micrograph of a mitochondrion.

A scanning electron micrograph shows the surface of a sample. In Figure 5 the outer surface of a mitochondrion can be seen. This micrograph also shows the outer surfaces of the structures inside the mitochondrion (cristae) because in this particular sample the outer membrane of the organelle has been cut open exposing the internal structures.

Producing electron micrographs

To prepare samples for use with electron microscopes they are treated with a solution of heavy metals (like lead) — this process is the equivalent of staining samples that are to be viewed with a light microscope (see page 44 for more about this). The metal ions act to scatter the electrons that are fired at the sample and give contrast between different structures.

The images produced by electron microscopy are always black and white, although colour can be added to images after they've been made to make them easier to interpret.

Comparing types of microscope

You need to know about the magnification and resolution of light microscopes and both types of electron microscope. All the important numbers are shown in Figure 6.

	light microscope	TEM	SEM
maximum resolution	0.2 μm	0.0002 μm	0.002 μm
maximum magnification	x 1500	can be more than x 1 000 000	usually less than x 500 000

Figure 6: Comparison table of light and electron microscope features.

Practice Questions — Application

Q1 Read the information in the table below.

object	diameter / μm
E. coli bacterium	2.0
nuclear pore	0.05
human egg cell	100
DNA helix	0.002
mitochondrion	0.7
influenza virus	0.1

For each object, state the type of microscope(s) it could be resolved by.

Q2 Two teams of scientists are studying the human immunodeficiency virus (HIV). HIV has a diameter of 0.12 μm. Team One are focusing on HIV surface proteins and how they bind to immune system cells. The second team is studying the internal structure of the virus. Suggest what specific type of microscope each team might use during their studies. Explain your answer.

Q3 A team of researchers are investigating the function of a particular set of proteins within a tissue. In a thick sample of tissue they have tagged the different types of protein with fluorescent dyes so that they can identify them.
Suggest the type of microscope that the team could use to gain an understanding of what is happening at different depths of the sample. Explain why your suggestion is suitable.

Exam Tip
If you understand the differences between the types of microscopes, you'll then be able to decide which microscope is the most useful in any given situation.

Practice Questions — Fact Recall

Q1 State the formula for calculating the magnification of a microscope.

Q2 Explain the difference between magnification and resolution.

Q3 In laser scanning confocal microscopy what type of dyes are used?

Q4 How do transmission electron microscopes work?

Q5 How do scanning electron microscopes work?

Q6 Which type of electron microscope can produce an image of the 3D surface of a sample?

Q7 What is the maximum resolution for:

a) a light microscope,

b) a transmission electron microscope,

c) a scanning electron microscope?

Q8 Which has a higher maximum magnification, a TEM or SEM?

Q9 What type of microscope would you use to study an object that is 0.001 μm long?

Exam Tip
Make sure you understand the difference between resolution and magnification — you could be asked to explain it in the exam.

5. Using Microscopes

Learning Objectives:

- Be able to explain the use of staining in light microscopy, including the use of differential staining to identify different cellular components and cell types.

- Understand representations of cell structure as seen under the light microscope using drawings and annotated diagrams of whole cells or cells in sections of tissue.

- Be able to prepare and examine microscope slides for use in light microscopy, including the use of an eyepiece graticule and stage micrometer (PAG1).

Specification Reference 2.1.1

Now you know how they work you need to grasp how to actually use them.

Microscopes — what you need to know

You need to know a few things about using microscopes. These are:

> PRACTICAL ACTIVITY GROUP **1**

- How to prepare a slide for use with a light microscope — this includes the use of stains.

- How to use a light microscope — this includes using an eyepiece graticule and stage micrometer to work out the size of specimens you're looking at.

- How to produce and interpret drawings and annotated diagrams of cells viewed under a light microscope.

Staining samples

In light microscopes the beam of light passes through the object being viewed. An image is produced because some parts of the object absorb more light than others. Sometimes the object being viewed is completely transparent. This makes the whole thing look white because the light rays just pass straight through. To get round this, the object can be stained.

For the light microscope, this means using some kind of dye. These dyes are called stains. Common stains include methylene blue and eosin (see below). The stain is taken up by some parts of the object more than others, which means that some parts become more heavily stained than others. The contrast between heavily stained and more lightly stained parts means that the different parts of cells can be seen.

Different stains can be used to make particular parts of cells show up.

Tip: An important thing to remember here is that an image is produced after staining because it makes some parts of the specimen appear darker (or a different colour) to other parts.

┌─ **Examples** ─────────────────────────────

Methylene blue can be used to stain DNA (see Figure 1) and Giemsa stain is commonly used to differentiate between different types of blood cells (Figure 2).

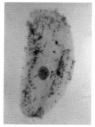

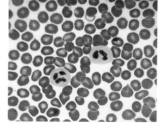

Figure 1: A cheek cell stained with methylene blue. The nucleus is visible as the roughly oval structure in the cell.

Figure 2: A human blood sample treated with Giemsa stain. Red blood cells are stained red and the nuclei present in the two white blood cells are stained purple.

It's possible to use more than one stain at once.

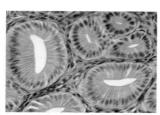

Figure 3: A light micrograph showing cells from the large intestine epithelium. Stained nuclei (purple) and cytoplasms (pink) are visible.

┌─ **Example** ──────────────────────────────

The stains haematoxylin and eosin are often used together (called H&E staining) to highlight different parts of cells (see Figure 3). Eosin dyes the cytoplasm pink. Haematoxylin stains the RNA and DNA present in cells a purple/blue colour — this highlights cell structures where these molecules are found (e.g. the nucleus and ribosomes).

How to prepare a microscope slide

If you want to look at a specimen under a light microscope, you need to stick it on a slide first. A slide is a strip of clear glass or plastic. Slides are usually flat, but some of them have a small dip or well in the centre (useful if your specimen's particularly big or a liquid).

There are two main ways of preparing a microscope slide:

Dry Mount

This is the simplest way of preparing a slide for examination under a microscope. This technique is particularly useful for observing specimens such as hairs, parts of insects, pollen, parts of flowers, etc.

Here's how to dry mount a specimen:

- Firstly, your specimen needs to let light through it for you to be able to see it clearly under the microscope. So if you've got quite a thick specimen, you'll need to take a thin slice to use on your slide.

- Use tweezers to pick up your specimen and put it in the middle of a clean slide.

- Pop a cover slip (a square of thin, transparent plastic or glass) on top. Your slide is now ready to use.

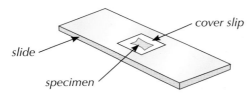

Figure 4: A dry mount slide.

Wet Mount

Wet mounts involve your specimen being in a liquid (usually water). They are more difficult to carry out than dry mounting but can produce slides that give a really clear view of a specimen. This technique can be used with a variety of specimens including living samples (e.g. tiny aquatic organisms).

Here's how to wet mount a specimen:

- Start by pipetting a small drop of water onto the slide. Then use tweezers to place your specimen on top of the water drop.

- To put the cover slip on, stand the slip upright on the slide, next to the water droplet. Then carefully tilt and lower it so it covers the specimen. Try not to get any air bubbles under there — they'll obstruct your view of the specimen.

- Once the cover slip is in position, you can add a stain. Put a drop of stain next to one edge of the cover slip. Then put a bit of paper towel next to the opposite edge. The stain will get drawn under the slip, across the specimen.

Figure 5: A wet mount slide.

Tip: Take care when preparing slides — glass slides and cover slips can expose sharp edges if they break. Also, make sure you do a risk assessment before doing any practical work like this to identify any other hazards, e.g. some stains are harmful chemicals.

Tip: In a dry mount there's just a (relatively) dry specimen under the cover slip.

Tip: Wet mounts are also used for liquid specimens (e.g. a sample of pond water). For these you won't need to add any water as your sample itself will provide the liquid. This is an example of when you might use a slide that has a well.

Tip: A smear slide is a special type of wet mount. These are often used for blood samples. It involves spreading the liquid thinly over the central area of the slide. A cover slip can then be applied and any excess liquid wiped off the slide.

How to use a light microscope

You're expected to be able to use a light microscope to view a specimen (e.g. a sample of plant tissue or a sample of human skin cells).

How to use a light microscope to view a specimen

1. Start by clipping the slide containing the specimen onto the stage.
2. Select the lowest-powered objective lens (i.e. the one that produces the lowest magnification).
3. Use the coarse adjustment knob to bring the stage up to just below the objective lens.
4. Look down the eyepiece (which contains the ocular lens). Use the coarse adjustment knob to move the stage downwards, away from the objective lens, until the image is roughly in focus.
5. Adjust the focus with the fine adjustment knob, until you get a clear image of what's on the slide.
6. If you need to see the slide with greater magnification, swap to a higher-powered objective lens and refocus.

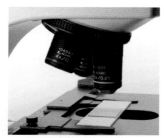

Figure 6: Some microscopes have a slide holder rather than clips. This grips the sides of a slide and allows fine movement of the slide on the stage.

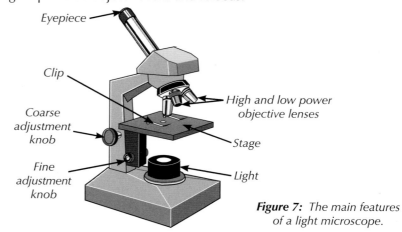

Figure 7: The main features of a light microscope.

(labels: Eyepiece, Clip, High and low power objective lenses, Coarse adjustment knob, Stage, Fine adjustment knob, Light)

If you're asked to draw what you can see when using a microscope to look at a specimen, make sure the relative sizes of objects in your drawing are accurate and that you write down the magnification the specimen was viewed under. You'll also need to label your drawing and give it a title.

How to use an eyepiece graticule and stage micrometer

Sometimes, you might want to know the size of your specimen. And that's where the eyepiece graticule and stage micrometer come in — they're a bit like rulers.

- An **eyepiece graticule** is fitted onto the eyepiece. It's like a transparent ruler with numbers, but no units. So when you look through the eyepiece you'll see a scale (see Figure 8 on the next page).

- The **stage micrometer** is placed on the stage — it is a microscope slide with an accurate scale (it has units) and it's used to work out the value of the divisions on the eyepiece graticule at a particular magnification.

This means that when you take the stage micrometer away and replace it with the slide containing your specimen, you'll be able to measure the size of the specimen. This works because you'll have worked out what lengths the divisions on your eyepiece graticule actually represent.

The example on the next page demonstrates how to use an eyepiece graticule and stage micrometer.

Example — Maths Skills

1. Line up the eyepiece graticule and the stage micrometer.
2. Each division on the stage micrometer is 0.1 mm long (see Figure 8).
3. At this magnification, 1 division on the stage micrometer is the same as 4.5 divisions on the eyepiece graticule.
4. To work out the size of 1 division on the eyepiece graticule, you need to divide 0.1 by 4.5:

    1 division on eyepiece graticule = 0.1 ÷ 4.5 = 0.02... mm

5. So if you look at an object under the microscope at this magnification and it's 20 eyepiece divisions long, you know it measures:

    20 × 0.02... = **0.4 mm** (1 s.f.)

   If you look at a different object under the microscope and it's 37 eyepiece divisions long, you know it measures:

    37 × 0.02... = **0.8 mm** (1 s.f.)

   But don't forget, if you change to a different magnification you'll need to re-do the calibration.

Tip: Remember: at a different magnification, 1 division on the stage micrometer will be equal to a different number of divisions on the eyepiece graticule — so the eyepiece graticule will need to be re-calibrated.

Tip: Each division on an eyepiece graticule can be called an eyepiece unit (epu).

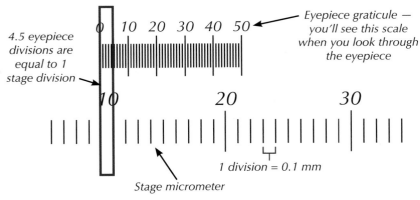

4.5 eyepiece divisions are equal to 1 stage division

Eyepiece graticule — you'll see this scale when you look through the eyepiece

1 division = 0.1 mm

Stage micrometer

Figure 8: Calibrating an eyepiece graticule to a stage micrometer.

Practice Question — Application

Q1 An eyepiece graticule and a stage micrometer are being calibrated. Each division on the stage micrometer is 2 μm long. At this magnification, 5 divisions on the stage micrometer is the same as 8 divisions on the eyepiece graticule.

   a) Calculate the size of one division on the eyepiece graticule.

   b) Calculate the width of the animal cell labelled X shown in the diagram below.

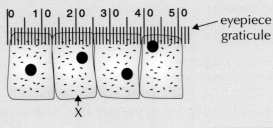

eyepiece graticule

X

Section Summary

Make sure you know:

- What prokaryotes and eukaryotes are.

- The ultrastructure of eukaryotic cells, such as animal and plant cells, and the cellular components that they contain, e.g. the different organelles that are present in different eukaryotic cells.

- The structure and function of the following cellular components: the plasma membrane, cell wall, nucleus, nuclear envelope, nucleolus, lysosomes, ribosomes, rough and smooth endoplasmic reticulum, vesicles, Golgi apparatus, mitochondria, chloroplasts, centrioles, cilia and flagella.

- That organelles work together to make proteins. Proteins are made at the ribosomes, then folded and processed in the rough endoplasmic reticulum. They are then transported to the Golgi apparatus in vesicles, processed further, and are transported around the cell before being secreted.

- That in eukaryotes the cytoplasm contains protein threads known as the cytoskeleton — arranged as microfilaments and microtubules. The cytoskeleton supports organelles, provides strength to the cell and maintains its shape, transports organelles and material within the cell and enables cell movement.

- The similarities and differences between the ultrastructure of prokaryotes and eukaryotes.

- How to use the magnification formula: magnification = image size ÷ object size. You also need to know how to manipulate this formula, e.g. how to rearrange it to calculate object size or image size.

- The difference between magnification (how much bigger the image is than the sample) and resolution (how detailed the image is).

- How microscopy allows the study of cells and cell structure.

- That a laser scanning confocal microscope uses laser beams to scan a specimen which is tagged with fluorescent dyes. The images produced result from fluorescent light emitted by specimens.

- That a transmission electron microscope (TEM) transmits a beam of electrons through a specimen and produces micrographs that show 2D images of the specimen.

- That a scanning electron microscope (SEM) scans a beam of electrons across a specimen and produces micrographs that show 3D images of the surface of the specimen.

- How to interpret photomicrographs of cellular components, including photos from TEMs and SEMs.

- The different magnification and resolution that can be achieved from a light microscope, a transmission electron microscope and a scanning electron microscope.

- How to understand drawings and annotated diagrams of whole cells or cells in sections of tissue as seen under the light microscope.

- That staining is often required before using a light microscope in order to see the different cellular structures and organelles, and that more than one stain can be used to highlight different parts.

- How to prepare slides for use in light microscopy (dry and wet mounts) and how to examine specimens and work out their size using an eyepiece graticule and stage micrometer.

Exam-style Questions

1 Abnormal mitochondria have been found in diseased heart tissue, suggesting a link between mitochondria and heart disease. To investigate this further, a group of scientists produced a strain of mice with abnormal mitochondria.

The abnormal mice developed symptoms of heart disease after just one year. Normal mice showed similar symptoms after two years.

(a) (i) Describe the main function of mitochondria.

(1 mark)

(ii) Suggest why abnormal mitochondria might be problematic in heart tissue.

(2 marks)

(b) **Fig. 1.1** shows mitochondria in the normal mice and the abnormal mice.

| Normal mice | Abnormal mice |

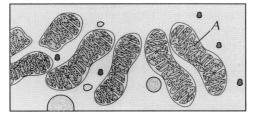 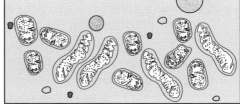

Fig. 1.1

(i) Describe **two** differences between the mitochondria found in the abnormal and normal mice.

(2 marks)

(ii) The mitochondrion labelled **A** in the normal mouse is about 1.5 μm in length. Calculate the magnification of the image.

(2 marks)

2 A scientist is studying secretory epithelial cells from the stomach under a light microscope.

The microscope has a magnification of × 100 and a resolution of 0.2 μm.

(a) (i) The ribosomes in the epithelial cells are 25 nm in diameter. Will the scientist be able to see them using the light microscope? Explain your answer.

(2 marks)

(ii) Explain the difference that you would expect to see if the ribosomes in the stomach cells were compared to those in bacterial cells.

(2 marks)

(iii) State **two** differences the scientist would observe if he compared the stomach cell to a plant cell.

(2 marks)

(iv) Before looking at the epithelial cells under the microscope the scientist applies two stains to the specimen.

Suggest why the scientist has done this.

(1 mark)

(b) The scientist sees an image of an epithelial cell that is 4 mm in diameter. Calculate the actual diameter of the cell. Give your answer in millimetres.

(2 marks)

(c)* One of the main functions of secretory epithelial cells in the stomach is to produce and secrete digestive enzymes.

Describe the role of each organelle involved in the production and secretion of these proteins.

(6 marks)

3 Penicillins are a group of antibiotics that are only effective against prokaryotic cells. They work by inhibiting cell wall synthesis, leading to cell lysis (bursting).

(a) Explain why penicillin antibiotics can clear bacterial infections in humans without harming the infected individual's cells.

(2 marks)

(b) The electron micrograph in **Fig. 3.1** shows an intact *Staphylococcus aureus* bacterium (right) and one undergoing lysis (left).

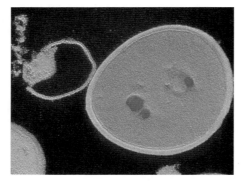

Fig. 3.1

(i) Suggest **one** reason why an electron microscope was used to view these cells rather than a light microscope.

(2 marks)

(ii) Name the type of electron microscope that was used to produce the micrograph seen in **Fig 3.1**. Give a reason for your answer.

(2 marks)

(c) Give **two** ways in which you could distinguish between a prokaryotic cell and a eukaryotic cell in an electron micrograph.

(2 marks)

* The quality of your response will be assessed in this question.

1. Water

Water is essential for life. The next few pages will show you what it is about water that makes it so important.

Functions of water

Water is vital to living organisms. It makes up about 80% of a cell's contents and has loads of important functions, inside and outside cells, such as:

- Water is a reactant in loads of important chemical reactions, including hydrolysis reactions (see page 54).
- Water is a solvent, which means some substances dissolve in it. Most biological reactions take place in solution (e.g. in the cytoplasm of eukaryotic and prokaryotic cells) so water's pretty essential.
- Water transports substances. The fact that it's a liquid and a solvent means it can easily transport all sorts of materials, like glucose and oxygen, around plants and animals.
- Water helps with temperature control because it has a high specific heat capacity and a high latent heat of evaporation (see next page).
- Water is a habitat. The fact that it helps with temperature control, is a solvent and becomes less dense when it freezes (see next page) means many organisms can survive and reproduce in it.

Structure of water

To understand the structure of water, you need to know a bit about the chemistry involved in holding water molecules together.

Polarity of water

A molecule of water (H_2O) is one atom of oxygen (O) joined to two atoms of hydrogen (H_2) by shared electrons — see Figure 1.

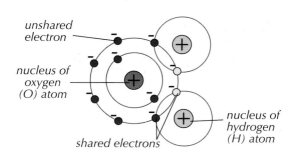

Figure 1: The structure of a water molecule.

Because the shared negative hydrogen electrons are pulled towards the oxygen atom, the other side of each hydrogen atom is left with a slight positive charge. The unshared negative electrons on the oxygen atom give it a slight negative charge. This makes water a polar molecule — it has a partial negative charge ($\delta-$) on one side and a partial positive charge ($\delta+$) on the other (see Figure 2).

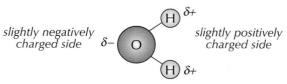

Figure 2: The slight charges on a water molecule.

Learning Objectives:

- Be able to describe how hydrogen bonding occurs between water molecules.
- Be able to relate the properties of water to the roles of water for living organisms, including as a solvent, transport medium, coolant and a habitat.
- Be able to illustrate these roles using examples of prokaryotes and eukaryotes.

Specification Reference 2.1.2

Exam Tip
Examiners like asking you to relate structure to properties and function, so make sure you're clear on the structure of water.

Tip: 'δ' is the Latin letter 'delta'. So you read $\delta+$ as 'delta positive' and $\delta-$ as 'delta negative'.

Exam Tip
Be careful not to write that a water molecule has a positive and a negative side — you must make it clear that one side has a partial positive charge and the other side has a partial negative charge.

Hydrogen bonding

The slightly negatively-charged oxygen atoms attract the slightly positively-charged hydrogen atoms of other water molecules. This attraction is called **hydrogen bonding** and it gives water some of its useful properties.

Exam Tip
If you're asked to draw water molecules in the exam, make sure you draw the hydrogen bonds as dashed lines and include the partial charges (δ+ or δ–) on all the atoms.

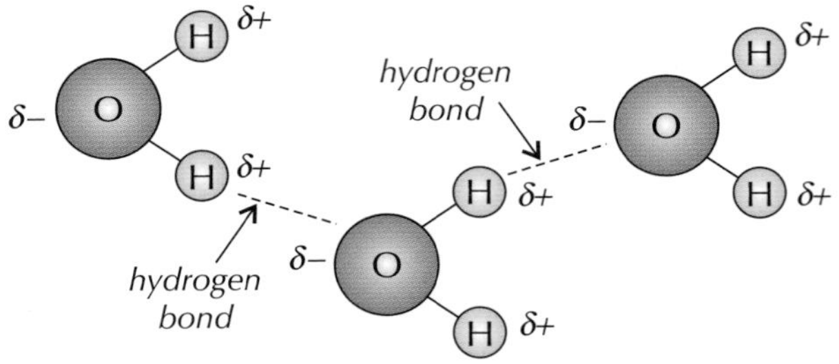

***Figure 3:** Diagram showing how hydrogen bonds hold water molecules together.*

Properties of water

The structure of a water molecule gives it some useful properties, and these help to explain many of its functions:

High specific heat capacity

Hydrogen bonds give water a high **specific heat capacity** — this is the energy needed to raise the temperature of 1 gram of a substance by 1 °C. The hydrogen bonds between water molecules can absorb a lot of energy. So water has a high specific heat capacity — it takes a lot of energy to heat it up. This means water doesn't experience rapid temperature changes, which is one of the properties that makes it a good habitat — the temperature under water is likely to be more stable than it is on land.

High latent heat of evaporation

It takes a lot of energy (heat) to break the hydrogen bonds between water molecules. So water has a high latent heat of evaporation — a lot of energy is used up when water evaporates (changes from a liquid to a gas). This is useful for living organisms because it means water's great for cooling things. This is why some mammals, like us, sweat when they're too hot. When sweat evaporates, it cools the surface of the skin.

Tip: Latent heat is the heat energy that's needed to change a substance from one state to another, e.g. from a liquid to a gas.

Very cohesive

Cohesion is the attraction between molecules of the same type (e.g. two water molecules). Water molecules are very cohesive (they tend to stick together) because they're polar. This helps water to flow, making it great for transporting substances. It also helps water to be transported up plant stems in the transpiration stream (see page 205).

Lower density when solid

At low temperatures water freezes — it turns from a liquid to a solid. Water molecules are held further apart in ice than they are in liquid water because each water molecule forms four hydrogen bonds to other water molecules, making a lattice shape. This makes ice less dense than liquid water — which is why ice floats. This is useful for living organisms because, in cold temperatures, ice forms an insulating layer on top of water — the water below doesn't freeze. So organisms that live in water, like fish, don't freeze and can still move around.

Good solvent

A lot of important substances in biological reactions are ionic (like salt, for example). This means they're made from one positively-charged atom or molecule and one negatively-charged atom or molecule (e.g. salt is made from a positive sodium ion and a negative chloride ion). Because water is polar, the slightly positive end of a water molecule will be attracted to the negative ion, and the slightly negative end of a water molecule will be attracted to the positive ion. This means the ions will get totally surrounded by water molecules — in other words, they'll dissolve (see Figure 4).

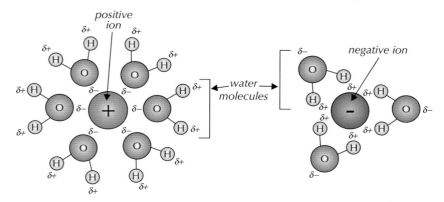

Figure 4: *A positive ion (left) and a negative ion (right) dissolved in water.*

Water's polarity makes it useful as a solvent in living organisms. E.g. in humans, important ions (see pages 66-67) can dissolve in the water in blood and then be transported around the body.

Tip: Most biological reactions take place in solution, so water's pretty essential.

Tip: Remember — a molecule is polar if it has a slightly negatively-charged side and a slightly positively-charged side.

Tip: Polar molecules, such as glucose, dissolve in water because hydrogen bonds form between them and the water molecules.

Practice Questions — Fact Recall

Q1 Give three functions of water that are important to living organisms.

Q2 Why is water classed as a polar molecule?

Q3 Label this diagram of a water molecule showing the name and charge on each atom.

Q4 What is a hydrogen bond?

Q5 Draw a diagram showing four water molecules hydrogen bonded together.

Q6 Explain why water has a high specific heat capacity.

Q7 Explain why water is good for cooling things.

Q8 Give two reasons why the polarity of water makes it good for transporting substances.

Q9 The diagrams on the right show molecular models of liquid water and ice.

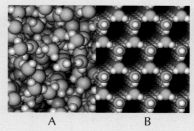

a) Which diagram, A or B, is a molecular model of ice? Give a reason for your answer.

b) Explain how the formation of ice can be beneficial for organisms.

Q10 Describe how an Mg^{2+} ion dissolves in water.

Exam Tip
If you're asked in the exam about how a particular ion dissolves in water, don't get put off by the ion itself — just figure out if it's positively charged or negatively charged. E.g. in Q10 here Mg^{2+} is a positively charged magnesium ion.

Learning Objectives:

- Understand the concept of monomers and polymers.
- Understand the importance of condensation and hydrolysis reactions in a range of biological molecules.

Specification Reference 2.1.2

Tip: Nucleic acids are also polymers. Their monomers are called nucleotides. There's more about nucleic acids on pages 83-84.

Tip: Lipids aren't classed as polymers because they do not consist of repeating units (monomers).

Exam Tip
If you're asked to show a condensation reaction, don't forget to put the water molecule in as a product.

Tip: A condensation reaction removes one molecule of water, but a hydrolysis reaction adds one molecule of water.

Tip: It's easy to remember what a hydrolysis reaction does as 'hydro' means water and 'lysis' means breaking down.

2. Macromolecules and Polymers

The cells of all living organisms are made up of loads of different types of biological molecules. Some of these are macromolecules and some are polymers as well...

What are macromolecules?

Macromolecules are complex molecules with a relatively large molecular mass. Examples of biological macromolecules include proteins, some carbohydrates and lipids. Polymers are a group of macromolecules.

What are polymers?

Most carbohydrates and all proteins are **polymers**. Polymers are large, complex molecules composed of long chains of **monomers** joined together.
Monomers are small, basic molecular units. Examples of monomers include monosaccharides (see next page) and amino acids (see p. 61).

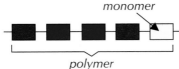

Figure 1: A polymer.

Making polymers

Most biological polymers are formed from their monomers by **condensation** reactions. A condensation reaction forms a chemical bond between monomers, releasing a molecule of water — see Figure 2.

Figure 2: Example of the formation of a polymer.

Breaking down polymers

Biological polymers can be broken down into monomers by **hydrolysis** reactions. A hydrolysis reaction breaks the chemical bond between monomers using a water molecule. It's basically the opposite of a condensation reaction.

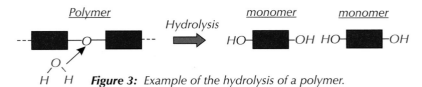

Figure 3: Example of the hydrolysis of a polymer.

Practice Questions — Fact Recall

Q1 What is a polymer?

Q2 What is a monomer?

Q3 Give two examples of monomers.

Q4 Explain what happens in a condensation reaction between two monomers.

Q5 What type of reaction involves the breakage of a chemical bond between two monomers using water?

3. Carbohydrates

Carbohydrates are needed by living organisms for things like energy storage and support — their function is related to their structure.

What are carbohydrates made from?

Most carbohydrates are polymers. All carbohydrates are made up of the same three chemical elements — carbon (C), hydrogen (H) and oxygen (O). For every carbon atom in the carbohydrate there are usually two hydrogen atoms and one oxygen atom.

The monomers that make up carbohydrates are called **monosaccharides**. You need to know the structures of two different monosaccharides — glucose and ribose.

Glucose

Glucose is a monosaccharide with six carbon atoms. This means it's a hexose monosaccharide. There are two forms of glucose — alpha (α) and beta (β). They both have a ring structure — see Figure 1.

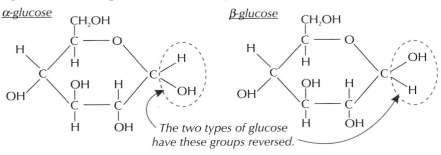

Figure 1: The structures of α-glucose and β-glucose.

Glucose's structure is related to its function as the main energy source in animals and plants. Its structure makes it soluble, so it can be easily transported. Its chemical bonds contain lots of energy.

Ribose

Ribose is a monosaccharide with five carbon atoms — this means it's a pentose monosaccharide. You need to know its structure (see Figure 2).

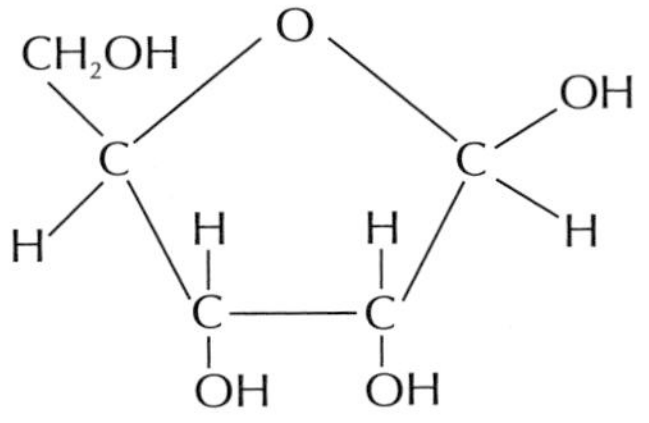

Ribose is the sugar component of RNA nucleotides (see p. 81).

Figure 2: The structure of ribose.

Polysaccharide formation

Monosaccharides are joined together by **glycosidic bonds**. During synthesis, a hydrogen atom on one monosaccharide bonds to a hydroxyl (OH) group on the other, releasing a molecule of water — this is a **condensation** reaction (see previous page). The reverse of this synthesis reaction is **hydrolysis** — a molecule of water reacts with the glycosidic bond, breaking it apart.

Learning Objectives:

- Know the chemical elements that make up carbohydrates (C, H and O).
- Understand the difference between a hexose and a pentose monosaccharide.
- Recall the ring structure and properties of glucose (a hexose monosaccharide) and the structure of ribose (a pentose monosaccharide).
- Understand the structural difference between α-glucose and β-glucose.
- Recall the synthesis and breakdown of disaccharides (including sucrose, lactose and maltose) and polysaccharides by the formation and breakage of glycosidic bonds.
- Recall the structure of starch (amylose and amylopectin), glycogen and cellulose molecules.
- Know how the structures and properties of glucose, starch, glycogen and cellulose molecules relate to their functions in living organisms.

Specification Reference 2.1.2

Tip: Although most carbohydrates are polymers, single monosaccharides are also called carbohydrates.

A **disaccharide** is formed when two monosaccharides join together:

Example

Two α-glucose molecules are joined together by a glycosidic bond to form maltose.

$$\text{synthesis} \rightleftharpoons \text{hydrolysis}$$

H_2O is removed

$+ H_2O$

glycosidic bond

Other disaccharides are formed in a similar way. Sucrose is a disaccharide formed when α-glucose and fructose join together. Lactose is a disaccharide formed by the joining together of galactose with either α-glucose or β-glucose.

A **polysaccharide** is formed when more than two monosaccharides join together:

Example

Lots of α-glucose molecules are joined together by glycosidic bonds to form amylose.

glycosidic bonds

Functions of carbohydrates

You need to know about the relationship between the structure and function of three polysaccharides — starch, glycogen and cellulose.

Starch

Starch is the main energy storage material in plants. Cells get energy from glucose and plants store excess glucose as starch (when a plant needs more glucose for energy it breaks down starch to release the glucose). Starch is insoluble in water so it doesn't cause water to enter cells by osmosis (see p. 126), which would make them swell. This makes it good for storage. Starch is a mixture of two polysaccharides of alpha-glucose — amylose and amylopectin:

- **Amylose** is a long, unbranched chain of α-glucose. The angles of the glycosidic bonds give it a coiled structure, almost like a cylinder. This makes it compact, so it's really good for storage because you can fit more in to a small space.

- **Amylopectin** is a long, branched chain of α-glucose. Its side branches allow the enzymes that break down the molecule to get at the glycosidic bonds easily. This means that the glucose can be released quickly.

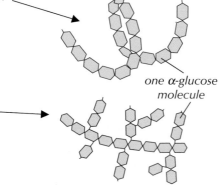

one α-glucose molecule

Figure 3: The structures of amylose (top) and amylopectin (bottom).

Tip: Structures aren't always drawn with everything on them, e.g. when you get a line with nothing on the end, like this

it just means there's a carbon there, with other elements (like hydrogen) attached to it.

Tip: You can test for the presence of starch using the iodine test (see page 69).

Tip: Hydrogen bonds between α-glucose molecules help to hold amylose in its helical structure.

Exam Tip
Always specify whether you're talking about α-glucose or β-glucose — you won't get a mark for only saying glucose.

Glycogen

Glycogen is the main energy storage material in animals. Animal cells get energy from glucose too, but animals store excess glucose as glycogen — another polysaccharide of alpha-glucose. Its structure is very similar to amylopectin, except that it has loads more side branches coming off it — see Figure 4. Loads of branches means that stored glucose can be released quickly, which is important for energy release in animals. It's also a very compact molecule, so it's good for storage.

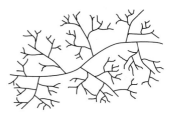

Figure 4: *The structure of glycogen.*

Exam Tip
If you're asked about the function of glycogen in the exam, make sure you say it acts as an energy store or reserve — you won't get marks just for saying it 'contains energy'.

Cellulose

Cellulose is the major component of cell walls in plants. It's made of long, unbranched chains of beta-glucose. When beta-glucose molecules bond, they form straight cellulose chains. The cellulose chains are linked together by **hydrogen bonds** to form strong fibres called **microfibrils** — see Figure 5. The strong fibres mean cellulose provides structural support for cells (e.g. in plant cell walls).

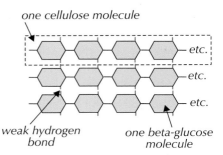

one cellulose molecule

etc.

etc.

etc.

weak hydrogen bond

one beta-glucose molecule

Figure 5: *The structure of a cellulose microfibril.*

Figure 6: *Coloured scanning electron micrograph (SEM) of cellulose microfibrils in a plant cell wall.*

Tip: A hydrogen bond is a relatively weak bond formed between hydrogen atoms and other atoms, e.g. nitrogen or oxygen.

Practice Question — Application

Q1 Look at the following monosaccharides.

α-glucose   galactose   fructose

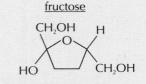

Draw the disaccharide that would be formed from a condensation reaction between:

a) α-glucose and galactose   b) α-glucose and fructose

Practice Questions — Fact Recall

Q1 What three chemical elements are found in carbohydrates?

Q2 What is the difference between a hexose monosaccharide and a pentose monosaccharide?

Q3 Draw the structure of:
   a) an α-glucose molecule,   b) a ribose molecule.

Q4 Name the bond that forms between two monosaccharides to make a disaccharide.

Q5 What two monosaccharides make up a sucrose molecule?

Q6 Describe the structure of glycogen and explain how its structure makes it suited to its function.

Q7 Sketch and label a diagram of a microfibril.

Exam Tip
Don't panic if you're asked to draw a diagram in the exam — you don't have to be the best artist in the world, but make sure you add labels to point out all the important bits.

4. Lipids

Lipids are commonly known as fats or oils. They're found in plants and animals, and have a variety of different functions.

Learning Objectives:

- Know the chemical elements that make up lipids (C, H and O).

- Recall the structure of a triglyceride as an example of a macromolecule.

- Be able to describe the synthesis and breakdown of triglycerides by the formation (esterification) and breakage of ester bonds between fatty acids and glycerol.

- Be able to outline the structure of a saturated and an unsaturated fatty acid.

- Recall the structure of a phospholipid as an example of a macromolecule.

- Be able to explain how the properties of triglyceride, phospholipid and cholesterol molecules relate to their functions in living organisms, including hydrophobic and hydrophilic regions and energy content, illustrated using examples of prokaryotes and eukaryotes.

Specification Reference 2.1.2

What are lipids?

Lipids are macromolecules — see page 54. They all contain the chemical elements carbon, hydrogen and oxygen. There are three types of lipid you need to know about — triglycerides, phospholipids and cholesterol.

Triglycerides

Triglycerides have one molecule of glycerol with three fatty acids attached to it. They're synthesised by the formation of an **ester bond** between each fatty acid and the glycerol molecule.

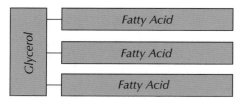

Figure 1: Structure of a triglyceride.

Ester bonds

One triglyceride molecule has three ester bonds. Each ester bond is formed by a condensation reaction (in which a water molecule is released). The process in which triglycerides are synthesised is called **esterification**. Triglycerides break down when the ester bonds are broken. Each ester bond is broken in a hydrolysis reaction (in which a water molecule is used up).

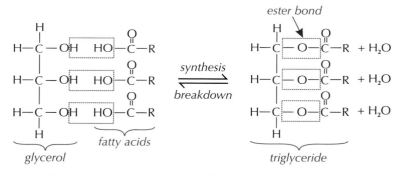

Figure 2: The esterification and breakdown of a triglyceride.

Fatty acids

Fatty acid molecules have long 'tails' made of hydrocarbons (compounds that contain only carbon and hydrogen atoms). The tails are 'hydrophobic' (they repel water molecules). These tails make lipids insoluble in water. All fatty acids have the same basic structure, but the hydrocarbon tail varies — see Figure 3.

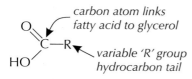

Figure 3: Structure of a fatty acid.

There are two kinds of fatty acids — saturated and unsaturated. The difference is in their hydrocarbon tails (see next page).

Tip: The variable R group can be any hydrocarbon.

- **Saturated fatty acids** don't have any double bonds between their carbon atoms in their hydrocarbon tails. The fatty acid is 'saturated' with hydrogen.

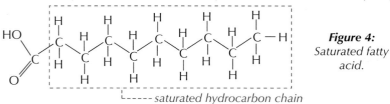

Figure 4: Saturated fatty acid.

Tip: Most animal fats are saturated — the fatty acids in these lipids are saturated so they have no double bonds.

Tip: The general formula for a saturated fatty acid is $C_nH_{(2n+1)}COOH$.

- **Unsaturated fatty acids** have at least one double bond between carbon atoms, which causes the chain to kink.

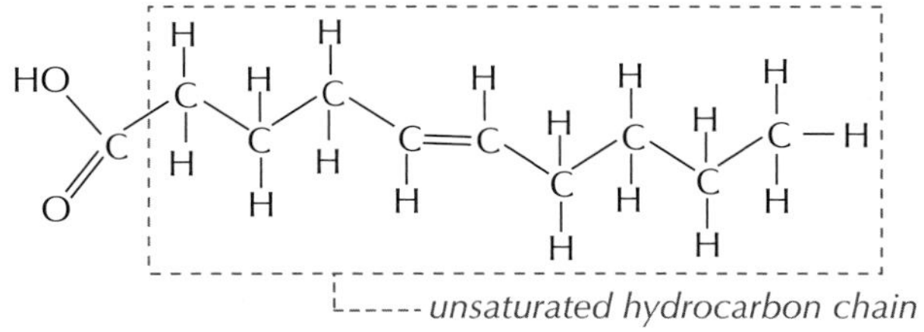

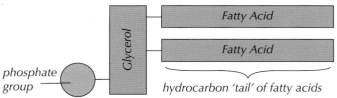

Figure 5: Unsaturated fatty acid.

Tip: Most plant fats are unsaturated — some of the fatty acids in these lipids are unsaturated meaning they have double bonds.

Phospholipids

Phospholipids are pretty similar to triglycerides, except one of the fatty acid molecules is replaced by a phosphate group. The phosphate group is hydrophilic (it attracts water molecules) and the fatty acid tails are hydrophobic.

Figure 6: Structure of a phospholipid.

Tip: Remember, a phospholipid has a phosphate group.

Cholesterol

Cholesterol is another type of lipid — it has a hydrocarbon ring structure attached to a hydrocarbon tail. The ring structure has a polar hydroxyl (OH) group attached to it.

hydroxyl → HO — | Hydrocarbon rings | — | Hydrocarbon tail |
group

Figure 7: Structure of cholesterol.

Tip: In a hydrocarbon ring structure, the carbon atoms are literally arranged in a ring-like shape instead of a long chain.

Functions of lipids

You need to know how the properties of triglycerides, phospholipids and cholesterol are related to their functions:

Triglycerides

In animals and plants, triglycerides are mainly used as energy storage molecules. Some bacteria (e.g. *Mycobacterium tuberculosis*) use triglycerides to store both energy and carbon. Triglycerides are good for storage because the long hydrocarbon tails of the fatty acids contain lots of chemical energy — a load of energy is released when they're broken down. Because of these tails, lipids contain about twice as much energy per gram as carbohydrates.

Tip: Storage molecules also need to be insoluble because otherwise they'd just dissolve (and release whatever they were storing) whenever they came into contact with water.

Triglycerides are also insoluble, so they don't cause water to enter the cells by osmosis (see p. 126) which would make them swell. The triglycerides bundle together as insoluble droplets in cells because the fatty acid tails are hydrophobic (water-repelling) — the tails face inwards, shielding themselves from water with their glycerol heads — see Figure 8.

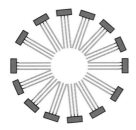

Figure 8: Diagram showing an insoluble triglyceride droplet.

Phospholipids

Tip: There's more about the role of phospholipids and cholesterol in cell membranes on pages 117-118.

Phospholipids are found in the cell membranes of all eukaryotes and prokaryotes. They make up what's known as the phospholipid bilayer (see p. 117). Cell membranes control what enters and leaves a cell. Phospholipid heads are hydrophilic and their tails are hydrophobic, so they form a double layer with their heads facing out towards the water on either side. The centre of the bilayer is hydrophobic, so water-soluble substances can't easily pass through it — the membrane acts as a barrier to those substances.

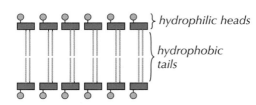

} hydrophilic heads

hydrophobic tails

Figure 9: A phospholipid bilayer.

Cholesterol

Tip: 'Polar' means it has a slightly negatively-charged bit and a slightly positively-charged bit — see p. 51.

In eukaryotic cells, cholesterol molecules help strengthen the cell membrane by interacting with the phospholipid bilayer. Cholesterol has a small size and flattened shape — this allows cholesterol to fit in between the phospholipid molecules in the membrane. They bind to the hydrophobic tails of the phospholipids, causing them to pack more closely together. This helps to make the membrane less fluid and more rigid.

cholesterol molecule

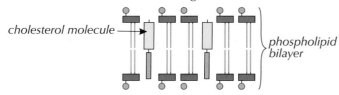

} phospholipid bilayer

Figure 10: Cholesterol molecules within a cell membrane.

Practice Questions — Fact Recall

Q1 What are the main three chemical elements that make up lipids?

Q2 What are the components of a triglyceride?

Q3 What type of bond links glycerol to a fatty acid in a triglyceride?

Q4 Explain the difference between a saturated fatty acid and an unsaturated fatty acid.

Q5 Give two reasons why triglycerides are used as energy storage molecules.

Q6 Explain how the structure of phospholipids make them suited to their function.

Q7 Describe the role cholesterol molecules have in cell membranes.

5. Proteins

Proteins have lots of useful functions in organisms. Their function is related to their structure, which is determined by the basic units they're made from and the bonds between them.

What are proteins made from?

Proteins are polymers. The monomers of proteins are amino acids. A **dipeptide** is formed when two amino acids join together. A **polypeptide** is formed when more than two amino acids join together. Proteins are made up of one or more polypeptides.

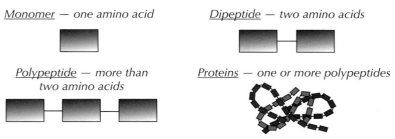

Monomer — one amino acid

Dipeptide — two amino acids

Polypeptide — more than two amino acids

Proteins — one or more polypeptides

Figure 1: *Amino acids join together to form peptides and proteins.*

Amino acid structure

All amino acids have the same general structure — a carboxyl group (-COOH) and an amino group (-NH$_2$) attached to a carbon atom. The difference between different amino acids is the variable group they contain (shown as R in Figure 2).

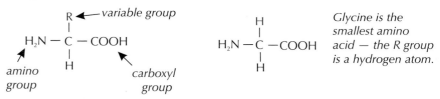

R ← variable group

$H_2N - C - COOH$

amino group

carboxyl group

Glycine is the smallest amino acid — the R group is a hydrogen atom.

$H_2N - C - COOH$

Figure 2: *The general structure of an amino acid (left) and the structure of glycine (right).*

All amino acids contain the chemical elements carbon, oxygen, hydrogen and nitrogen. Some also contain sulfur.

Dipeptide and polypeptide formation

Amino acids are linked together by **peptide bonds** to form dipeptides and polypeptides. A molecule of water is released during the reaction — it's a **condensation reaction**. The reverse of this reaction adds a molecule of water to break the peptide bond — it's a **hydrolysis** reaction.

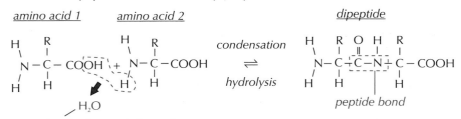

amino acid 1   *amino acid 2*   *dipeptide*

condensation ⇌ hydrolysis

peptide bond

H_2O

a molecule of water is formed during condensation.

Figure 3: *Dipeptide formation.*

Learning Objectives:

- Know the general structure of an amino acid (C, H, O, N and S).
- Know the chemical elements that make up proteins.
- Understand the synthesis and breakdown of dipeptides and polypeptides by the formation and breakage of peptide bonds.
- Recall the levels of protein structure, including primary, secondary, tertiary and quaternary structure.
- Understand the role of hydrogen bonds, ionic bonds, hydrophobic and hydrophilic interactions and disulfide bonds in the structure of proteins.
- Recall the structure and function of globular proteins, including a conjugated protein, using examples of haemoglobin (as a conjugated protein), a named enzyme and insulin.
- Recall the properties and functions of fibrous proteins, including collagen, keratin and elastin.

Specification Reference 2.1.2

Tip: Remember, condensation reactions <u>form</u> a water molecule, hydrolysis reactions <u>use</u> a water molecule.

Practice Questions — Application

Q1 Look at the following amino acid structures.

Glycine

$$H_2N - \underset{\underset{H}{|}}{\overset{\overset{H}{|}}{C}} - COOH$$

Alanine

$$H_2N - \underset{\underset{H}{|}}{\overset{\overset{CH_3}{|}}{C}} - COOH$$

Valine

$$H_2N - \underset{\underset{H}{|}}{\overset{\overset{\overset{H_3C \quad CH_3}{\diagdown \diagup}}{CH}}{\underset{|}{C}}} - COOH$$

Draw the dipeptides and polypeptide that would be formed from a condensation reaction between:

a) glycine and valine.

b) alanine and glycine.

c) glycine, alanine and valine.

Q2 Draw the amino acids produced from the hydrolysis of the dipeptide below.

$$H_2N - \underset{\underset{H}{|}}{\overset{\overset{H}{|}}{C}} - \overset{\overset{O}{||}}{C} - \underset{\underset{H}{|}}{\overset{\overset{H}{|}}{N}} - \underset{\underset{H}{|}}{\overset{\overset{CH_2OH}{|}}{C}} - COOH$$

Protein structure

Proteins are big, complicated molecules. They're much easier to explain if you describe their structure in four 'levels'. These levels are a protein's primary, secondary, tertiary and quaternary structures. The four structural levels of a protein are held together by different kinds of bonds.

Primary structure

This is the sequence of amino acids in the polypeptide chain. Different proteins have different sequences of amino acids in their primary structure. A change in just one amino acid may change the structure of the whole protein. It is held together by the peptide bonds between the amino acids.

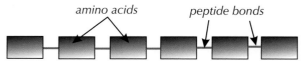

amino acids   *peptide bonds*

Figure 4: *A protein's primary structure.*

Secondary structure

The polypeptide chain doesn't remain flat and straight. Hydrogen bonds form between the –NH and –CO groups of the amino acids in the chain. This makes it automatically coil into an alpha (α) helix or fold into a beta (β) pleated sheet — this is the secondary structure.

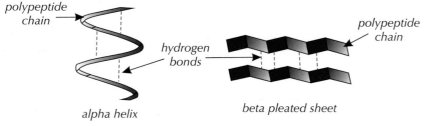

polypeptide chain

hydrogen bonds

polypeptide chain

alpha helix

beta pleated sheet

Figure 5: *A protein's secondary structure.*

Tertiary structure

The coiled or folded chain of amino acids is often coiled and folded further. More bonds form between different parts of the polypeptide chain such as:

- **Ionic bonds** — these are attractions between negatively-charged R groups and positively-charged R groups on different parts of the molecule — see Figure 7.

- **Disulfide bonds** — whenever two molecules of the amino acid cysteine come close together, the sulfur atom in one cysteine bonds to the sulfur in the other cysteine, forming a disulfide bond — see Figure 6.

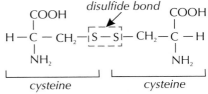

Figure 6: A disulfide bond.

- **Hydrophobic and hydrophilic interactions** — when hydrophobic (water-repelling) R groups are close together in the protein, they tend to clump together. This means that hydrophilic (water-attracting) R groups are more likely to be pushed to the outside, which affects how the protein folds up into its final structure — see Figure 7.

- **Hydrogen bonds** — these weak bonds form between slightly positively-charged hydrogen atoms in some R groups and slightly negatively-charged atoms in other R groups on the polypeptide chain — see Figure 7.

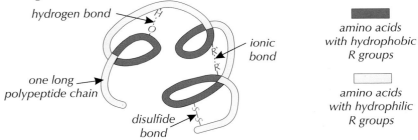

Figure 7: Examples of bonding in a protein's tertiary structure.

For proteins made from a single polypeptide chain, the tertiary structure forms their final 3D structure.

Quaternary structure

Some proteins are made of several different polypeptide chains held together by bonds. The quaternary structure is the way these polypeptide chains are assembled together.

> **Example**
>
> Haemoglobin is made of four polypeptide chains, bonded together — see Figure 9 on the next page.

The quaternary structure tends to be determined by the tertiary structure of the individual polypeptide chains being bonded together. Because of this, it can be influenced by all the bonds mentioned above. For proteins made from more than one polypeptide chain, the quaternary structure is the protein's final 3D structure.

Investigating protein structure

Computer modelling can create 3D interactive images of proteins. This is really handy for investigating the different levels of structure in a protein molecule.

Tip: Remember, an R group is an amino acid's variable group. It's also called an amino acid's 'side chain'.

Exam Tip
Make sure you spell the name of a bond correctly in the exam, otherwise you won't get the mark.

Tip: Heating a protein to a high temperature will break up its ionic bonds, hydrophobic/hydrophilic interactions and hydrogen bonds. In turn this will cause a change in the protein's 3D shape.

Tip: Not all proteins have a quaternary structure — some are made of only <u>one</u> polypeptide chain.

Tip: Figures 8, 10, 11 and 12 on the next page are examples of images of proteins made by computer modelling.

Globular proteins

Globular proteins are round and compact. In a globular protein, the hydrophilic R groups on the amino acids tend to be pushed to the outside of the molecule. This is caused by the hydrophobic and hydrophilic interactions in the protein's tertiary structure (see previous page). This makes globular proteins soluble, so they're easily transported in fluids.

Globular proteins have a range of functions in living organisms.

Exam Tip
You need to learn how the structures of haemoglobin, insulin and amylase (or another named enzyme) relate to their function.

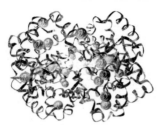

Figure 8: A molecular model of haemoglobin.

Tip: It's the iron-containing haem groups in haemoglobin that bind to oxygen.

Example — Haemoglobin

Haemoglobin is a globular protein that carries oxygen around the body in red blood cells (see page 191). It's known as a **conjugated protein** — this means it's a protein with a non-protein group attached. The non-protein part is called a **prosthetic group**. Each of the four polypeptide chains in haemoglobin has a prosthetic group called haem. A haem group contains iron, which oxygen binds to.

haem group

polypeptide chains

Figure 9: Haemoglobin's quaternary structure.

Example — Insulin

Insulin is a hormone secreted by the pancreas. It helps to regulate the blood glucose level. Its solubility is important — it means it can be transported in the blood to the tissues where it acts. An insulin molecule consists of two polypeptide chains, which are held together by disulfide bonds. When they're in the pancreas, six of these molecules bind together to form a large, globular structure (see Figure 10).

Figure 10: The quaternary structure of insulin.

Example — Amylase

Amylase is an enzyme (see page 97) that catalyses the breakdown of starch in the digestive system. It is made of a single chain of amino acids. Its secondary structure contains both alpha-helix and beta-pleated sheet sections. Most enzymes are globular proteins.

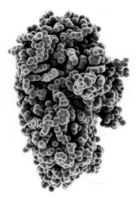

Figure 11: A molecular model of amylase.

Fibrous proteins

Fibrous proteins are tough and rope-shaped. They're also insoluble and strong. They're structural proteins and are fairly unreactive (unlike many globular proteins). You need to know about these three fibrous proteins:

Figure 12: A molecular model of collagen.

Example — Collagen

Collagen is found in animal connective tissues, such as bone, skin and muscle. It is a very strong molecule. Minerals can bind to the protein to increase its rigidity, e.g. in bone.

Figure 13: The structure of a collagen molecule.

Example — Keratin

Keratin is found in many of the external structures of animals, such as skin, hair, nails, feathers and horns. It can either be flexible (as it is in skin) or hard and tough (as it is in nails).

Example — Elastin

Elastin is found in elastic connective tissue, such as skin, large blood vessels and some ligaments. It is elastic, so it allows tissues to return to their original shape after they have been stretched.

Figure 14: Keratin layers within a nail.

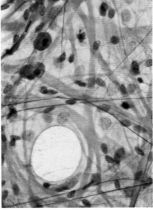

Figure 15: Light micrograph showing elastin fibres (thin dark lines) and collagen (thicker pink lines) in connective tissue.

Practice Questions — Fact Recall

Q1   What are the monomers of proteins?

Q2   What is a polypeptide?

Q3   Draw the general structure of an amino acid.

Q4   What are the main five elements found in proteins?

Q5   What is the name of the bond that forms between amino acids?

Q6   What sort of reaction:

a)   links amino acids together?   b)   breaks amino acids apart?

Q7   Describe how the secondary structure of a protein is formed.

Q8   Look at the diagram of the polypeptide chain on the right.

a)   What level of a protein's structure does it show?

b)   Name the bonds labelled A-C.

c)   Describe how the bond labelled C is formed.

Q9   What is the quaternary structure of a protein?

Q10 Explain how the globular structure of haemoglobin makes it suited to its function.

Q11 What is a conjugated protein?

Q12 State two properties of a globular protein that are different to those of a fibrous protein.

Q13 a)   What is the function of collagen?

b)   How is collagen suited to its function?

6. Inorganic Ions

Inorganic ions may be small, but they're essential for many biological processes. All the key inorganic ions you need to know about are on these two pages...

What are inorganic ions?

An ion is an atom (or group of atoms) that has an electric charge. An inorganic ion is one which doesn't contain carbon (although there are a few exceptions to this rule). Inorganic ions are really important in biological processes. The ones you need to know about are listed below and on the next page.

Cations

An ion with a positive charge is called a cation.

Name of cation	Chemical Symbol	Example(s) of roles in biological processes
Calcium	Ca^{2+}	Involved in the transmission of nerve impulses and the release of insulin from the pancreas. Acts as a cofactor for many enzymes, e.g. those involved in blood clotting. Is important for bone formation.
Sodium	Na^+	Important for generating nerve impulses, for muscle contraction and for regulating fluid balance in the body.
Potassium	K^+	Important for generating nerve impulses, for muscle contraction and for regulating fluid balance in the body. Activates essential enzymes needed for photosynthesis in plant cells.
Hydrogen	H^+	Affects the pH of substances (more H^+ ions than OH^- ions in a solution creates an acid). Also important for photosynthesis reactions that occur in the thylakoid membranes inside chloroplasts (see p. 33) and respiration reactions that occur in the inner membrane of mitochondria (p. 33).
Ammonium	NH_4^+	Absorbed from the soil by plants and is an important source of nitrogen (which is then used to make, e.g. amino acids, nucleic acids).

Learning Objectives:

- Know the key inorganic ions that are involved in biological processes, including the correct symbols for:

  - Cations: calcium ions (Ca^{2+}), sodium ions (Na^+), potassium ions (K^+), hydrogen ions (H^+), and ammonium ions (NH_4^+).
  - Anions: nitrate ions (NO_3^-), hydrogencarbonate ions (HCO_3^-), chloride ions (Cl^-), phosphate ions (PO_4^{3-}), and hydroxide ions (OH^-).

  Specification Reference 2.1.2

Tip: Children who don't receive enough calcium may develop rickets — a condition that causes the bones to become soft and weak.

Tip: An enzyme cofactor is a non-protein substance that is required for an enzyme's activity. There's more about enzyme cofactors on page 108.

Tip: Plants need nitrogen to produce chlorophyll (the green pigment found in leaves and stems). If a plant doesn't get enough nitrogen, its leaves will turn yellow.

Anions

An ion with a negative charge is called an anion.

Name of anion	Chemical Symbol	Example(s) of roles in biological processes
Nitrate	NO_3^-	Absorbed from the soil by plants and is an important source of nitrogen (which is then used to make, e.g. amino acids, nucleic acids).
Hydrogencarbonate	HCO_3^-	Acts as a buffer, which helps to maintain the pH of the blood.
Chloride	Cl^-	Involved in the 'chloride shift' which helps to maintain the pH of the blood during gas exchange (see p. 194). Acts as a cofactor for the enzyme amylase (see p. 108). Also involved in some nerve impulses.
Phosphate	PO_4^{3-}	Involved in photosynthesis and respiration reactions. Needed for the synthesis of many biological molecules, such as nucleotides (including ATP), phospholipids, and calcium phosphate (which strengthens bones).
Hydroxide	OH^-	Affects the pH of substances (more OH^- ions than H^+ ions in a solution creates an alkali).

Figure 1: *A plant with nitrogen deficiency.*

Tip: Maintaining pH in the body is really important — a pH that is too high or too low will cause proteins (including enzymes) in the body to denature (see p. 102) and so lose their function.

Tip: ATP stands for adenosine triphosphate — its structure contains three phosphate groups (in blue below):

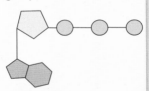

See p. 81 for more.

Practice Question — Application

Q1 Which of the ions below acts as an enzyme cofactor for amylase?

    A Na^+ **B** OH^- **C** Cl^- **D** K^+

Practice Questions — Fact Recall

Q1 Write the chemical symbol for each of the following:
   a) a hydrogen ion,
   b) an ammonium ion,
   c) a phosphate ion,
   d) a hydroxide ion.

Q2 Which ion is essential for forming strong bones?

Q3 Name two ions that are important for generating nerve impulses.

Q4 Give two sources of nitrogen for plants.

Q5 Name an ion that acts as a buffer in the blood.

Q6 What would be the effect of adding OH^- ions to a solution?

Exam Tip
Make sure you know all the chemical symbols for the ions on these pages, as well as their names — some of them are trickier than others.

- Know how to carry out and interpret the results of the following chemical tests (all PAG9):
  - the biuret test for proteins,
  - the iodine test for starch,
  - the emulsion test for lipids,
  - the Benedict's test for reducing and non-reducing sugars,
  - reagent test strips for reducing sugars.
- Know how to use quantitative methods to determine the concentration of a chemical substance in a solution using:
  - colorimetry (PAG5),
  - biosensors.

Specification Reference 2.1.2

Figure 1: A negative (left) and positive (right) biuret test result.

Tip: If you're using dilute sodium hydroxide for this test, you'll need to wear safety goggles.

Exam Tip
When a question says 'suggest' you're not expected to know the exact answer — you're expected to use your knowledge to come up with a sensible answer.

7. Biochemical Tests for Molecules

The next few pages are all about tests you can do to find out if a substance contains proteins, carbohydrates or lipids. You never know when you might need to find out exactly what is in a food sample...

Qualitative testing

PRACTICAL ACTIVITY GROUP **9**

The next three pages are about qualitative testing, which is how you determine whether a substance is present in a sample or not. There are different qualitative tests for different biological molecules. You need to know how to do these tests and how to interpret the results. Don't forget to do a risk assessment before carrying out each one — see page 7 for the kinds of things you need to look out for.

The biuret test for proteins

If you needed to find out if a substance contained protein you'd use the biuret test. There are two stages to this test.

1. The test solution needs to be alkaline, so first you add a few drops of sodium hydroxide solution.
2. Then you add some copper(II) sulfate solution.

If protein is present, the solution turns purple. If there's no protein, the solution will stay blue — see Figures 1 and 2. The colours can be fairly pale, so you might need to look carefully.

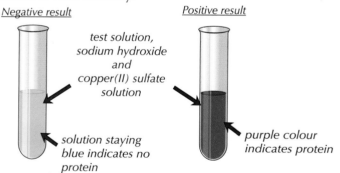

Negative result   *Positive result*

test solution, sodium hydroxide and copper(II) sulfate solution

solution staying blue indicates no protein

purple colour indicates protein

Figure 2: A positive and negative biuret test result.

Practice Questions — Application

A biuret test was carried out to determine which liquids contained protein. The results of the experiment are shown in the table below.

Liquid	Result
De-ionised water	Blue
Cow's milk	Blue
Orange juice	Purple
Orange squash	Blue
Goat's milk	Purple

Q1 Which of the liquids in the table gave a positive test result?

Q2 Suggest why the scientist tested de-ionised water.

The iodine test for starch

If you want to test for the presence of starch in a sample, you'll need to do the iodine test. Just add iodine dissolved in potassium iodide solution to the test sample. If starch is present, the sample changes from browny-orange to a dark, blue-black colour — see Figures 3 and 4. If there is no starch, it stays browny-orange.

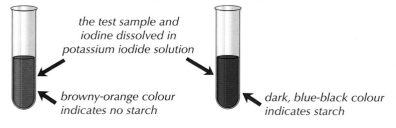

the test sample and iodine dissolved in potassium iodide solution

browny-orange colour indicates no starch

dark, blue-black colour indicates starch

Figure 3: *A negative (left) and positive (right) iodine test result.*

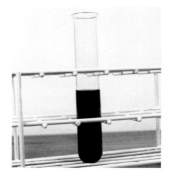

Figure 4: *A dark blue-black colour indicates the presence of starch in an iodine test.*

The emulsion test for lipids

If you want to test for the presence of lipids in a sample, you'll need to do the emulsion test. To do this you shake the test substance with ethanol for about a minute, then pour the solution into water. If lipid is present, the solution will turn milky — see Figures 5 and 6. The more lipid there is, the more noticeable the milky colour will be. If there's no lipid, the solution will stay clear.

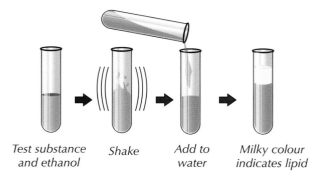

Test substance and ethanol   *Shake*   *Add to water*   *Milky colour indicates lipid*

Figure 5: *The emulsion test for lipids.*

Figure 6: *A positive result using the emulsion test.*

The Benedict's test for sugars

Sugar is a general term for monosaccharides and disaccharides. All sugars can be classified as reducing or non-reducing. To test for sugars you use the Benedict's test. The test differs depending on the type of sugar you are testing for.

Reducing sugars

Reducing sugars include all monosaccharides (e.g. glucose) and some disaccharides (e.g. maltose and lactose). You add Benedict's reagent (which is blue) to a sample and heat it in a water bath that's been brought to the boil. If the test's positive it will form a coloured precipitate — solid particles suspended in the solution. The colour of the precipitate changes as shown in Figure 7 (see next page).

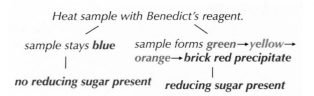

Heat sample with Benedict's reagent.

sample stays **blue**   sample forms **green**→**yellow**→
                                        orange→**brick red precipitate**

no reducing sugar present   reducing sugar present

Figure 7: Benedict's test for reducing sugars.

The higher the concentration of reducing sugar, the further the colour change goes — you can use this to compare the amount of reducing sugar in different solutions. (A more accurate way of doing this is to filter the solution and weigh the precipitate.)

Non-reducing sugars

If the result of the reducing sugars test is negative, there could still be a non-reducing sugar present. To test for non-reducing sugars, like sucrose, first you have to break them down into monosaccharides. You do this by getting a new sample of the test solution (i.e. not the same one you've already added Benedict's reagent to) adding dilute hydrochloric acid and carefully heating it in a water bath that's been brought to the boil. You then neutralise it with sodium hydrogencarbonate. Then just carry out the Benedict's test as you would for a reducing sugar — see Figure 9.

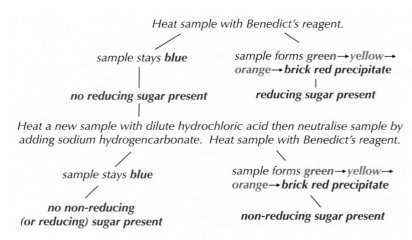

Heat sample with Benedict's reagent.

sample stays **blue**   sample forms **green**→**yellow**→
                                        orange→**brick red precipitate**

no reducing sugar present   reducing sugar present

Heat a new sample with dilute hydrochloric acid then neutralise sample by adding sodium hydrogencarbonate. Heat sample with Benedict's reagent.

sample stays **blue**   sample forms **green**→**yellow**→
                                        orange→**brick red precipitate**

no non-reducing   **non-reducing sugar present**
(or reducing) sugar present

Figure 9: Benedict's test for non-reducing sugars.

Figure 8: A blue colour (left) indicates a negative Benedict's test result and a brick red colour (right) indicates a positive result.

Practice Question — Application

Q1 Samples from two different solutions, A and B, were heated with Benedict's reagent. The sample of solution A remained blue, while the sample of solution B formed a brick red precipitate. What conclusions can you draw from these results?

Test strips for glucose

Glucose can also be tested for using test strips coated in a reagent. The strips are dipped in a test solution and change colour if glucose is present. The colour change can be compared to a chart to give an indication of the concentration of glucose present — see Figure 10. The strips are useful for testing a person's urine for glucose, which may indicate they have diabetes.

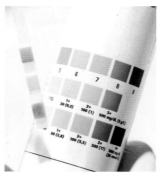

Figure 10: A urine test strip being compared to a results chart. The result shows an elevated level of glucose.

Quantitative tests

Quantitative tests tell you the amount (i.e. concentration) of a substance that is present in a sample. You need to know how to use colorimetry to find out the concentration of a substance in a sample, as well as how a biosensor works.

Colorimetry and the Benedict's test

PRACTICAL ACTIVITY GROUP **5**

You can use Benedict's reagent and a colorimeter to get a quantitative estimate of how much glucose (or other reducing sugar) there is in a solution.

What is a colorimeter?

A colorimeter is a device that measures the strength of a coloured solution by seeing how much light passes through it — see Figure 12. A colorimeter measures absorbance (the amount of light absorbed by the solution). The more concentrated the colour of the solution, the higher the absorbance is.

Figure 11: A colorimeter is used to measure the amount of light absorbed by a substance.

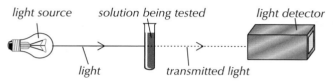

Figure 12: A diagram showing how a colorimeter works.

To find out the glucose concentration of an unknown solution, you first need to make up several solutions of known glucose concentrations, then measure the absorbance of these solutions, and finally plot these absorbances on a graph to make a calibration curve (see p. 72). You can then use the calibration curve to estimate the concentration of glucose in the unknown solution.

It's easiest to measure the concentration of the blue Benedict's solution that's left after the test (the paler the solution, the more glucose there was). So, the higher the glucose concentration, the lower the absorbance of the solution.

Tip: Don't forget to do a risk assessment before starting this experiment.

Making known concentrations of glucose

You can make up glucose solutions of different, known concentrations using a serial dilution technique:

--- Example ---

This is how you'd make five serial dilutions with a dilution factor of 2, starting with an initial glucose concentration of 40 mM.

1. Line up five test tubes in a rack.

2. Add 10 cm^3 of the initial 40 mM sucrose solution to the first test tube and 5 cm^3 of distilled water to the other four test tubes (see Figure 13).

3. Then, using a pipette, draw 5 cm^3 of the solution from the first test tube, add it to the distilled water in the second test tube and mix the solution thoroughly. You now have 10 cm^3 of solution that's half as concentrated as the solution in the first test tube (it's 20 mM).

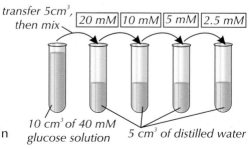

transfer 5cm^3, then mix

20 mM 10 mM 5 mM 2.5 mM

10 cm^3 of 40 mM glucose solution

5 cm^3 of distilled water

Figure 13: How to make serial dilutions.

4. Repeat this process three more times to create solutions of 10 mM, 5 mM and 2.5 mM.

Tip: You don't have to dilute solutions by a factor of 2. E.g. to dilute by a factor of 10, take 1 cm^3 from your original sample and add it to 9 cm^3 of water.

Measuring the absorbance of known solutions

Tip: In the negative control, there's no glucose. If there's no glucose, none of the Benedict's reagent will react and so the solution will remain blue — this should give you the highest absorbance value.

Once you've got your glucose solutions, you need to find out the absorbance of each one. Here's how:

- Do a Benedict's test on each solution (plus a negative control of pure water). Use the same amount of Benedict's solution in each case.
- Remove any precipitate — either leave for 24 hours (so that the precipitate settles out) or centrifuge them.
- Use a colorimeter to measure the absorbance of the Benedict's solution remaining in each tube. The method is outlined below.

  1. Switch the colorimeter on and allow five minutes for it to stabilise. Then set up the colorimeter so you're using a red filter (or a wavelength of 630 nm).

Tip: In a centrifuge, solutions are spun at high speed so the precipitate is separated from the solution.

  2. Add distilled water to a cuvette so it is three quarters full (a cuvette is a small container that fits inside a colorimeter). Put the cuvette into the colorimeter. Two of the cuvette's sides may be ridged or frosted — you need to make sure you put the cuvette into the colorimeter the correct way, so that the light will be passing through the clear sides. Calibrate the machine to zero.

  3. Next, use a pipette to transfer a sample of the solution from the first test tube to a clean cuvette — again it should be about three quarters full.

Tip: When you're handling cuvettes you need to wipe away any marks or moisture from the sides the light will be passing through. You should also gently tap the cuvette to remove any air bubbles.

  4. Put the cuvette in the colorimeter and read and record the absorbance of the solution.

  5. Repeat steps 1-4 for the remaining solutions (using a clean pipette and cuvette each time).

Making and using a calibration curve

To make a calibration curve, plot a graph of your results showing absorbance (on the *y*-axis) against glucose concentration (on the *x*-axis).

Tip: Your teacher will show you how to calibrate the colorimeter you are using to zero.

Then you can test the unknown solution in the same way as the known concentrations and use the calibration curve to find its concentration.

--- **Example** — **Maths Skills** ---

To find the glucose concentration of an unknown solution with an absorbance value of 0.5, you need to follow these steps:

1. Find 0.5 on the *y*-axis (vertical axis) of the calibration graph.
2. Read across from this value to the curve.
3. Read down from the curve to the *x*-axis.

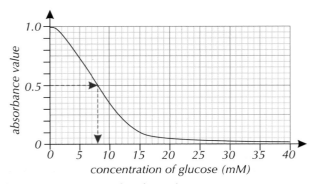

4. Read the concentration value from the *x*-axis.

   *The unknown solution has a glucose concentration of **8 mM**.*

Biosensors

A biosensor is a device that uses a biological molecule, such as an enzyme (see page 97) to detect a chemical. The biological molecule produces a signal (e.g. a chemical signal), which is converted to an electrical signal by a transducer (another part of the biosensor). The electrical signal is then processed and can be used to work out other information.

Figure 15: Glucose biosensors can be used to monitor blood sugar levels.

Example — Glucose biosensors

A glucose biosensor is used to determine the concentration of glucose in a solution. It does this using the enzyme glucose oxidase and electrodes. The enzyme catalyses the oxidation of glucose at the electrodes — this creates a charge, which is converted into an electrical signal by the electrodes (the transducer). The electrical signal is then processed to work out the initial glucose concentration.

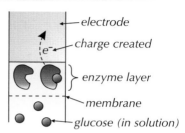

Figure 14: How a glucose biosensor works.

Practice Question — Application

Q1 A student used a colorimeter to measure the absorbance of known concentrations of starch solution, after doing the iodine test on them. She then drew the calibration curve on the right. The student also carried out the iodine test on a solution with an unknown concentration of starch. The absorbance of the unknown solution was 0.85. Find the concentration of the solution using the calibration curve.

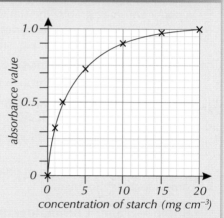

Practice Questions — Fact Recall

Q1 The biuret test is used to test for proteins.
   a) What is added to the test solution to make it alkaline?
   b) What is added next to the solution?
   c) What would a positive test result look like?

Q2 Name a test to find out if starch is present in a sample or not.

Q3 Describe a test you could do to find out if a sample contains lipids, including what observation would indicate a positive result.

Q4 Describe how to test for reducing sugars and say what a positive and a negative result would look like.

Q5 a) What is a colorimeter?
   b) Assuming a calibration curve had already been created, describe how you would use a colorimeter and the calibration curve to measure the glucose concentration of an unknown solution.

Q6 Describe a biosensor and outline how it works.

8. Separating Molecules

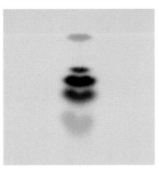

Figure 1: *Plant pigments that have been separated by thin-layer chromatography.*

Tip: The pattern of spots you end up with is called a chromatogram.

Tip: The sample of mixture is also called a blot.

Tip: Don't forget to do a risk assessment before you do this experiment to identify all the safety precautions you need to take.

Chromatography is a useful way of identifying what molecules you've got in a mixture, and you need to know all about it...

Chromatography

Chromatography is used to separate stuff in a mixture — once it's separated out, you can often identify the components. For example, chromatography can be used to separate out and identify biological molecules such as amino acids, carbohydrates, vitamins and nucleic acids.

There are quite a few different types of chromatography — you only need to know about paper chromatography and thin-layer chromatography.

How does chromatography work?

All types of chromatography (including paper and thin-layer) have the same basic set up:

- A **mobile phase** — where the molecules can move.
  In both paper and thin-layer chromatography the mobile phase is a liquid solvent, such as ethanol or water.

- A **stationary phase** — where the molecules can't move.
  In paper chromatography the stationary phase is a piece of chromatography paper. In thin-layer chromatography the stationary phase is a thin (0.1-0.3 mm) layer of solid, e.g. silica gel, on a glass or plastic plate.

They all use the same basic principle:

- The mobile phase moves through or over the stationary phase.

- The components in the mixture spend different amounts of time in the mobile phase and the stationary phase.

- The components that spend longer in the mobile phase travel faster or further.

- The time spent in the different phases is what separates out the components of the mixture.

Example — Paper Chromatography

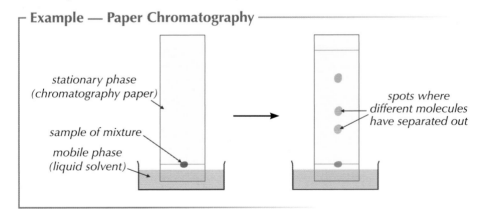

Identifying unknown molecules

In the exam you might be asked how chromatography can be used to identify the biological molecules in a mixture. An example of how paper chromatography can be used to identify amino acids in a mixture is shown on the next page.

Example — Separating amino acids

You need to make sure you're wearing gloves, safety goggles and a lab coat throughout the experiment — the solvent used for amino acids is harmful and corrosive, and ninhydrin irritates the skin and eyes. The gloves will also prevent amino acids from your skin getting on the chromatography paper.

1. Draw a pencil line near the bottom of a piece of chromatography paper and put a concentrated spot of the mixture of amino acids on it. It's best to carefully roll the paper into a cylinder with the spot on the outside so it'll stand up.

2. Add a small amount of prepared solvent (a mixture of butan-1-ol, glacial ethanoic acid and water is usually used for amino acids) to a beaker and dip the bottom of the paper into it (not the spot). This should be done in a fume cupboard. Cover with a lid to stop the solvent evaporating — see Figure 2 (top).

3. As the solvent spreads up the paper, the different amino acids (solutes) move with it, but at different rates, so they separate out.

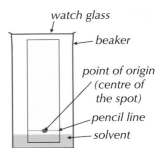
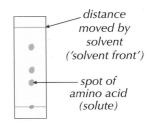

Figure 2: Setting up paper chromatography to separate amino acids (top) and the results (bottom).

4. When the solvent's nearly reached the top, take the paper out and mark the solvent front with pencil. Then you can leave the paper to dry out before you analyse it (see below and next page).

5. Amino acids aren't coloured, which means you won't be able to see them on the paper. So before you can analyse them, you have to spray the paper with ninhydrin solution to turn the amino acids purple — see Figure 2 (bottom). This should also be done in a fume cupboard.

Tip: A lot of chromatography solvents are highly flammable, so you shouldn't work with them near any open flames (e.g. from Bunsen burners).

Tip: Make sure you use a pencil (not a pen) to draw the line, and that the pencil line is above the solvent level.

Tip: Both the solvent and ninhydrin are volatile (evaporate easily) and are harmful if inhaled, so make sure you use them in a fume cupboard.

Tip: If you're trying to identify different biological molecules, the method will vary slightly (e.g. a different solvent might be used) but the basic principle will be the same.

Tip: You can't use ninhydrin to detect all biological molecules, only proteins and amino acids.

R_f values

Once the chromatogram is dry, you can use R_f values to identify the separated molecules. An R_f value is the ratio of the distance travelled by a solute to the distance travelled by the solvent. You can calculate it using this formula:

$$R_f \text{ value} = \frac{\text{distance moved by the solute}}{\text{distance moved by the solvent}}$$

When you're measuring how far a solute has travelled, you measure from the point of origin to the vertical centre of the spot (see Figure 3).

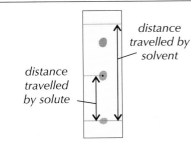

Figure 3: Diagram to show the distances to measure in order to work out the R_f value of a solute on a chromatogram.

Tip: R_f stands for 'retention (or retardation) factor'.

Tip: The substances in the sample mixture (e.g. amino acids) dissolve as the solvent passes over it, so they are called solutes.

Tip: You could also compare your chromatogram to the chromatogram of a known mixture and identify the components that way — if two solutes have travelled the same distance in the solvent, they will be the same molecule.

Tip: The stationary phase and solvent that you use will affect the R_f value. Temperature can have an effect on the R_f value as well. If you're looking up R_f values, you need to check that they were recorded under the same conditions as your experiment.

Tip: R_f values are always between 0 and 1.

Example — Maths Skills

A solution containing a mixture of three amino acids is separated using paper chromatography.
The chromatogram is shown in Figure 4.
Calculate the R_f value of solute X.

To find the R_f value of solute X, all you have to do is stick the numbers into the formula:

$$R_f \text{ value} = \frac{\text{distance moved by the solute}}{\text{distance moved by the solvent}}$$

$= 2.3 \text{ cm} \div 8.8 \text{ cm} = \mathbf{0.26}$

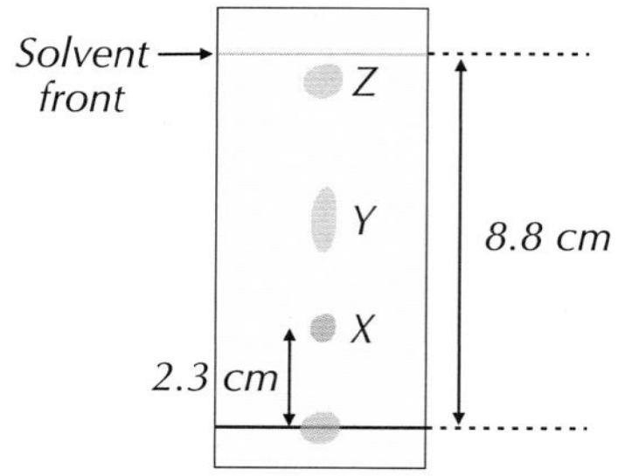

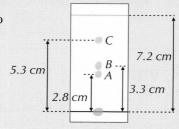

Figure 4: A sample chromatogram.

You can work out what was in a mixture by looking up the R_f value of each solute in a database, or table, of known values.

Example

Figure 5 shows the R_f values of five amino acids under the conditions used in the experiment above.
Use the table to identify solute X.

Solute X has an R_f value of 0.26.
Glycine also has an R_f value of 0.26, so solute X must be glycine.

Amino acid	R_f value
Glycine	0.26
Alanine	0.39
Tyrosine	0.46
Valine	0.61
Leucine	0.74

Figure 5: R_f values of amino acids.

Practice Question — Application

Q1 A student used paper chromatography to separate out a mixture of three amino acids. The chromatogram that she produced is shown on the right.

a) Calculate the R_f values of the three solutes, A, B and C.

b) Use the table in Figure 5 to identify the solutes A, B and C.

Practice Questions — Fact Recall

Q1 What is chromatography used for?

Q2 What would be used for the mobile phase in paper chromatography?

Q3 Describe the stationary phase in thin-layer chromatography.

Q4 Give the formula for calculating R_f values.

Section Summary

Make sure you know...

- That water molecules are polar (they have a slight negative charge on one side and a slight positive charge on the other).

- That a hydrogen bond is a weak bond between a slightly positively-charged hydrogen atom in one molecule and a slightly negatively-charged atom in another molecule.

- The properties of water (high specific heat capacity, high latent heat of evaporation, very cohesive, lower density when solid, good solvent) and how they relate to the functions of water.

- That polymers are big molecules made from large numbers of smaller units called monomers.

- What is meant by a condensation reaction and a hydrolysis reaction, and how each one works.

- The chemical elements that make up carbohydrates, lipids and proteins.

- The molecular structures of the monosaccharides α-glucose and β-glucose, and how they differ.

- The molecular structure of ribose (a pentose monosaccharide) and how it differs from glucose (a hexose monosaccharide).

- That glycosidic bonds are formed between monosaccharides during condensation reactions to form disaccharides (e.g. maltose) and polysaccharides (e.g. amylose), and broken during hydrolysis reactions.

- The structure of starch (amylose and amylopectin), glycogen (long, branched chains of α-glucose) and cellulose (long, unbranched chains of β-glucose held together by hydrogen bonds to form microfibrils), and how their structures and properties are related to their functions.

- The structure of a triglyceride (one molecule of glycerol with three fatty acids) and a phospholipid (one molecule of glycerol, two fatty acids and a phosphate group) as examples of macromolecules.

- That ester bonds are formed between glycerol and fatty acids during condensation reactions (to form triglycerides) and are broken during hydrolysis reactions.

- The general structure of a saturated and an unsaturated fatty acid.

- How the properties of a triglyceride, phospholipid and cholesterol are related to their functions.

- The structure of an amino acid (carboxyl group, amino group and R group).

- That peptide bonds are formed between amino acids during condensation reactions (to form dipeptides and polypeptides) and broken during hydrolysis reactions.

- That a protein's primary structure is the sequence of amino acids, held together by peptide bonds.

- That a protein's secondary structure is an alpha (α) helix or beta (β) pleated sheet, held together by hydrogen bonding between the -NH and -CO groups of amino acids in the chain.

- That a protein's tertiary structure is the further coiling or folding of the polypeptide chain, held together by ionic bonds, disulfide bonds, hydrophobic and hydrophilic interactions, and hydrogen bonds.

- That a protein's quaternary structure is the way in which two or more polypeptide chains are assembled together.

- That haemoglobin (a conjugated protein), insulin and most enzymes (e.g. amylase) are globular proteins and how their structures relate to their functions.

- That collagen, keratin and elastin are fibrous proteins and how their properties relate to their functions.

- The key inorganic ions that are involved in biological processes, including their chemical symbols.

- How to test a substance for the presence of proteins (biuret test), starch (iodine test), lipids (emulsion test) and sugars (Benedict's test and reagent test strips) and interpret the results.

- How to use a colorimeter to determine the concentration of a substance (e.g. glucose) in a solution.

- How biosensors can be used to determine the concentration of a chemical substance (e.g. glucose).

- How to use paper and thin-layer chromatography to separate biological molecules in a solution.

- How to calculate retention (R_f) values from a chromatogram using the formula R_f = distance moved by the solute ÷ distance moved by the solvent, and use R_f values to identify molecules in a solution.

Exam-style Questions

1   Photosynthesis is the process by which plants synthesise glucose from carbon dioxide and water using light as an energy source. Glucose is stored as starch in a plant.

(a)   A student investigating photosynthesis kept two plants, A and B, under different conditions. They tested a leaf from each plant for the presence of starch, using the iodine test. **Table 1.1** below shows the results of the test. Complete the table to show the observation from the iodine test on each of the leaves.

	Observation	Starch present
Leaf A		Yes
Leaf B		No

Table 1.1

(2 marks)

(b)   Amylose is one of the polysaccharides that forms starch.
    (i)   Name the other polysaccharide present in starch molecules.

(1 mark)

    (ii)   Describe the structure of amylose and explain how its structure makes it suited to its function.

(3 marks)

(c)   Cellulose is also a polysaccharide found in plants.
    (i)   Describe **three** ways in which cellulose differs from starch.

(3 marks)

    Fig. 1.1 shows a glucose molecule that makes up cellulose.

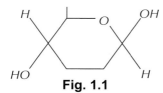

Fig. 1.1

    (ii)   Draw how two molecules of glucose link together to form part of a cellulose molecule.

(1 mark)

    (iii)   Describe how a cellulose molecule is broken apart into molecules of glucose.

(3 marks)

2   The human body contains many different proteins.
    Each of these proteins has a primary, secondary and tertiary structure.

(a)   Describe the primary structure of a protein.

(2 marks)

(b) The tertiary structure of a protein is held in place by different types of bonds. Complete the following passage about these bonds.

To form the tertiary structure of a protein, ... bonds form between negatively and positively charged R groups on different parts of the polypeptide chain. Whenever two molecules of the amino acid cysteine come close together they can become joined by their sulfur atoms to form .... bonds. Weak bonds called .... bonds also form between slightly ....-charged hydrogen atoms in some R groups and slightly ....-charged atoms in other R groups on the polypeptide chain.

(5 marks)

(c) The biuret test can be used to test for the presence of protein in a urine sample. Describe how this test would be carried out, including what observations would indicate positive and negative results.

(4 marks)

3 Plants use a variety of pigments in their leaves to capture sunlight for photosynthesis. A scientist uses thin-layer chromatography to separate out the photosynthetic pigments from a mixture obtained from plant leaves. **Fig. 3.1** shows the thin-layer chromatogram that he produces.

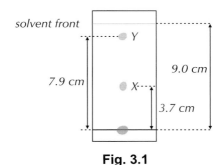

solvent front

Y

9.0 cm

7.9 cm

X

3.7 cm

Fig. 3.1

(a) Explain why the different pigments separate as they travel up the plate.

(2 marks)

(b) The equation for calculating R_f values is given below.

$$R_f \text{ value} = \frac{\text{distance travelled by spot}}{\text{distance travelled by solvent}}$$

Calculate the R_f value of **spot X**.

(1 mark)

Another scientist repeats the experiment above using the same mixture of pigments but the chromatogram does not give the same R_f values.

(c) Suggest **two** possible variations in the method that could have produced these different results.

(2 marks)

Tip: The structure of a nucleotide is the same in all living organisms.

Tip: Nucleic acids are an essential part of how characteristics are passed on from one generation to another (this is known as heredity).

Tip: A polynucleotide is a polymer made up of nucleotide monomers.

1. Nucleotides

DNA and RNA are molecules that are essential for the function of living organisms and they're both made up of nucleotides...

Nucleotide structure

A nucleotide is a type of biological molecule. It's made from: a pentose sugar (that's a sugar with 5 carbon atoms), a nitrogenous (nitrogen-containing) base and a phosphate group (see Figure 1). All nucleotides contain the elements C, H, O, N and P.

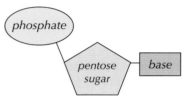

Figure 1: *A nucleotide.*

Importance of nucleotides

Nucleotides are really important. For a start they're the monomers (see page 54) that make up DNA and RNA. DNA and RNA are both types of nucleic acid. They're found in all living cells. **DNA** is used to store genetic information — the instructions an organism needs to grow and develop. **RNA** is used to make proteins from the instructions in DNA.

There are also special types of nucleotide, such as ADP and ATP (see next page). They're used to store and transport energy in cells.

DNA nucleotides

The nucleotides in DNA all contain the same pentose sugar called deoxyribose. (DNA stands for deoxyribonucleic acid.) Each DNA nucleotide also has the same phosphate group. The base on each nucleotide can vary though. There are four possible bases — adenine (A), thymine (T), cytosine (C) and guanine (G). Figure 2 shows the structure of a DNA nucleotide.

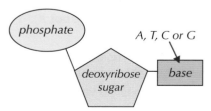

Figure 2: *A DNA nucleotide.*

A molecule of DNA contains two polynucleotide chains — each chain is made up of lots of nucleotides joined together. There's more on how polynucleotides form on page 83.

RNA nucleotides

RNA (ribonucleic acid) contains nucleotides with a ribose sugar (not deoxyribose). Like DNA, an RNA nucleotide also has a phosphate group and one of four different bases. In RNA though, uracil replaces thymine as a base. An RNA molecule is made up of a single polynucleotide chain. Figure 3 shows the structure of a RNA nucleotide.

Tip: Remember, ribose is an example of a pentose sugar.

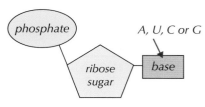

Figure 3: A RNA nucleotide.

Purines and pyrimidines

There are two types of base present in DNA and RNA nucleotides — these are called **purines** and **pyrimidines**. Each of the bases present in DNA or RNA nucleotides can be classed as one of these types. Adenine and guanine are both purines. Cytosine, thymine and uracil are pyrimidines.

The difference between these types of bases is in their structures. A purine base contains two carbon-nitrogen rings joined together, whereas a pyrimidine base only has one carbon-nitrogen ring. So a pyrimidine base is smaller than a purine base (see Figure 4).

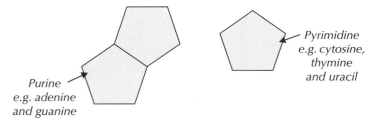

Tip: You can remember that cytosine and thymine are pyrimidines because of the 'y'.

Figure 4: Basic structures of a purine and a pyrimidine (not to scale).

ADP and ATP

ADP and ATP are phosphorylated nucleotides. To phosphorylate a nucleotide, you add one or more phosphate groups to it. ADP (adenosine diphosphate) contains the base adenine, the sugar ribose and two phosphate groups (see Figure 5). ATP (adenosine triphosphate) contains the base adenine, the sugar ribose and three phosphate groups (see Figure 6).

Tip: To remember the difference between adenosine diphosphate and adenosine triphosphate just remember 'di' means two and 'tri' means three. So adenosine diphosphate must contain two phosphate groups, and adenosine triphosphate must contain three phosphate groups.

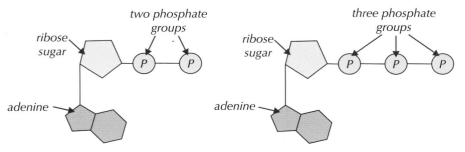

Figure 5: A molecule of ADP.   *Figure 6:* A molecule of ATP.

Making and using ATP

Plant and animal cells release energy from glucose — this process is called respiration. A cell can't get its energy directly from glucose. So, in respiration, the energy released from glucose is used to make ATP and then molecules of ATP provide energy for chemical reactions in the cell.

ATP is synthesised from ADP and inorganic phosphate (P_i). The ADP is phosphorylated to form ATP and a phosphate bond is formed (see Figure 8).

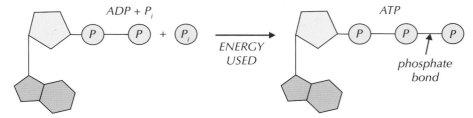

Figure 8: Synthesis of ATP from ADP and P_i.

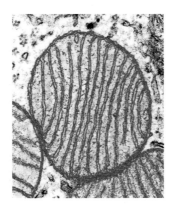

Figure 7: A transmission electron micrograph showing mitochondria, the site of ATP synthesis in cells.

Energy is stored in the phosphate bond. When this energy is needed by a cell, ATP is broken back down into ADP and inorganic phosphate (P_i). Energy is released from the phosphate bond and used by the cell (see Figure 9).

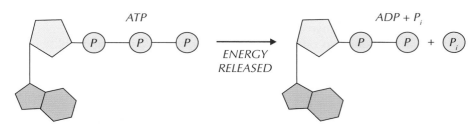

Figure 9: Breakdown of ATP to form ADP and P_i.

Practice Questions — Fact Recall

Q1 What is the name for the monomers that make up nucleic acids?

Q2 The diagram shows a DNA nucleotide. Name parts A, B and C.

Q3 How would the structure in the diagram above be different if it was an RNA nucleotide?

Q4 Name the purine bases that can be present in DNA and RNA.

Q5 Name the pyrimidines that can be present in RNA.

Q6 Outline the difference between the structure of a purine and a pyrimidine base.

Q7 What is added to a nucleotide to phosphorylate it?

Q8 Describe the structure of a molecule of ADP.

2. Polynucleotides and DNA

DNA is actually two strings of nucleotides joined together...

Polynucleotide structure

Nucleotides join together to form **polynucleotides**. The nucleotides join up between the phosphate group of one nucleotide and the sugar of another via a condensation reaction (see page 54). This forms a **phosphodiester** bond (consisting of the phosphate group and two ester bonds). The chain of sugars and phosphates is known as the sugar-phosphate backbone (see Figure 1). Polynucleotides can be broken down into nucleotides again by breaking the phosphodiester bonds using hydrolysis reactions.

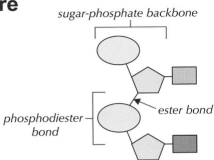

Figure 1: *Structure of a single polynucleotide strand.*

DNA structure

DNA is composed of two polynucleotide strands joined together to form a double-helix shape. The two strands join together by hydrogen bonding between the bases. Each base can only join with one particular partner — this is called complementary base pairing. Adenine always pairs with thymine (A - T) and guanine always pairs with cytosine (G - C) — see Figure 2. This means that a purine (A or G) always pairs with a pyrimidine (T or C). Two hydrogen bonds form between A and T, and three hydrogen bonds form between C and G.

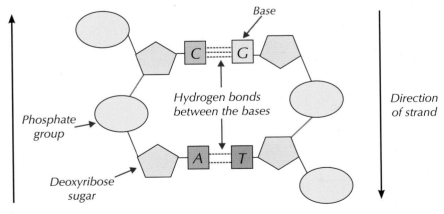

Figure 2: *Complementary base pairing in DNA molecules.*

The two polynucleotide strands are antiparallel — this means they run in opposite directions. Two antiparallel strands twist to form a DNA double-helix. Overall, the structure of a DNA molecule looks like the one in Figure 4 on the next page.

Learning Objectives:

- Understand the synthesis and breakdown of polynucleotides by the formation and breakage of phosphodiester bonds.
- Know the structure of DNA (deoxyribonucleic acid) including how hydrogen bonding between complementary base pairs (A to T, G to C) on two antiparallel DNA polynucleotides leads to the formation of a DNA molecule, and how the twisting of DNA produces its 'double-helix' shape.
- Be able to carry out practical investigations into the purification of DNA by precipitation (PAG9).

Specification Reference 2.1.3

Tip: If you're struggling to remember which base pairs with which, just think — you eat **A**pple **T**urnover with **G**loopy **C**ustard.

Tip: The two ends of a polynucleotide strand are different — one end has a phosphate group and the other has a hydroxyl (OH) group attached to the sugar. That's how you can tell which direction a strand is running in.

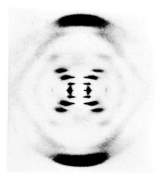

Figure 3: X-ray diffraction picture of DNA. The cross of bands shows that the molecule is a helix.

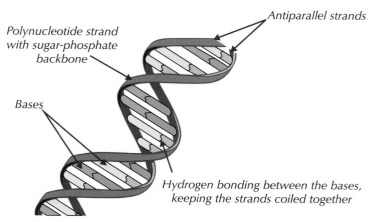

Antiparallel strands

Polynucleotide strand with sugar-phosphate backbone

Bases

Hydrogen bonding between the bases, keeping the strands coiled together

Figure 4: The DNA double-helix.

You can use computer modelling to investigate the structure of DNA and other nucleic acids. For example, the computer software RasMol can be used to produce graphical representations of molecules.

Purifying DNA

PRACTICAL ACTIVITY GROUP **9**

Scientists often need to extract a pure DNA sample from cells in order to analyse it, e.g. for use in forensics. DNA can be purified using a precipitation reaction. You need to know how to purify DNA by precipitation, so here's how to do it:

1. Break up the cells in your sample (e.g. some onion or tomato). You can do this using a blender for about 10 seconds.

2. Make up a solution of detergent (a dilute washing-up liquid will do), salt (sodium chloride) and distilled water.

3. Add the broken-up cells to a beaker containing the detergent solution — Figure 5.

4. Incubate the beaker in a water bath at 60 °C for 15 minutes (see Figure 5). Whilst in the water bath, the detergent in the mixture breaks down the cell membranes. The salt binds to the DNA and causes it to clump together. The temperature of the water bath should be high enough to stop enzymes in the cells from working properly and breaking down the DNA.

5. Once incubated, put your beaker in an ice bath to cool the mixture down (see Figure 5).

Tip: Remember to do a risk assessment before carrying out this experiment. For example, enzymes (see p. 97) can irritate the skin and may cause an allergic reaction so they need to be handled with care.

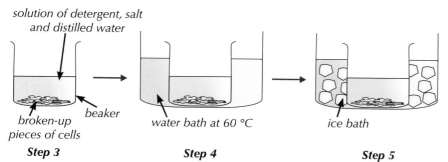

solution of detergent, salt and distilled water

broken-up pieces of cells

beaker

Step 3

water bath at 60 °C

Step 4

ice bath

Step 5

Figure 5: Steps 3-5 in DNA purification.

6. When it's cooled, filter the mixture using coffee filter paper (or gauze) and a funnel. Transfer a sample of your filtered mixture to a clean boiling tube and discard the contents of the filter paper.

7. Add protease enzymes to the filtered mixture. These will break down some proteins in the mixture, e.g. proteins bound to the DNA.

8. Slowly dribble some cold ethanol down the side of the tube, so that it forms a layer on top of the DNA-detergent mixture (see Figure 6).

9. If you leave the tube for a few minutes, the DNA will form a white precipitate (solid) (see Figure 6 and Figure 7), which you can remove from the tube using a glass rod (or a hooked instrument like a bent paper clip).

Tip: See pages 97-112 for more about enzymes.

Tip: You could also add RNase enzymes to the mixture to breakdown any RNA present. This would have to be added before the protease though to prevent the RNase (a protein) being destroyed by the protease.

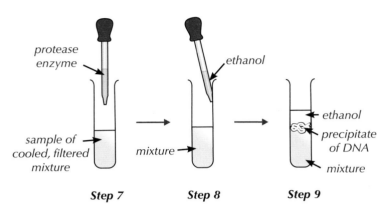

Figure 6: Steps 7-9 in DNA purification.

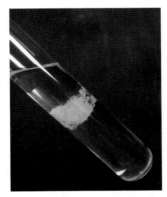

Figure 7: White precipitate of DNA formed after addition of ethanol during DNA purification.

Practice Questions — Application

Q1 Here are the base sequences of two short stretches of DNA. For each one, write down the sequence of bases they would pair up with:

a) ACTGTCGTAGTCGATGCTA

b) TGCACCATGTGGTAAATCG

Q2 In a DNA purification experiment, some onion cells are broken up and then mixed together with salt, diluted washing-up liquid and distilled water. The mixture is then placed in a water bath at 30 °C for 15 minutes. Suggest what affect using this temperature might have on the result of the experiment.

Q3 Scientists analysed a section of double stranded DNA. There were 68 bases in total (34 base pairs) and 22 of the bases were adenine. How many of the bases were:

a) thymine?   b) cytosine?   c) guanine?

Practice Questions — Fact Recall

Q1 a) What type of bonds join nucleotides together in a polynucleotide?

b) Which parts of the nucleotides are joined by these bonds?

Q2 Describe how a DNA double-helix is formed from two polynucleotide strands.

Q3 Describe how you could purify DNA from a sample of cells using a precipitation reaction.

Exam Tip
Questions on the structure of DNA are easy marks in the exam and they come up a lot. Make sure you know the structure inside out.

■ Understand semi-
conservative DNA
replication, including
the roles of the
enzymes helicase and
DNA polymerase.

■ Know the importance
of replication in
conserving genetic
information with
accuracy.

■ Understand that
random, spontaneous
mutations can occur
during replication.

**Specification
Reference 2.1.3**

3. DNA replication

DNA is able to replicate itself and does so regularly when cells are dividing.

Why does DNA replicate?

DNA copies itself before cell division (see p. 139) so that each new cell has the full amount of DNA. This is important for making new cells and for passing genetic information from generation to generation (see p. 139-146).

How is DNA replicated?

A DNA molecule has a paired base structure (see page 83), which makes it easy for DNA to copy itself. Here's how it works:

| 1 | **DNA helicase** (an enzyme) breaks the hydrogen bonds between the two polynucleotide DNA strands. The helix unzips to form two single strands. |

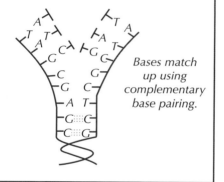

Helicase breaks hydrogen bonds

DNA helix

| 2 | Each original single strand acts as a template for a new strand. Free-floating DNA nucleotides join to the exposed bases on each original template strand by complementary base pairing — A with T and G with C. |

Bases match up using complementary base pairing.

Tip: Phosphodiester bonds form between the DNA nucleotides on the new strand (see page 83).

| 3 | The nucleotides on the new strand are joined together by the enzyme **DNA polymerase**. This forms the sugar-phosphate backbone. Hydrogen bonds form between the bases on the original and new strand. | The strands twist to form a double-helix. Each new DNA molecule contains one strand from the original DNA molecule and one new strand. |

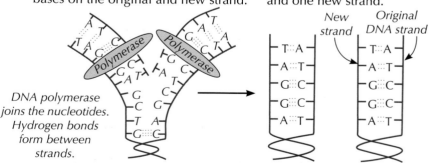

DNA polymerase joins the nucleotides. Hydrogen bonds form between strands.

New strand   Original DNA strand

Exam Tip
If you're asked to describe the process of semi-conservative replication in the exam, you need to make sure you do it in the correct order or you won't get all the marks. Get the sequence clear in your head now.

This type of copying is called **semi-conservative replication** because half of the strands in each new DNA molecule are from the original piece of DNA (i.e. the new molecule contains one old strand and one new strand).

Accuracy of DNA replication

DNA replication is really accurate — it has to be, to make sure genetic information is conserved (stays the same) each time the DNA in a cell is replicated. Every so often though, a random, spontaneous mutation occurs. A mutation is any change to the DNA base sequence. Mutations don't always have an effect, but they can alter the sequence of amino acids in a protein. This can cause an abnormal protein to be produced. The abnormal protein might function better than the normal protein — or it might not work at all.

Practice Question — Application

Q1 The evidence that DNA replicated semi-conservatively came from an experiment carried out by Meselson and Stahl. Their experiment used two isotopes of nitrogen — heavy nitrogen (^{15}N) and light nitrogen (^{14}N).

Two samples of bacteria were grown — one in a nutrient broth containing light nitrogen, and one in a broth with heavy nitrogen. As the bacteria reproduced, they took up nitrogen from the broth to help make new DNA. The bacteria that had been grown in the heavy nitrogen broth were then grown in a light nitrogen broth and left for one round of DNA replication.

At each stage of the experiment, the composition of the bacterial DNA was analysed. The results are shown in the table below.

	Bacteria grown in light nitrogen broth only	Bacteria grown in heavy nitrogen broth only	Bacteria grown in heavy nitrogen broth, then in light nitrogen broth
% of heavy nitrogen in one DNA molecule	0	100	50
% of light nitrogen in one DNA molecule	100	0	50

a) DNA is copied by semi-conservative replication. Explain how the results shown in the table above provide evidence that DNA replicates semi-conservatively.

b) Scientists predicted that DNA could replicate semi-conservatively because of the paired base structure of a double-stranded DNA molecule. Explain how a paired base structure helps DNA to replicate semi-conservatively.

c) Suggest one way in which Meselson and Stahl may have made sure that their results were valid.

Tip: See page 5 for more about valid results.

Practice Questions — Fact Recall

Q1 Which bonds need to break in a DNA molecule before replication can begin?

Q2 Describe the role of DNA polymerase in DNA replication.

Q3 Why is it important that DNA replication is accurate?

Q4 Mutations can occur during DNA replication. What is a mutation?

4. Genes and Protein Synthesis

Learning Objectives:

- Understand how a gene determines the sequence of amino acids in a polypeptide (the primary structure of a protein).

- Know the roles of messenger RNA (mRNA), transfer RNA (tRNA) and ribosomal RNA (rRNA).

- Understand the nature of the genetic code, including the triplet, non-overlapping degenerate and universal nature of the code.

Specification Reference 2.1.3

DNA and RNA have starring roles in protein synthesis. Here's why...

Genes

DNA contains genes. A **gene** is a sequence of DNA nucleotides that codes for a polypeptide. The sequence of amino acids in a polypeptide forms the primary structure of a protein (see page 62).

Different proteins have a different number and order of amino acids. It's the order of nucleotide bases in a gene that determines the order of amino acids in a particular protein. Each amino acid is coded for by a sequence of three bases (called a **triplet**) in a gene. Different sequences of bases code for different amino acids. This is the genetic code — see next page for more. So the sequence of bases in a section of DNA is a template that's used to make proteins during protein synthesis.

Tip: A triplet is a sequence of three bases as shown below.

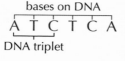

bases on DNA

A T C T C A

DNA triplet

Tip: For more about ribosomes, see page 32.

Tip: There's more about transcription and translation on pages 91-93.

DNA, RNA and protein synthesis

DNA molecules are found in the nucleus of the cell, but the organelles that make proteins (ribosomes) are found in the cytoplasm. DNA is too large to move out of the nucleus, so a section is copied into mRNA (see Figure 1). This process is called **transcription**. The mRNA leaves the nucleus and joins with a ribosome in the cytoplasm, where it can be used to synthesise a protein. This process is called **translation**. Figure 1 summarises this.

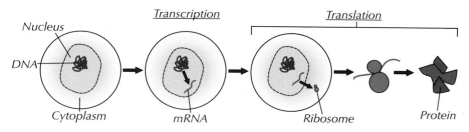

Figure 1: *Making a protein from DNA.*

RNA

Remember, RNA is a single polynucleotide strand and it contains uracil (U) as a base instead of thymine (see page 81). Uracil always pairs with adenine during protein synthesis. RNA isn't all the same though.
You need to know about:

Tip: mRNA is copied from DNA — so its sequence is complementary to the DNA sequence. See page 91 for more.

Messenger RNA (mRNA)

mRNA is a single polynucleotide strand (see Figure 2). It's made in the nucleus during transcription. mRNA carries the genetic code from the DNA in the nucleus to the cytoplasm, where it's used to make a protein during translation. In mRNA, groups of three adjacent bases are usually called **codons**.

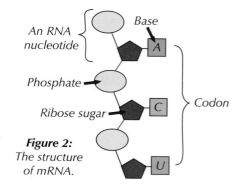

Figure 2:
The structure of mRNA.

Transfer RNA (tRNA)

tRNA is a single polynucleotide strand that's folded into a clover shape (see Figure 3). Hydrogen bonds between specific base pairs hold the molecule in this shape. Every tRNA molecule has a specific sequence of three bases at one end called an **anticodon**. They also have an amino acid binding site at the other end. tRNA is found in the cytoplasm where it's involved in translation. It carries the amino acids that are used to make proteins to the ribosomes.

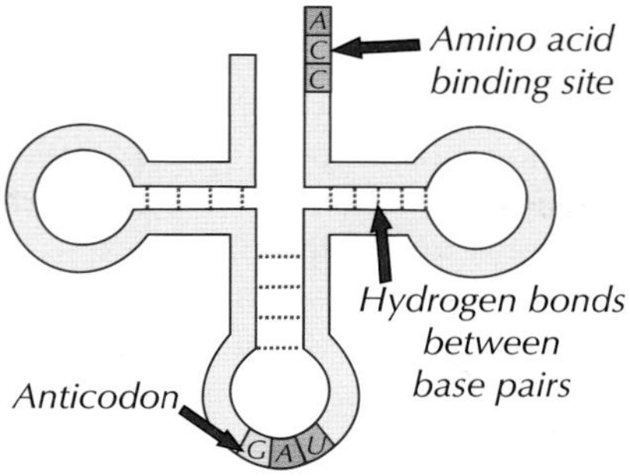

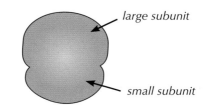

Amino acid binding site

Hydrogen bonds between base pairs

Anticodon

Figure 3: *The structure of tRNA.*

Tip: Transfer RNA is so called because it transfers amino acids to the ribosomes. There's more about this on pages 92-93.

Tip: Codons and anticodons are sometimes referred to as triplets.

Ribosomal RNA (rRNA)

rRNA forms the two subunits in a ribosome, along with proteins (see Figure 4). The ribosome moves along the mRNA strand during protein synthesis. The rRNA in the ribosome helps to catalyse the formation of peptide bonds between the amino acids.

large subunit

small subunit

Figure 4: *The structure of a ribosome.*

Tip: Amino acids in a polypeptide are joined together by peptide bonds — see p. 61.

The genetic code

The genetic code is the sequence of base triplets (codons) in DNA or mRNA, which codes for specific amino acids. In the genetic code, each base triplet is read in sequence, separate from the triplet before it and after it. Base triplets don't share their bases — the code is **non-overlapping**.

Examples

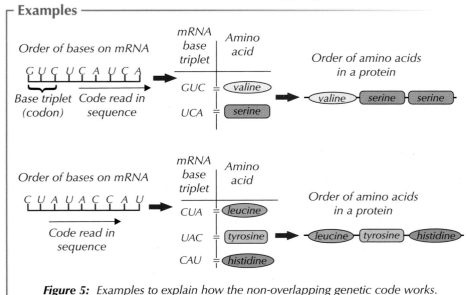

Figure 5: *Examples to explain how the non-overlapping genetic code works.*

Exam Tip
You'll be pleased to know you don't need to learn which base sequences code for which amino acids — all the information you need to answer any questions will be given to you in the exam.

The genetic code is also **degenerate** — there are more possible combinations of triplets than there are amino acids (20 amino acids but 64 possible triplets). This means that some amino acids are coded for by more than one base triplet, e.g. tyrosine can be coded for by UAU or UAC. Not all triplets code for amino acids though. For example, some triplets are used to tell the cell when to stop production of a protein — these are called stop signals. They're found at the end of the mRNA. E.g. UAG is a stop signal. (There are also start signals at the start of the mRNA which tell the cell when to start protein production, but these code for a specific amino acid called methionine.)

The genetic code is also **universal** — the same specific base triplets code for the same amino acids in all living things. E.g. UAU codes for tyrosine in all organisms.

Tip: Start and stop signals are also called start and stop codons.

Exam Tip
You won't always get information about mRNA codons and amino acids presented in a table like this in the exam, e.g. it could be in the form of a graph or diagram. Don't let that throw you though. The trick is to read the question carefully, then apply what you know.

Practice Questions — Application

Q1 How many amino acids do the following mRNA sequences code for?
   a) GAUGGUUAUGACC
   b) UAUUGCGACCACAGAGAC
   c) ACGGACCAUAGGAGGUACUAUUGCGAUCA

The table below shows six amino acids and some of the codons that code for them:

Amino acid:	His	Arg	Gly	Tyr	Cys	Asp
mRNA codon:	CAU/ CAC	AGA/ AGG	GGC/ GGU	UAC/ UAU	UGC/ UGU	GAC/ GAU

Q2 Use the table to determine the amino acid sequence coded for by the following mRNA sequences:
   a) CAUUACUACAGAGGCUGCCAUAGAGGC
   b) AGGUACGACGACUGUCACGGUUAUCAC

Q3 Use the table to determine a mRNA sequence that could code for the following amino acid sequence:
   Asp - Tyr - Cys - Arg - Arg - Gly - Cys - Gly - Tyr - His - Gly - Asp

Practice Questions — Fact Recall

Q1 What is the genetic code?
Q2 Name the molecule responsible for:
   a) carrying the genetic code from the nucleus to the cytoplasm.
   b) carrying the amino acids used to make proteins to the ribosomes.
Q3 What is the role of rRNA in the ribosome?
Q4 a) What is an mRNA codon?
   b) Describe the function of mRNA codons.
   c) What is another name for an mRNA codon?
Q5 Explain why the genetic code is thought of as:
   a) non-overlapping,
   b) universal.

5. Transcription and Translation

Proteins are synthesised (made) using the instructions in DNA.
Protein synthesis involves two main stages: transcription and translation.

Transcription

Transcription is the first stage of protein synthesis. During transcription an mRNA copy of a gene (a section of DNA) is made in the nucleus. Here's how:

1. RNA polymerase attaches to the DNA

Transcription starts when **RNA polymerase** (an enzyme) attaches to the DNA double-helix at the beginning of a gene.
The hydrogen bonds between the two DNA strands in the gene break, separating the strands, and the DNA molecule uncoils at that point. One of the strands is then used as a template to make an mRNA copy — see Figure 1.

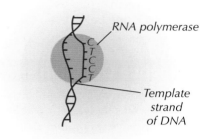

Figure 1: *RNA polymerase attaches to the DNA double-helix.*

2. Complementary mRNA is formed

The RNA polymerase lines up free RNA nucleotides alongside the template strand. Complementary base pairing means that the mRNA strand ends up being a complementary copy of the DNA template strand (except the base T is replaced by U in RNA). Once the RNA nucleotides have paired up with their specific bases on the DNA strand, they're joined together by RNA polymerase, forming an mRNA strand — see Figure 2.

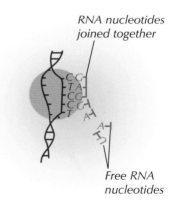

Figure 2: *A complementary mRNA strand starts to form.*

3. RNA polymerase moves down the DNA strand

The RNA polymerase moves along the DNA, assembling the mRNA strand. The hydrogen bonds between the uncoiled strands of DNA re-form once the RNA polymerase has passed by and the strands coil back into a double-helix — see Figure 3.

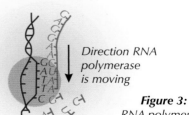

Direction RNA polymerase is moving

Figure 3: *RNA polymerase moves down the DNA strand.*

Learning Objectives:

- Understand the transcription and translation of genes resulting in the synthesis of polypeptides, including the role of RNA polymerase.

Specification Reference 2.1.3

Tip: In prokaryotes, the DNA strands are separated by RNA polymerase. In eukaryotes, the strands are separated by a complex of proteins including DNA helicase.

Tip: Free RNA nucleotides aren't bound to anything in the nucleus — they're just floating freely.

Tip: The DNA template strand is also called the antisense strand.

Tip: Here's an example of complementary base pairing:

DNA triplet
A T C
U A G
codon on mRNA

Tip: It's easy to remember that <u>R</u>NA polymerase is involved in the making of m<u>R</u>NA. Don't confuse it with DNA polymerase, which is involved in the making of DNA (see page 86).

4. mRNA leaves the nucleus

When RNA polymerase reaches a stop codon, it stops making mRNA and detaches from the DNA. The mRNA moves out of the nucleus through a nuclear pore and attaches to a ribosome in the cytoplasm, where the next stage of protein synthesis takes place (see below).

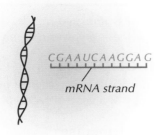

CGAAUCAAGGAG

mRNA strand

Figure 4: mRNA detaches from the DNA.

Practice Question — Application

Q1 α–amanitin is a deadly toxin produced by some mushrooms. It works by inhibiting RNA polymerase. What effect will this have on protein synthesis? Explain your answer.

Translation

Translation is the second stage of protein synthesis. It takes place at the ribosomes in the cytoplasm. During translation, amino acids are joined together by a ribosome to make a polypeptide chain (protein), following the sequence of codons carried by the mRNA. Here's how it works:

The mRNA attaches itself to a ribosome and transfer RNA (tRNA) molecules carry amino acids to the ribosome.

Tip: See pages 88-89 for more on the structures of mRNA and tRNA.

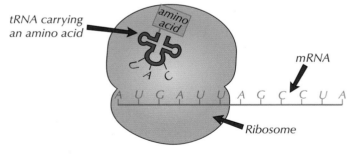

tRNA carrying an amino acid

amino acid

mRNA

Ribosome

Figure 5: mRNA (turquoise) attached to a bacterial ribosome.

A tRNA molecule, with an anticodon that's complementary to the start codon on the mRNA, attaches itself to the mRNA by complementary base pairing. A second tRNA molecule attaches itself to the next codon on the mRNA in the same way.

Tip: Here's an example of a tRNA anticodon complementary to a start codon on mRNA:

tRNA anticodon

U A C

A U G

codon on mRNA

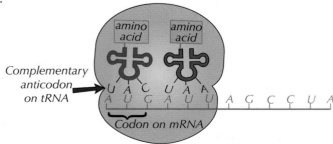

amino acid   amino acid

Complementary anticodon on tRNA

Codon on mRNA

Ribosomal RNA (rRNA) in the ribosome catalyses the formation of a peptide bond between the two amino acids attached to the tRNA molecules. This joins the amino acids together. The first tRNA molecule moves away, leaving its amino acid behind.

Tip: Once the amino acids are lined up in the correct order, the ribosome joins them together.

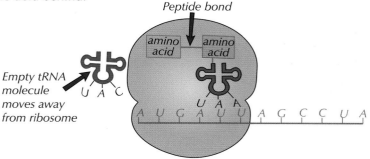

Tip: Ribosomes are actually complexes made up of rRNA (ribosomal RNA) and loads of different proteins. See page 89 for more about rRNA.

A third tRNA molecule binds to the next codon on the mRNA. Its amino acid binds to the first two and the second tRNA molecule moves away. This process continues, producing a chain of linked amino acids (a polypeptide chain), until there's a **stop codon** on the mRNA molecule.

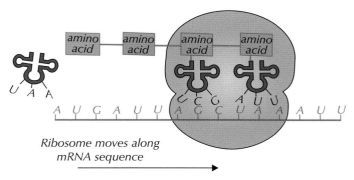

Tip: Protein synthesis happens this way in all eukaryotic cells (e.g. plants, animals and fungi). It's a bit different in prokaryotes (e.g. bacteria).

The polypeptide chain (protein) then moves away from the ribosome and translation is complete.

Tip: Protein synthesis is also called polypeptide synthesis as it makes a polypeptide (protein).

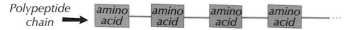

Practice Questions — Application

Q1 Diamond-Blackfan anaemia is an inherited condition caused by one of several gene mutations. The mutations can affect the function of the proteins that make up ribosomes. What effect could this have on protein synthesis? Explain your answer.

Q2 An error occurs during transcription that accidentally inserts a stop codon into the middle of an mRNA sequence. What effect could this have on the protein that is eventually produced? Explain your answer.

Tip: A mutation is any change to the DNA base sequence. See page 87 for more.

Practice Questions — Fact Recall

Q1 What is produced during transcription?
Q2 What is RNA polymerase? Describe its role in protein synthesis.
Q3 What happens to the uncoiled strands of DNA once RNA polymerase has passed along them during transcription?

Q4 a) Explain how tRNA molecules pair up with mRNA.

b) During which stage of protein synthesis does this happen?

c) What feature on the mRNA strand results in the termination of protein synthesis?

Section Summary

Make sure you know...

- That nucleotides are made up of a pentose sugar, a nitrogenous (nitrogen-containing) base (adenine, cytosine, guanine, thymine or uracil) and a phosphate group.
- That nucleotides are the monomers that make up nucleic acids, such as DNA and RNA.
- The differences between DNA and RNA nucleotides, including bases (RNA contains uracil instead of thymine) and type of pentose sugar (RNA contains ribose instead of deoxyribose).
- That there are two types of nitrogenous base in nucleotides, pyrimidines (cytosine, thymine and uracil) and purines (guanine and adenine), which have different structures.
- That ADP and ATP are both phosphorylated nucleotides made up of the base adenine and the sugar ribose, but that ADP contains two phosphate groups, while ATP contains three phosphate groups.
- That polynucleotides (polymers made up of nucleotides) are made by the formation of phosphodiester bonds, and are broken up by the breakage of these bonds.
- That DNA is made up of two antiparallel polynucleotide strands with hydrogen bonds between complementary base pairs (A and T, G and C).
- That the two antiparallel DNA strands twist together forming a double-helix.
- How to carry out an experiment to purify DNA using a precipitation reaction.
- Understand how semi-conservative DNA replication works and the roles that the enzymes DNA helicase and DNA polymerase play in this process.
- That the process of DNA replication is very accurate and that this is important for the conservation of genetic information.
- That random, spontaneous mutations can occur in DNA replication that alter DNA's base sequence.
- That a gene is a sequence of DNA nucleotides and how this sequence determines the order of amino acids in a polypeptide (which is a protein's primary structure).
- That each amino acid is coded for by a sequence of three bases called a triplet.
- That mRNA molecules carry the genetic code from the DNA in the nucleus to the cytoplasm, where it's used to make a protein during translation.
- That tRNA molecules carry amino acids to the ribosomes during translation.
- That rRNA in ribosomes catalyses the formation of peptide bonds between the amino acids.
- That the genetic code is the sequence of base triplets (codons) in DNA or mRNA which codes for specific amino acids.
- That the genetic code is non-overlapping (triplets don't share bases), degenerate (there are more possible combinations of triplets than there are amino acids) and universal (the same base triplets code for the same amino acids in all living things).
- That polypeptide (protein) synthesis involves the transcription and translation of genes.
- That transcription is the first stage of protein synthesis and involves the production of an mRNA copy of a gene in the nucleus.
- That during transcription the enzyme RNA polymerase attaches to the DNA double helix and the two DNA strands separate. RNA polymerase then lines up free RNA nucleotides alongside the DNA template strand and assembles the mRNA strand.
- That translation is the second stage of protein synthesis in which amino acids are joined together by ribosomes to make a polypeptide strand (protein) based on the order of codons in mRNA.

Exam-style Questions

1   Which of the following statements about semi-conservative replication is/are correct?

Statement 1:   DNA helicase breaks hydrogen bonds between the two
polynucleotide DNA strands.

Statement 2:   DNA polymerase attaches to the original template strand by
complementary base pairing.

Statement 3:   Free-floating RNA nucleotides join to the exposed bases
on each original template strand.

A   1, 2 and 3   **C**   Only 2 and 3

B   Only 1 and 2   **D**   Only 1

(1 mark)

2   Which of these statements correctly describes the components of a molecule of ATP?

A   Ribose, adenine and three phosphate groups.

B   Deoxyribose, thymine and three phosphate groups.

C   Deoxyribose, adenine and two phosphate groups.

D   Ribose, thymine and two phosphate groups.

(1 mark)

3   Researchers have been studying a genetic disease with the aim of developing
a treatment for it. The genetic disease is caused by the production of a specific
enzyme.

(a)   Part of the DNA sequence for the enzyme is shown in **Fig. 1.1**.

T   C   G   C   C   A   A   C   A   A   C   A   C   T   C

Fig. 1.1

State the complementary mRNA sequence to the sequence shown in **Fig. 1.1**
and how many amino acids this DNA sequence would code for.
(Assume there are no start or stop codons present).

(2 marks)

(b)   The researchers are exploring a possible treatment for the genetic disease
that would involve disrupting the process of translation.

(i)   Name the organelle that mRNA attaches to during translation.

(1 mark)

(ii)* Once mRNA has attached to this organelle, translation begins.
Describe the process of translation from this point, including the roles of
rRNA and tRNA.

(6 marks)

*The quality of your response will be assessed in this question.

4 (a) DNA is a polynucleotide.
State the **three** components that make up a DNA nucleotide.

(3 marks)

(b) (i) Urea is a weak alkali. Adding urea to a solution of double-stranded DNA will severely disrupt the hydrogen bonding in the DNA.
Explain what effect this will have on the structure of the DNA.

(2 marks)

(ii) Depurination of DNA results in the loss of purine bases.
Name the **two** DNA bases that would be lost during depurination.

(2 marks)

(c) (i) Use the most appropriate terms to complete the passage on DNA replication below.

Hydrogen bonds between the two polynucleotide strands break and the DNA

double-helix .... to form two separate strands. Each original strand

acts as a .... for the new strand. Free-floating DNA nucleotides join on

to the exposed bases by .... base pairing — for example, thymine pairs

with .... The nucleotides on the new strands are then joined together

by the enzyme .... and bonds form between the new and

original strands.

(5 marks)

(ii) What is the name given to the method by which DNA replicates itself?

(1 mark)

5 mRNA and DNA both play important roles in protein synthesis.
(a) Give **three** ways in which the structure of mRNA is different to the structure of DNA.

(3 marks)

(b) Describe the role of mRNA in protein synthesis.

(2 marks)

(c) DNA contains genes.
(i) Give the definition of a **gene**.

(1 mark)

(ii) Suggest how random, spontaneous mutations in a gene during DNA replication could affect the protein produced.

(3 marks)

(d) DNA carries the genetic code.
Explain why this code is described as being degenerate.

(1 mark)

1. Action of Enzymes

Enzymes are proteins that speed up the rate of chemical reactions. Without enzymes, bodily processes such as digestion would not happen.

Enzymes as biological catalysts

Enzymes speed up chemical reactions by acting as biological catalysts. A catalyst is a substance that speeds up a chemical reaction without being used up in the reaction itself — biological catalysts are those found in living organisms. They catalyse metabolic reactions — both at a cellular level (e.g. respiration) and for the organism as a whole (e.g. digestion in mammals).

Enzymes can affect structures in an organism (e.g. enzymes are involved in the production of collagen, an important protein in the connective tissues of animals) as well as functions (like respiration). Enzyme action can be **intracellular** — within cells, or **extracellular** — outside cells.

Example — Intracellular enzyme

Catalase is an enzyme that works inside cells to catalyse the breakdown of hydrogen peroxide to harmless oxygen (O_2) and water (H_2O).

Hydrogen peroxide (H_2O_2) is the toxic by-product of several cellular reactions. If left to build up, it can kill cells.

Examples — Extracellular enzymes

Amylase and trypsin both work outside cells in the human digestive system.

Amylase is found in saliva. It's secreted into the mouth by cells in the salivary glands. It catalyses the hydrolysis (breakdown, see page 54) of starch into maltose (a sugar) in the mouth.

Trypsin catalyses the hydrolysis of peptide bonds — turning big polypeptides into smaller ones (which then get broken down into amino acids by other enzymes). Trypsin is produced by cells in the pancreas and secreted into the small intestine.

Enzyme structure

Enzymes are globular proteins (see page 64). They have an **active site**. The active site is the part of the enzyme where the **substrate** molecules (the substance that the enzyme interacts with) bind to. The active site has a specific shape, which is determined by the enzyme's tertiary structure (see page 63).

For the enzyme to work, the substrate has to fit into the active site (its shape has to be complementary). If the substrate shape doesn't match the active site, the reaction won't be catalysed (see Figure 1 on the next page). This means that enzymes are very specific and work with very few substrates — usually only one. When a substrate binds to an enzyme's active site, an **enzyme-substrate complex** is formed.

Learning Objectives:

- Know the role of enzymes in catalysing reactions that affect metabolism at a cellular and whole organism level.
- Understand that enzymes affect both structure and function.
- Understand the role of enzymes in catalysing both intracellular and extracellular reactions, including catalase as an example of an enzyme that catalyses intracellular reactions and amylase and trypsin as examples of enzymes that catalyse extracellular reactions.
- Understand the mechanism of enzyme action, with reference to:
  - the tertiary structure,
  - specificity,
  - the active site,
  - the lock and key hypothesis,
  - the induced-fit hypothesis,
  - enzyme-substrate complexes,
  - enzyme-product complexes,
  - product formation,
  - lowering of activation energy.

Specification Reference 2.1.4

Tip: Metabolic reactions are reactions that occur in living cells.

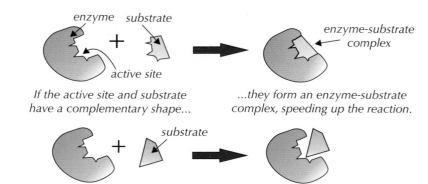

If the active site and substrate have a complementary shape...

...they form an enzyme-substrate complex, speeding up the reaction.

*If the active site and substrate **do not** have a complementary shape...*

*...the substrate can't fit into the active site so the reaction **can't** be catalysed.*

Figure 1: *An enzyme's active site has a complementary shape to the substrate.*

Exam Tip
When describing enzyme action you need to say the active site and the substrate have a complementary shape, rather than the <u>same</u> shape.

Tip: Understanding how enzymes function and the factors that affect them (see pages 101-103) has improved our knowledge about how biological processes work. This has allowed us to utilise enzymes in industrial processes, e.g. cellulase enzymes are used in the production of biofuels.

Tip: Imagine you have to get to the top of a mountain to start a chemical reaction. It would take a lot of energy to get to the top. An enzyme effectively reduces the height of the mountain, so it doesn't take as much energy to start the reaction.

How enzymes speed up reactions

In a chemical reaction, a certain amount of energy needs to be supplied to the chemicals before the reaction will start. This is called the **activation energy** — it's often provided as heat. Enzymes reduce the amount of activation energy that's needed (see Figure 2), often making reactions happen at a lower temperature than they could without an enzyme. This speeds up the rate of reaction.

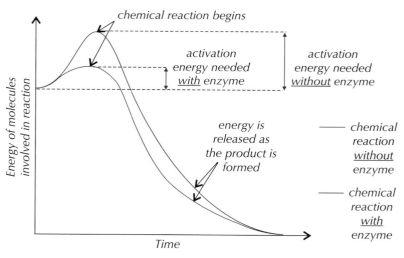

Figure 2: *A graph to show the activation energy needed for a reaction with and without an enzyme.*

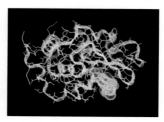

Figure 3: *Computer model of an enzyme-substrate complex. The substrate (yellow) has bound to the enzyme's active site.*

When a substance binds to an enzyme's active site, an enzyme-substrate complex is formed (see Figure 1 above) — it's this that lowers the activation energy. Here are two reasons why:

- If two substrate molecules need to be joined, attaching to the enzyme holds them close together, reducing any repulsion between the molecules so they can bond more easily.

- If the enzyme is catalysing a breakdown reaction, fitting into the active site puts a strain on bonds in the substrate. This strain means the substrate molecule breaks up more easily.

Models of enzyme action

Scientists now have a pretty good understanding of how enzymes work. As with most scientific theories, this understanding has changed over time.

The 'lock and key' model

Enzymes are a bit picky — they only work with substrates that fit their active site. Early scientists studying the action of enzymes came up with the 'lock and key' model. This is where the substrate fits into the enzyme in the same way that a key fits into a lock — the active site and substrate have a complementary shape.

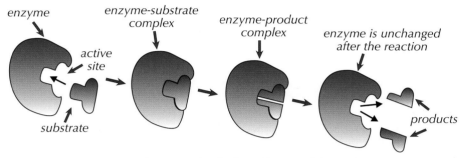

Figure 4: The 'lock and key' model.

> **Tip:** An enzyme-product complex is formed when the substrate has been converted into its products, but they've not yet been released from the active site.

Scientists soon realised that the lock and key model didn't give the full story. The enzyme and substrate do have to fit together in the first place, but new evidence showed that the enzyme-substrate complex changed shape slightly to complete the fit. This locks the substrate even more tightly to the enzyme. Scientists modified the old lock and key model and came up with the 'induced fit' model.

> **Tip:** The 'lock and key' model can also be called the 'lock and key' hypothesis, and the 'induced fit' model can also be called the 'induced fit' hypothesis.

The 'induced fit' model

The 'induced fit' model helps to explain why enzymes are so specific and only bond to one particular substrate. The substrate doesn't only have to be the right shape to fit the active site, it has to make the active site change shape in the right way as well. This is a prime example of how a widely accepted theory can change when new evidence comes along. The 'induced fit' model is still widely accepted — for now, anyway.

> **Tip:** The diagrams on this page show how enzymes break substrates down (e.g. one substrate molecule goes into the active site and two products come out). Enzymes can also catalyse synthesis reactions (e.g. two substrate molecules go into the active site, bind together and one product comes out).

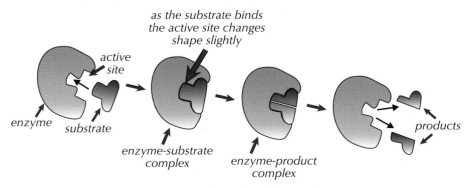

Figure 5: The 'induced fit' model.

Practice Question — Application

Q1 The enzyme maltase can be used in the industrial production of glucose syrup. It catalyses this reaction:

$$\text{maltose} \xrightarrow{\text{maltase}} \text{glucose}$$

An error in the process at a factory carrying out this industrial process meant that the enzyme sucrase, instead of maltase, was added to the maltose. Sucrase catalyses this reaction:

$$\text{sucrose} \xrightarrow{\text{sucrase}} \text{glucose}$$

No glucose was produced from this batch.

Using your knowledge of enzyme action, explain why no glucose was produced.

Practice Questions — Fact Recall

Q1 What is a catalyst?

Q2 What term is used to describe an enzyme that acts:

a) within cells?

b) outside cells?

Q3 a) Explain why the action of catalase is important to some cells.

b) Is catalase an example of an intracellular or an extracellular enzyme?

Q4 What reaction does amylase catalyse?

Q5 a) What role does trypsin play in human digestion?

b) Is trypsin an example of an intracellular or an extracellular enzyme?

Q6 What determines the shape of an enzyme's active site?

Q7 What is formed when a substrate binds with an active site?

Q8 Look at the graph below.

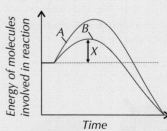

a) Which line shows a reaction with the presence of an enzyme?

b) What does the line labelled X represent?

Q9 Explain, in terms of activation energy, why an enzyme enables reactions to happen at lower temperatures than they could without an enzyme.

Q10 Describe the 'lock and key' model of enzyme action.

Q11 What is the main difference between the 'lock and key' model and the 'induced fit' model?

2. Factors Affecting Enzyme Activity

Learning Objective:
- Know the effects of pH, temperature, enzyme concentration and substrate concentration on enzyme activity, including reference to the temperature coefficient (Q_{10}), which is calculated using the formula: $Q_{10} = R_2 \div R_1$.
  Specification Reference 2.1.4

Enzymes are great at speeding up reactions, but there are several factors that affect how fast they work.

Temperature

Like any chemical reaction, the rate of an enzyme-controlled reaction increases when the temperature's increased. More heat means more kinetic energy, so molecules move faster. This makes the substrate molecules more likely to collide with the enzymes' active sites. The energy of these collisions also increases, which means each collision is more likely to result in a reaction. The rate of reaction continues to increase until the enzyme reaches its **optimum temperature** — this is the temperature at which the rate of an enzyme-controlled reaction is at its fastest.

But, if the temperature gets too high, the reaction stops. The rise in temperature makes the enzyme's molecules vibrate more. If the temperature goes above a certain level, this vibration breaks some of the bonds that hold the enzyme in shape. The active site changes shape and the enzyme and substrate no longer fit together. At this point, the enzyme is **denatured** — it no longer functions as a catalyst (see Figures 1 and 2).

Tip: Every enzyme has an optimum temperature. For most human enzymes it's around 37 °C but some enzymes, like those used in biological washing powders, can work well at 60 °C.

Tip: High temperatures break the weak bonds in an enzyme's tertiary structure, e.g. hydrogen bonds and ionic bonds. See page 63 for more on protein bonds.

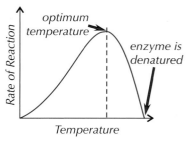

Figure 1: Effect of temperature on the rate of an enzyme-controlled reaction.

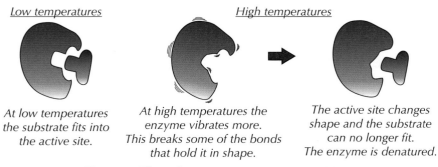

At low temperatures the substrate fits into the active site.

At high temperatures the enzyme vibrates more. This breaks some of the bonds that hold it in shape.

The active site changes shape and the substrate can no longer fit. The enzyme is denatured.

Figure 2: Effect of temperature on enzyme activity.

Exam Tip
Make sure you don't say the enzyme's killed by high temperatures — it's <u>denatured</u>.

The temperature coefficient (Q_{10})

The temperature coefficient or Q_{10} value for a reaction shows how much the rate of a reaction changes when the temperature is raised by 10 °C. You can calculate the Q_{10} value using this equation:

$$Q_{10} = \frac{R_2 \text{ (rate at higher temperature)}}{R_1 \text{ (rate at lower temperature)}}$$

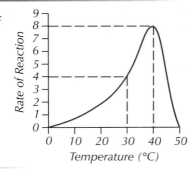

Example — Maths Skills

1. The graph on the right shows the rate of a reaction between 0 °C and 50 °C.

2. Here's how to calculate the Q_{10} value of the reaction using the rate at 30 °C and at 40 °C:

$$Q_{10} = \frac{R_2}{R_1} = \frac{\text{rate at 40 °C}}{\text{rate at 30 °C}} = \frac{8}{4} = 2$$

At temperatures before the optimum, a Q_{10} value of 2 means that the rate doubles when the temperature is raised by 10 °C. A Q_{10} value of 3 would mean that the rate trebles. Most enzyme-controlled reactions have a Q_{10} value of around 2.

pH

Exam Tip
Don't forget — both a pH that's too high and one that's too low will denature an enzyme, not just one that's too high.

All enzymes have an optimum pH value — this is the pH at which the rate of an enzyme-controlled reaction is at its fastest. Most human enzymes work best at pH 7 (neutral), but there are exceptions. Pepsin, for example, works best at acidic pH 2, which is useful because it's found in the stomach. Above and below the optimum pH, the H^+ and OH^- ions found in acids and alkalis can break the ionic bonds and hydrogen bonds that hold the enzyme's tertiary structure in place. This makes the active site change shape, so the enzyme is denatured.

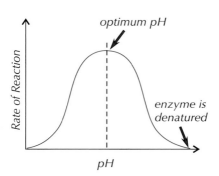

Figure 3: Effect of pH on the rate of an enzyme-controlled reaction.

Enzyme concentration

Tip: The enzyme concentration graph initially shows a linear (straight line) relationship between the concentration and the rate of reaction. This means you can use the gradient of the line to work out how fast the rate is changing — see page 20 for more on finding a gradient.

The more enzyme molecules there are in a solution, the more likely a substrate molecule is to collide with one and form an enzyme-substrate complex. So increasing the concentration of the enzyme increases the rate of reaction.

But, if the amount of substrate is limited, there comes a point when there's more than enough enzyme molecules to deal with all the available substrate, so adding more enzyme has no further effect.

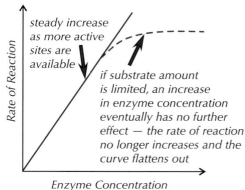

Figure 4: A graph to show the rate of an enzyme-controlled reaction against enzyme concentration.

Substrate concentration

The higher the substrate concentration, the faster the reaction. More substrate molecules means a collision between substrate and enzyme is more likely, so more active sites will be occupied and more enzyme-substrate complexes will be formed. This is only true up until a 'saturation' point though. After that, there are so many substrate molecules that the enzymes have about as much as they can cope with (all the active sites are full), and adding more makes no difference — the enzyme concentration becomes the limiting factor.

Substrate concentration decreases with time during a reaction (unless more substrate is added to the reaction mixture), so if no other variables are changed, the rate of reaction will decrease over time too. This makes the initial rate of reaction (the reaction rate right at the start of the reaction, close to time 0) the highest rate of reaction.

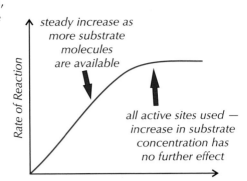

steady increase as more substrate molecules are available

all active sites used — increase in substrate concentration has no further effect

Substrate Concentration

Figure 5: *A graph to show the rate of an enzyme-controlled reaction against substrate concentration.*

Tip: The graphs showing how different factors affect enzyme activity show the rate of reaction (i.e. the speed of the reaction). When the line on the graph levels off it doesn't mean the reaction has stopped, just that it isn't going any faster.

Tip: A limiting factor is a variable that can slow down the rate of a reaction.

Tip: This graph shows how the substrate concentration decreases over the course of an enzyme-controlled reaction:

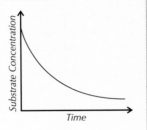

Time

Practice Question — Application

Q1 Hyperthermophilic bacteria are found in hot springs where temperatures reach 80 °C. Psychrotrophic bacteria are found in very cold environments. The graph on the right shows the rate of reaction for an enzyme from three different bacteria.

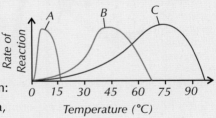

a) Explain which curve on the graph shows the enzyme from:
   i) hyperthermophilic bacteria,
   ii) psychrotrophic bacteria.
b) Explain what would happen to enzyme activity for each type of bacteria shown on the graph if they were put into an environment with a temperature range of 60-75 °C.

Practice Questions — Fact Recall

Q1 Explain why an increase in temperature increases the rate of enzyme activity.

Q2 Explain how a very high temperature can stop an enzyme from working.

Q3 What would a temperature coefficient of 4 tell you about the effect of temperature on the rate of an enzyme-controlled reaction?

Q4 Give a factor other than temperature that can denature an enzyme.

Q5 Explain the effect of increasing the enzyme concentration on the rate of an enzyme-controlled reaction.

Q6 Explain what happens to the rate of an enzyme-controlled reaction when the substrate concentration is increased after the saturation point.

Learning Objective:

■ Be able to investigate the effects of pH, temperature, enzyme concentration and substrate concentration on enzyme activity (PAG4).

Specification Reference 2.1.4

The rate of enzyme-controlled reactions can be determined by experiments.

Measuring rates of reactions

PRACTICAL ACTIVITY GROUP **4**

You need to know how the effects of pH, temperature, enzyme concentration and substrate concentration can be investigated experimentally. Here are two ways of measuring the rate of an enzyme-controlled reaction:

1. You can measure how fast the product of the reaction appears and use this to compare the rate of reaction under different conditions.

Tip: Don't forget to do a risk assessment before you do either of the experiments on these next two pages. You should always take basic safety precautions including wearing goggles and a lab coat.

— **Example** ——————

Catalase catalyses the breakdown of hydrogen peroxide into water and oxygen. It's easy to measure the volume of oxygen produced and to work out how fast it's given off. In this investigation, temperature is the independent variable — the thing you change. The dependent variable (the thing you measure) will be the volume of oxygen produced.
You need to control all the other variables that could affect the outcome of the investigation (i.e. keep them constant). That includes the pH, the enzyme concentration, the substrate concentration, etc.

Figure 1 below shows the apparatus you'll need. The oxygen released displaces the water from the measuring cylinder. (A stand and clamp would also be pretty useful to hold the cylinder upside down, as would a stopwatch and a water bath.)

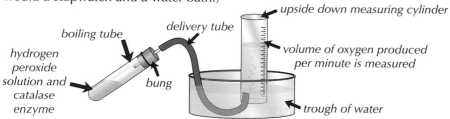

Figure 1: *Apparatus needed for investigating the breakdown of hydrogen peroxide.*

Here's how to carry out the experiment:

1. Set up boiling tubes containing the same volume and concentration of hydrogen peroxide. To keep the pH constant, add equal volumes of a suitable buffer solution to each boiling tube.

2. Set up the rest of the apparatus as shown in the diagram.

Tip: A buffer solution is able to resist changes in pH when small amounts of acid or alkali are added.

3. Put each boiling tube in a water bath set to a different temperature (e.g. 10 °C, 20 °C, 30 °C and 40 °C) along with another tube containing catalase. Wait 5 minutes before moving onto the next step so the enzyme gets up to temperature.

4. Use a pipette to add the same volume and concentration of catalase to each boiling tube. Then quickly attach the bung and delivery tube.

5. Record how much oxygen is produced in the first minute (60 s) of the reaction. Use a stopwatch to measure the time.

Tip: A negative control reaction, i.e. a boiling tube not containing catalase, should also be carried out at each temperature.

6. Repeat the experiment at each temperature three times, and use the results to find a mean volume of oxygen produced.

7. Calculate the mean rate of reaction at each temperature by dividing the volume of oxygen produced by the time taken (i.e. 60 s). The units will be cm^3 s^{-1}.

2. You can measure how fast the substrate is broken down and use this
    to compare the rate of reaction under different conditions.

Tip: Which method
you use to measure the
rate of a reaction will
normally depend on
whether the product or
the substrate is easier to
test for.

Example

The enzyme amylase catalyses the breakdown of starch to maltose.
In this experiment, the independent variable is the concentration of amylase
and the dependent variable is the time taken to break down starch
to maltose. All other variables need to be controlled. Figure 2 below shows
how the experiment can be set up. You'll need the apparatus shown in the
diagram as well as a stopwatch.

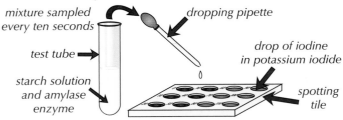

Figure 2: *Apparatus needed for investigating the breakdown of starch.*

1. Put a drop of iodine in potassium iodide solution into each well
    on a spotting tile. Label the wells to help you read your results.
2. Mix together a known concentration and volume of amylase and starch
    in a test tube.
3. Use a dropping pipette to put a drop of this mixture into one of the wells
    containing the iodine solution at regular intervals (e.g. every 10 seconds).
4. Observe the resulting colour. The iodine solution goes dark blue-black
    when starch is present but remains its normal browny-orange colour
    when there's no starch around.
5. You can see how fast amylase is working by recording how long it takes
    for the iodine solution to no longer turn blue-black when starch/amylase
    mixture is added — see Figure 3.

Exam Tip
You might have learnt
different methods for
measuring the rate of
an enzyme-controlled
reaction to those shown
here and on the previous
page — it doesn't matter
which ones you revise,
so long as you know
them well enough to
describe in the exam.

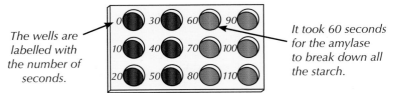

Figure 3: *Example results from investigating the breakdown of starch.*

6. Repeat the experiment using different concentrations of amylase.
7. Make sure that you also repeat the experiment three times at each
    amylase concentration and use your results to find the mean time taken.

Tip: This experiment
uses the starch test —
see page 69.

Variables

The experiments on this page and the previous one show you how you can
investigate the effects of temperature and enzyme concentration on the rate of
enzyme-controlled reactions.

    You can also alter these experiments to investigate the effect of a
different variable, such as pH (by adding a buffer solution with a different
pH to each test tube or boiling tube) or substrate concentration (you could
use serial dilutions to make substrate solutions with different concentrations).
The key to experiments like this is to remember to only change one variable
— everything else should stay the same.

Tip: There's more about
controlling variables on
page 5.

Estimating the initial rate of reaction

You can use a **tangent** to estimate the initial rate of reaction from a graph. As you know from page 103, the initial rate of reaction is the rate of reaction right at the start of the reaction, close to time equals zero (t = 0) on the graph. To work out the initial rate of reaction carry out the following steps:

1. Draw a tangent to the curve at t = 0, using a ruler. Do this by positioning the ruler so it's an equal distance from the curve at both sides of where it's touching it. Here you'll have to estimate where the curve would continue if it carried on below zero. Then draw a line along the ruler.

Tip: For more details on how to draw a tangent, see page 21.

2. Calculate the **gradient** of the tangent — this is the initial rate of reaction. The equation for the gradient of a straight line is:
    Gradient = change in y axis ÷ change in x axis.

3. Finally, you need to work out the units of the rate. The units will vary depending on what was measured in the experiment. To work out the units of rate from a graph, divide the units of the y axis by the units of the x axis (which should always be time).

Tip: If you're comparing the initial rate of reaction for two different reactions, you can work out the ratio of the rates to give you a quick and easy comparison. E.g. if the initial rate of a reaction at 30 °C is 1.2 cm³ s⁻¹ and the initial rate at 60 °C is 3.0 cm³ s⁻¹, you could write the ratio of the initial rates of reaction at 30 °C : 60 °C as 1 : 2.5. There's more about working out ratios on pages 13-14.

Example — Maths Skills

The graph below shows the volume of product released by an enzyme-controlled reaction at 37 °C.

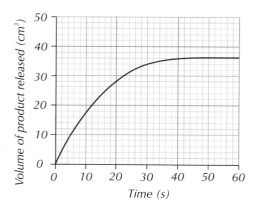

To work out the initial rate of reaction:

1. **Draw a tangent at t = 0.**
    (See the red line on the graph on the right.)

2. **Calculate the gradient of the tangent.**
    The gradient at t = 0 is:
    change in y ÷ change in x
    = 50 ÷ 18 = 2.8

3. **Work out the units.**
    units of y ÷ units of x
    = cm³ ÷ s = cm³ s⁻¹

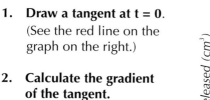

So the initial rate of reaction is **2.8 cm³ s⁻¹**.

Practice Questions — Application

Q1 The graph below shows the increase in the concentration of product from an enzyme-catalysed reaction at 25 °C.

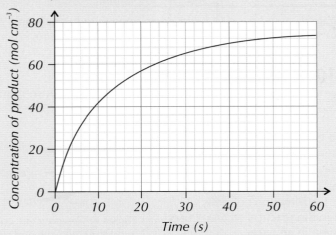

Use this graph to calculate the initial rate of reaction.

Q2 A group of students were investigating the effect of hydrogen peroxide concentration on the rate of breakdown of hydrogen peroxide by the enzyme catalase. They measured the volume of oxygen released by the reaction. Their results are shown in the graph below.

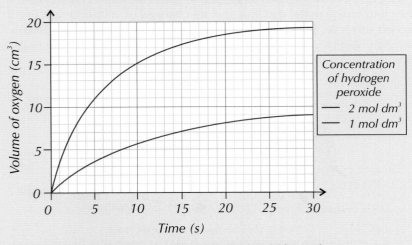

a) Name two variables that the students should keep the same during this investigation.

b) Calculate the ratio of the initial rates of reaction at 2 mol dm³ : 1 mol dm³ hydrogen peroxide.
Write your answer in the form X : 1.

Practice Question — Fact Recall

Q1 Describe how you could measure the rate of the breakdown of hydrogen peroxide by catalase at different temperatures, including the equipment you would use.

- Understand the need for coenzymes, cofactors and prosthetic groups in some enzyme-controlled reactions, including Cl⁻ as a cofactor for amylase, Zn^{2+} as a prosthetic group for carbonic anhydrase and vitamins as a source of coenzymes.

- Understand the effects of inhibitors on the rate of enzyme-controlled reactions, including competitive and non-competitive and reversible and non-reversible inhibitors, with reference to the action of metabolic poisons and some medicinal drugs, and the role of product inhibition.

- Understand that some enzymes involved in metabolic pathways are synthesised as inactive precursors (covered at A level only).

Specification Reference 2.1.4

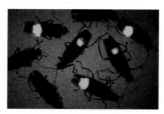

Figure 3: *The chemical reaction that makes fireflies glow is catalysed by the enzyme luciferase and an organic cofactor, ATP.*

Exam Tip
You need to learn the Cl⁻ and Zn^{2+} examples here for the exam.

4. Cofactors and Enzyme Inhibition

Some substances might need to be present for an enzyme to work. But other substances can slow enzymes down or stop them working altogether.

Cofactors and coenzymes

Some enzymes will only work if there is another non-protein substance bound to them. These non-protein substances are called cofactors.

Inorganic cofactors

Some cofactors are inorganic molecules or ions. They work by helping the enzyme and substrate to bind together (see Figure 1). They don't directly participate in the reaction so aren't used up or changed in any way.

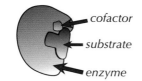

Figure 1: *An inorganic cofactor bound to an enzyme and substrate.*

┌ **Example** ──────────────────
Chloride ions (Cl⁻) are inorganic cofactors for the enzyme amylase.

Organic cofactors (coenzymes)

Some cofactors are organic molecules — these are called coenzymes. They participate in the reaction and are changed by it (they're just like a second substrate, but they aren't called that). They often act as carriers, moving chemical groups between different enzymes. They're continually recycled during this process (see Figure 2).

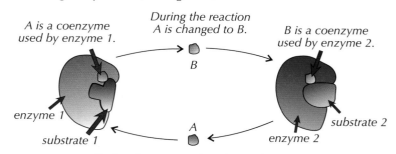

During the reaction B is changed to A (i.e. the coenzyme is recycled by enzyme 2)

Figure 2: *The recycling of coenzymes.*

Vitamins are often sources of coenzymes. For example, the coenzyme NAD is derived from vitamin B3.

Prosthetic Groups

If a cofactor is tightly bound to the enzyme, it's known as a prosthetic group.

┌ **Example** ──────────────────
Zinc ions (Zn^{2+}) are a prosthetic group for carbonic anhydrase (an enzyme in red blood cells, which catalyses the production of carbonic acid from water and carbon dioxide). The zinc ions are a permanent part of the enzyme's active site.

Enzyme inhibitors

Enzyme activity can be prevented by enzyme inhibitors — molecules that bind to the enzyme that they inhibit. Inhibition can be competitive or non-competitive.

Competitive inhibitors

Competitive inhibitor molecules have a similar shape to that of substrate molecules. They compete with the substrate molecules to bind to the active site, but no reaction takes place. Instead they block the active site, so no substrate molecules can fit in it — see Figure 4.

How much the enzyme is inhibited depends on the relative concentrations of the inhibitor and substrate. If there's a high concentration of the inhibitor, it'll take up nearly all the active sites and hardly any of the substrate will get to the enzyme. But if there's a higher concentration of substrate, then the substrate's chances of getting to an active site before the inhibitor increase. So increasing the concentration of substrate will increase the rate of reaction (up to a point) — see Figure 5.

Exam Tip
Don't say that the inhibitor molecule and the substrate have the same shape — they have a <u>similar</u> shape.

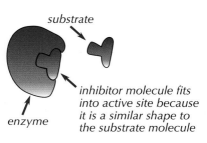

Figure 4: Competitive inhibition.

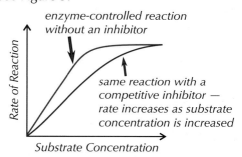

Figure 5: Effect of a competitive inhibitor on the rate of an enzyme-controlled reaction.

Tip: If you have a competitive inhibitor, increasing the concentration of substrate will reverse its effects — the substrate will out-compete the inhibitor for the active site.

Non-competitive inhibitors

Non-competitive inhibitor molecules bind to the enzyme away from its active site. The site they bind to is known as the enzyme's allosteric site. This causes the active site to change shape so the substrate molecules can no longer bind to it — see Figure 6.

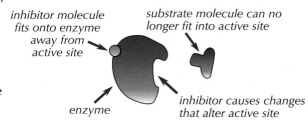

Figure 6: Non-competitive inhibition.

Exam Tip
When you're talking about shape change, always refer to the <u>active site</u> — don't just say the enzyme's changed shape.

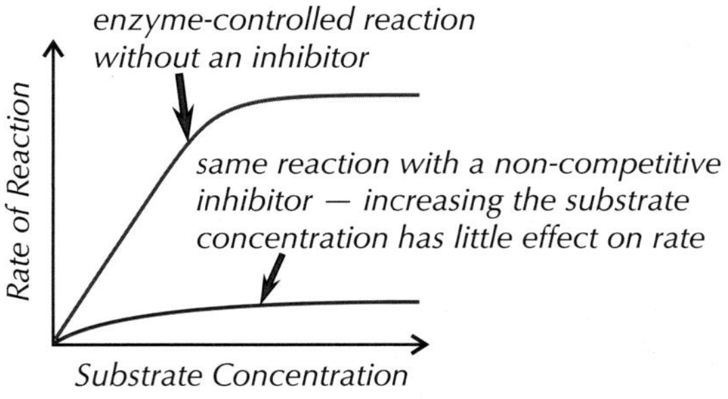

Non-competitive inhibitor molecules don't 'compete' with the substrate molecules to bind to the active site because they are a different shape. Increasing the concentration of substrate won't make any difference — enzyme activity will still be inhibited.

Figure 7: Effect of a non-competitive inhibitor on the rate of an enzyme-controlled reaction.

Reversible and non-reversible inhibition

Inhibitors can be reversible (not bind permanently to an enzyme) or non-reversible (bind permanently to an enzyme). Which one they are depends on the strength of the bonds between the enzyme and the inhibitor.

- If they're strong, covalent bonds, the inhibitor can't be removed easily and the inhibition is irreversible.
- If they're weaker hydrogen bonds or weak ionic bonds, the inhibitor can be removed and the inhibition is reversible.

Tip: A covalent bond is formed between two atoms that share electrons.

Exam Tip
This is exactly the kind of question you could get in the exam — enzyme-inhibition is a favourite with examiners, so make sure you know it inside out.

Practice Questions — Application

Q1 Methanol is broken down in the body into formaldehyde. The build up of formaldehyde can cause death. The enzyme that hydrolyses the reaction is alcohol dehydrogenase. The enzyme-substrate complex formed is shown on the right.

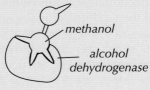

a) A diagram of ethanol is shown on the right. If someone had been poisoned with methanol, they could be helped by being given ethanol as soon as possible. Explain why.

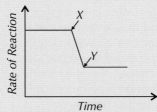

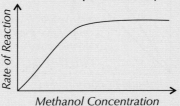

b) The graph shows the rate of the reaction with no ethanol present. Sketch a graph with the same axes showing the rate of reaction with the presence of ethanol.

Q2 Scientists have identified a substance (substance A) that inhibits the enzyme glycogen phosphorylase. This enzyme is responsible for the breakdown of glycogen into glucose. Substance A inhibits glycogen phosphorylase by binding to it away from the active site.

a) Is substance A a competitive or non-competitve inhibitor? Explain your answer.

The scientists test the effect of substance A in a solution containing glycogen and glycogen phosphorylase. The graph on the right shows the rate of the reaction over time.

b) At point X the scientists increase the concentration of substance A in the test solution. Describe and explain the shape of the graph between points X and Y.

c) Explain which of the graphs below represents the effect of:
  i) increasing the glycogen concentration at point Z.
  ii) increasing the glycogen phosphorylase concentration at point Z.

Tip: It might help you to jot down the role of each substance to answer these questions, e.g. glycogen = substrate, glucose = product, substance A = inhibitor.

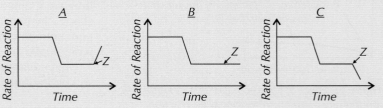

Drugs

Some medicinal drugs are enzyme inhibitors, for example:

Examples

- Some antiviral drugs (drugs that stop viruses) — e.g. reverse transcriptase inhibitors are a class of antiviral developed to treat HIV. They work by inhibiting the enzyme reverse transcriptase, which catalyses the replication of viral DNA. This prevents the virus from replicating.

- Some antibiotics — e.g. penicillin inhibits the enzyme transpeptidase, which catalyses the formation of proteins in bacterial cell walls. This weakens the cell wall and prevents the bacterium from regulating its osmotic pressure. As a result the cell bursts and the bacterium is killed.

Tip: Human Immunodeficiency virus (HIV) is a virus that causes AIDS.

Metabolic poisons

Metabolic poisons interfere with metabolic reactions (the reactions that occur in cells), causing damage, illness or death — they're often enzyme inhibitors. In the exam you might be asked to describe the action of one named poison.

Examples

- Cyanide is a non-competitive, irreversible inhibitor of cytochrome c oxidase, an enzyme that catalyses respiration reactions. Cells that can't respire die.

- Malonate is a competitive inhibitor of succinate dehydrogenase (which also catalyses respiration reactions).

- Arsenic is a non-competitive inhibitor of pyruvate dehydrogenase, yet another enzyme that catalyses respiration reactions.

Exam Tip
It doesn't matter which metabolic poison you learn for the exam, so long as you know an example and can describe how it works.

Product inhibition

Metabolic pathways are regulated by **end-product inhibition**. A metabolic pathway is a series of connected metabolic reactions. The product of the first reaction takes part in the second reaction — and so on. Each reaction is catalysed by a different enzyme. Many enzymes are inhibited by the product of the reaction they catalyse. This is known as product inhibition. End-product inhibition is when the final product in a metabolic pathway inhibits an enzyme that acts earlier on in the pathway — see Figure 8.

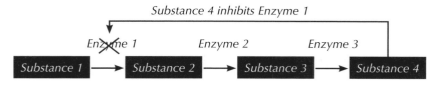

Figure 8: End-product inhibition

End-product inhibition is a nifty way of regulating the pathway and controlling the amount of end-product that gets made.

Example

Phosphofructokinase is an enzyme involved in the metabolic pathway that breaks down glucose to make ATP. ATP inhibits the action of phosphofructokinase — so a high level of ATP prevents more ATP from being made.

Both product and end-product inhibition are reversible. So when the level of product starts to drop, the level of inhibition will start to fall and the enzyme can start to function again — this means that more product can be made.

Enzyme inhibition to protect cells

Enzymes are sometimes synthesised as **inactive precursors** in metabolic pathways to prevent them causing damage to cells. Part of the precursor molecule inhibits its action as an enzyme. Once this part is removed (e.g. via a chemical reaction) the enzyme becomes active.

Exam Tip
You won't be tested on inactive precursors in your AS exams. You'll only be tested on them if you're doing the A-level exams.

┌ **Example** ───

Some proteases (which break down proteins) are synthesised as inactive precursors to stop them damaging proteins in the cell in which they're made.

Practice Question — Application

Q1 The diagram below shows two interlinked metabolic pathways.

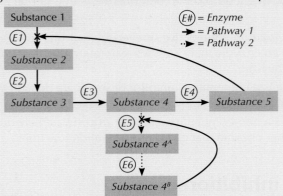

a) Substance 4^B is able to regulate its own production from substance 4 by inhibiting enzyme 5. What is this process called?

b) Suggest what immediate effect inhibition of enzyme 5 (in pathway 2) would have on the amount of substance 2 being produced (in pathway 1)? Explain your answer.

Practice Questions — Fact Recall

Q1 What is a cofactor?

Q2 Describe how a coenzyme is recycled during an enzyme-controlled reaction.

Q3 What is a prosthetic group?

Q4 Where do the following molecules bind to an enzyme:

a) a non-competitive inhibitor?   b) a competitive inhibitor?

Q5 State the bonds present between an enzyme and a:

a) reversible inhibitor.   b) non-reversible inhibitor.

Q6 Name a poison that inhibits enzyme action and describe how it works.

Q7 Explain the method of enzyme inhibition that can be used to protect cells that synthesise potentially damaging enzymes.

Section Summary

Make sure you know:

- That an enzyme is a biological catalyst (a substance that speeds up chemical reactions in living organisms without being used up in the reaction itself).

- That an enzyme can affect both the structure and function of an organism.

- That enzyme action may be intracellular (within cells) or extracellular (outside cells).

- That catalase is an enzyme that catalyses intracellular reactions and amylase and trypsin are enzymes that catalyse extracellular reactions.

- That enzymes are globular proteins with a specific tertiary structure and that the active site is the part of the enzyme that binds to a substrate to form an enzyme-substrate complex.

- That an enzyme's active site has a specific shape complementary to the shape of the substrate, and so enzymes will usually only work with one substrate.

- That the formation of an enzyme-substrate complex lowers the activation energy needed for a reaction, and the reasons why.

- That an enzyme-product complex is formed when the substrate has been converted into its products, but the products are still bound to the enzyme's active site.

- How to describe the 'lock and key' model and the 'induced fit' model of enzyme action.

- That increasing the temperature increases the rate of an enzyme-controlled reaction by:
    - increasing the kinetic energy of substrate and enzyme molecules, which increases the likelihood of a collision between them.
    - increasing the energy of collisions between substrate and enzyme molecules, which means collisions are more likely to result in a reaction.

- That enzymes have an optimum temperature and if the temperature becomes too high, the enzyme will become denatured.

- That the temperature coefficient (Q_{10}) value for a reaction shows how much the reaction rate changes in response to the temperature being raised by 10 °C and the formula is: $Q_{10} = R_2 \div R_1$.

- That enzymes have an optimum pH at which the rate of an enzyme-controlled reaction is at its fastest and that if the pH is too high or too low, the enzyme will become denatured.

- That increasing enzyme concentration will increase the rate of a reaction until the amount of substrate becomes the limiting factor.

- That increasing substrate concentration will increase the rate of a reaction until the saturation point is reached and all active sites are full (enzyme concentration is the limiting factor). And that over the course of a reaction substrate concentration will decrease, decreasing the rate of reaction.

- How to describe experiments that investigate the effects of pH, temperature, enzyme concentration and substrate concentration on the rate of an enzyme-controlled reaction.

- How to draw a tangent to a graph and use it to work out the initial rate of a reaction.

- That cofactors and coenzymes are non-protein substances needed to activate some enzymes, and are able to explain how they work. Cl⁻ ions are an example of a cofactor (for amylase).

- That prosthetic groups are a type of cofactor that is tightly bound to an enzyme and that Zn^{2+} ions are an example of a prosthetic group for the enzyme carbonic anhydrase.

- That competitive inhibitors have a similar shape to a substrate and inhibit enzymes by binding to the active site and that non-competitive inhibitors inhibit enzyme activity by binding to them away from the active site, causing the active site to change shape.

- That some enzyme inhibitors are reversible and some are irreversible, and are able to explain why.

- That some metabolic poisons and medicinal drugs work by inhibiting enzymes.

- That product inhibition is when a product inhibits the enzyme that has catalysed its formation and end-product inhibition is when the final product in a metabolic pathway inhibits an enzyme that acts earlier in the pathway.

Exam-style Questions

1   Apples contain a substance called catechol and the enzyme catecholase. When an apple is cut open and exposed to oxygen, the following chemical reaction takes place:

$$\text{catechol} + \tfrac{1}{2}O_2 \xrightarrow{\text{catecholase}} \text{benzoquinone} + H_2O$$

(a) (i) What effect do enzymes have on the activation energy of a reaction?

(1 mark)

(ii) Explain why enzymes have this effect.

(2 marks)

(b) (i)* Use the **'induced fit' model** of enzyme activity to explain how catecholase catalyses the reaction shown above.

In your answer you should make clear how the shape of the enzyme relates to its function.

(6 marks)

(ii) Name **another model** of enzyme action not mentioned in part **(i)** and describe how it differs to the induced fit model.

(2 marks)

(c)   Benzoquinone has a brown colour and its production is responsible for the 'browning' of apples once they have been cut.

To reduce the browning of an apple once it has been cut, would it be best to store the apple at room temperature or in a fridge? Explain your answer.

(4 marks)

(d)   Catecholase uses copper as a cofactor.
(i) Describe how copper enables catecholase to function.

(3 marks)

(ii) Give **two** differences between organic and inorganic cofactors.

(2 marks)

(e)   Copper binds more easily to a chemical called PTU than it does to catecholase.

Suggest why the rate of apple browning would be **lower** in the presence of PTU.

(3 marks)

* The quality of your response will be assessed in this question.

2   Triglycerides are a type of fat found in foods. In the stomach, gastric lipase acts as a catalyst to break triglycerides down into diglycerides and fatty acids.

$$triglyceride \xrightarrow{\text{gastric lipase}} diglyceride + fatty\ acid$$

(a)   Fig. 2.1 shows the rate of reaction for gastric lipase at different pH values.

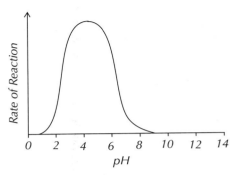

Fig. 2.1

(i) What is the **optimum pH** of gastric lipase?

(1 mark)

(ii) At what pH value(s) is gastric lipase **denatured**? Give a reason for your answer.

(2 marks)

(iii) Explain what happens when an enzyme is denatured by an extreme pH value.

(3 marks)

(iv) Suggest **two** variables you would control if you were investigating the activity of gastric lipase at different pH values.

(2 marks)

(b)   The weight-loss drug, orlistat, stops triglycerides from being broken down. Orlistat is a competitive inhibitor of gastric lipase.

Fig. 2.2 shows the reaction with and without orlistat present.

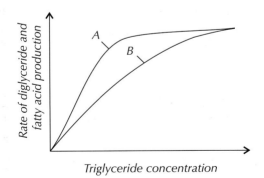

Fig. 2.2

(i) Which curve on Fig 2.2 shows the reaction **without** the presence of orlistat? Give a reason for your answer.

(1 mark)

(ii) Explain the action of orlistat in this reaction.

(3 marks)

Learning Objectives:

- Understand the roles of membranes at the surface of cells and within cells, including their role as:
  - partially permeable barriers between the cell and its environment, between organelles and the cytoplasm, and within organelles
  - sites of cell communication (cell signalling)
  - sites of chemical reactions.
- Know the fluid mosaic model of membrane structure and the roles of the following components:
  - phospholipids
  - cholesterol
  - proteins
  - glycolipids
  - glycoproteins.
- Understand the factors affecting membrane structure and permeability, including the effects of solvents and temperature.
- Know how to carry out practical investigations into factors affecting membrane structure and permeability (PAG5 and PAG8).

Specification Reference 2.1.5

1. Cell Membranes — The Basics

Cell membranes are the boundaries of cells, but there's an awful lot more to them than that...

Membrane function

Cells (and many of the organelles inside them) are surrounded by membranes that have a wide range of functions. You need to be able to describe the functions of membranes at the cell surface, as well as those within cells.

Membranes at the cell surface (plasma membranes)

Plasma membranes are a barrier between the cell and its environment, controlling which substances enter and leave the cell. They're **partially permeable** — they let some molecules through but not others.

Substances can move across the plasma membrane by **diffusion**, **osmosis** or **active transport** (see pages 124-132). Plasma membranes also allow recognition by other cells (e.g. the cells of the immune system, see p. 222) and cell communication (sometimes called cell signalling, see p. 122).

Membranes within cells

The membranes around organelles (see p. 32-33) divide the cell into different compartments — they act as a barrier between the organelle and the cytoplasm. This makes different functions more efficient.

> **Example**
>
> The substances needed for respiration (like enzymes) are kept together inside a mitochondrion by the mitochondrion's outer membrane.

Membranes can form vesicles to transport substances between different areas of the cell (see pages 132-133).

> **Example**
>
> Proteins are transported in vesicles from the rough endoplasmic reticulum to the Golgi apparatus during protein synthesis.

Membranes within cells are also partially permeable so they can control which substances enter and leave the organelle.

> **Example**
>
> RNA (see page 88) leaves the nucleus via the nuclear membrane (also called the nuclear envelope). DNA is too large to pass through the partially permeable membrane, so it remains in the nucleus.

You can also get membranes within organelles — these act as barriers between the membrane contents and the rest of the organelle.

> **Example**
>
> Thylakoid membranes in chloroplasts (see p. 33) keep the components needed for the light-dependent reactions of photosynthesis together.

Membranes within cells can be the site of chemical reactions. The membranes of some organelles are folded, increasing their surface area and making chemical reactions more efficient.

> **Example**
>
> The inner membrane of a mitochondrion contains enzymes needed for respiration. It has a large surface area, which increases the number of enzymes present and makes respiration more efficient.

Membrane structure

The structure of all membranes is basically the same. They're all composed of lipids (mainly a type called phospholipids), proteins and carbohydrates (usually attached to proteins or lipids).

In 1972, the **fluid mosaic model** was suggested to describe the arrangement of molecules in the membrane — see Figure 1. In the model, phospholipid molecules form a continuous, double layer (called a bilayer). This bilayer is 'fluid' because the phospholipids are constantly moving. Protein molecules are scattered through the bilayer, like tiles in a mosaic. Some proteins have a carbohydrate attached — these are called **glycoproteins**. Some lipids also have a carbohydrate attached — these are called **glycolipids**. Cholesterol molecules are also present within the bilayer.

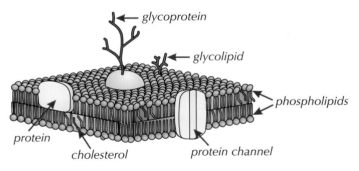

Figure 1: The fluid mosaic model of a cell membrane.

Membrane components

There are five main components you need to know about:

Phospholipids

Phospholipid molecules form a barrier to dissolved (water-soluble) substances. Phospholipids have a 'head' and a 'tail'. The head is **hydrophilic** — it attracts water. The tail is **hydrophobic** — it repels water. The molecules automatically arrange themselves into a bilayer — the heads face out towards the water on either side of the membrane (see Figure 3).

The centre of the bilayer is hydrophobic so the membrane doesn't allow water-soluble substances (like ions and polar molecules) to diffuse through it — it acts as a barrier to these dissolved substances. Fat-soluble substances, e.g. fat-soluble vitamins, dissolve in the bilayer and pass directly through the membrane.

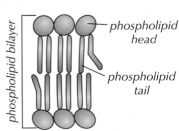

Figure 3: Phospholipid bilayer.

Tip: For more on models and theories, see page 1.

Tip: The phospholipid bilayer is ~ 7 nm thick.

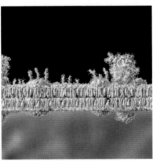

Figure 2: *A computer model of the fluid mosaic model.*

Tip: A polar molecule has one end with a slightly positive charge and one end with a slightly negative charge. These charges are nowhere near as strong as the positive or negative charge on an ion, but they do help polar molecules to dissolve in water. Non-polar substances have no charges.

Tip: Water is actually a polar molecule, but it can diffuse (by osmosis) through the cell membrane because it's so small (see page 124).

Cholesterol

Cholesterol gives the membrane stability. It is a type of lipid that's present in all cell membranes (except bacterial cell membranes). Cholesterol molecules fit between the phospholipids (see Figure 4). They bind to the hydrophobic tails of the phospholipids, causing them to pack more closely together. This makes the membrane less fluid and more rigid. Cholesterol also has hydrophobic regions, so it's able to create a further barrier to polar substances moving through the membrane.

Tip: There's more on phospholipids and cholesterol on pages 59-60.

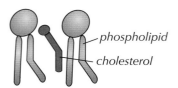

Figure 4: Cholesterol in the membrane.

Proteins

Tip: Charged particles include ions and polar molecules.

Proteins control what enters and leaves the cell. Some proteins form channels in the membrane (see pages 131-132) — these allow small, charged particles through. Other proteins (called carrier proteins) transport larger molecules and charged particles across the membrane by active transport and facilitated diffusion (see pages 131-132). Proteins also act as receptors for molecules (e.g. hormones) in cell signalling (see page 122). When a molecule binds to the protein, a chemical reaction is triggered inside the cell.

Glycolipids and glycoproteins

Tip: A hydrogen bond is a weak bond that forms between a slightly positively-charged hydrogen atom in one molecule and a slightly negatively-charged atom or group in another molecule, e.g. oxygen.

Glycolipids and glycoproteins stabilise the membrane by forming hydrogen bonds with surrounding water molecules. They act as receptors for messenger molecules in cell signalling and are sites where drugs, hormones and antibodies bind (see pages 122-123). They're also antigens — cell surface molecules involved in self-recognition and the immune response (see p. 222).

Tip: Remember, glyco*lipids* are carbohydrates attached to *lipids*, and glyco*proteins* are carbohydrates attached to *proteins*. Glyco is Greek for sweet or sugar and it refers to the carbohydrate bit.

Practice Questions — Application

Q1 Suggest a function of each of the following membranes:
  a) the membrane surrounding a chloroplast.
  b) the membrane surrounding a bacterial cell.

Q2 Chloride ions (Cl^-) need to pass through the plasma membrane to get inside the cell. How might they move across the membrane?

Q3 The protein content of a typical cell membrane is around 50%. In energy-releasing organelles, such as mitochondria, the amount rises to around 75%. Suggest a reason for this difference.

Factors affecting membrane permeability

Anything that affects the structure of a cell membrane can affect its permeability. You need to know the effects that solvents and temperature can have on cell membranes.

Solvents

The permeability of cell membranes depends on the solvent surrounding them. This is because some solvents (such as ethanol) dissolve the lipids in a cell membrane, so the membrane loses its structure. Some solvents increase membrane permeability more than others, e.g. ethanol increases membrane permeability more than methanol. Increasing the concentration of the solvent will also increase membrane permeability. For example, Figure 5 shows the effect of increasing alcohol concentration on membrane permeability.

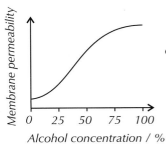

Figure 5: *The effect of increasing alcohol concentration on membrane permeability.*

> **Tip:** A solvent is any substance (usually a liquid) that can dissolve other substances.

Temperature

Cell membranes are affected by temperature — it affects how much the phospholipids in the bilayer can move, which affects membrane structure and permeability.

- **Temperatures below 0 °C** — The phospholipids don't have much energy, so they can't move very much. They're packed closely together and the membrane is rigid. But channel proteins and carrier proteins in the membrane denature (lose structure and function), increasing the permeability of the membrane (see Point 1, Figure 6). Ice crystals may form and pierce the membrane, making it highly permeable when it thaws.

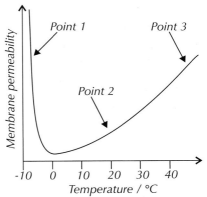

Figure 6: *Graph to show the effect of temperature on membrane permeability.*

> **Tip:** You may remember from Module 2: Section 4 that proteins (e.g. enzymes) denature at high temperatures. Well, very cold temperatures (i.e. those below 0 °C) can cause proteins to denature too.

- **Temperatures between 0 and 45 °C** — The phospholipids can move around and aren't packed as tightly together — the membrane is partially permeable (see Point 2, Figure 6). As the temperature increases the phospholipids move more because they have more energy — this increases the permeability of the membrane.

- **Temperatures above 45 °C** — The phospholipid bilayer starts to melt (break down) and the membrane becomes more permeable. Water inside the cell expands, putting pressure on the membrane. Channel proteins and carrier proteins in the membrane denature so they can't control what enters or leaves the cell — this increases the permeability of the membrane (Point 3, Figure 6).

> **Tip:** Think about what happens when you cook fruit or vegetables — as you apply heat, the food softens and liquid is released. This is partly because the cell membranes start to break down and become more permeable.

Investigating cell membrane permeability

You can investigate how different variables (e.g. solvent concentration and temperature) affect cell membrane permeability by doing experiments using beetroot. Beetroot cells contain a coloured pigment that leaks out — the higher the permeability of the membrane, the more pigment leaks out of the cell.

PRACTICAL ACTIVITY GROUP **5**

PRACTICAL ACTIVITY GROUP **8**

Tip: You should assess all safety risks before proceeding with this experiment. Be careful when using a scalpel — make sure you cut away from yourself and that the blade is clean and sharp.

Example — Investigating temperature

Here's how you could investigate the effect of temperature on beetroot membrane permeability:

1. Use a scalpel to carefully cut five equal sized pieces of beetroot. (Make sure you do your cutting on a cutting board.) Rinse the pieces to remove any pigment released during cutting.

2. Add the five pieces to five different test tubes, each containing 5 cm³ of water. Use a measuring cylinder or pipette to measure the water.

3. Place each test tube in a water bath at a different temperature, e.g. 10 °C, 20 °C, 30 °C, 40 °C, 50 °C, for the same length of time (measured using a stopwatch).

4. Remove the pieces of beetroot from the tubes, leaving just the coloured liquid.

Tip: Place the tubes into the water bath gently to avoid splashing hot water on yourself. Use tongs to remove them after the experiment — they may be hot.

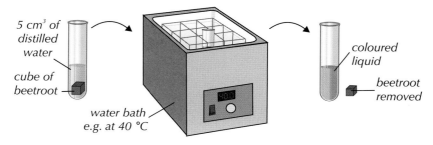

5 cm³ of distilled water

cube of beetroot

water bath e.g. at 40 °C

coloured liquid

beetroot removed

Figure 7: *Investigating the effect of temperature on beetroot cell membrane permeability.*

5. Now you need to use a **colorimeter**. Firstly, switch the colorimeter on and allow five minutes for it to stabilise. Then set up the colorimeter so you're using a blue filter (or a wavelength of about 470 nm).

6. Add distilled water to a cuvette and then put it into the colorimeter. Calibrate the machine to zero — your teacher will show you how to do this.

7. Next, use a pipette to transfer a sample of the liquid from the first test tube to a clean cuvette.

8. Put the cuvette in the colorimeter and read and record the absorbance of the solution.

9. Repeat steps 7-8 for the liquids in the remaining four test tubes (using a clean pipette and cuvette each time).

10. You're now ready to analyse your results. Bear in mind that the higher the absorbance reading, the more pigment released, so the higher the permeability of the membrane.

Depending on the resources you have available, you may be able to connect the colorimeter to a computer and use software to collect the data and draw a graph of the results.

Tip: See page 71 for more on colorimeters.

Tip: Your cuvettes should be about three quarters full of the sample liquid (or water) before they go into the colorimeter.

Q1 A person leaves some frozen raspberries on a plate to defrost. When he returns, there's a red puddle on the plate around the fruit. Use your knowledge of cell membranes to explain what has happened.

Q2 An experiment was carried out to investigate the effect of increasing methanol concentration on the permeability of beetroot cell membranes. Beetroot cubes were soaked in varying concentrations of methanol for a set amount of time, then a colorimeter was used to read the absorbance of the liquid once the beetroot cubes had been removed. The results of the experiment were used to produce a graph.

    a) Give four variables that should be controlled in this experiment.

    b) Give two things that should be done with the colorimeter before it is used to measure the absorbance of the liquid samples.

    c) Suggest which of the graphs below (A or B) was produced using the results of the experiment. Explain your answer.

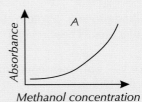

Q1 Explain what is meant when a cell membrane is described as being 'partially permeable'.

Q2 Give three functions of membranes within cells.

Q3 Identify the structures labelled A-E in the diagram below.

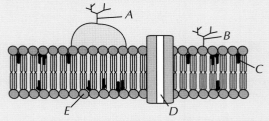

Q4 Explain the meaning of the terms 'hydrophilic' and 'hydrophobic'.

Q5 Explain why the plasma membrane is an effective barrier against water-soluble substances.

Q6 How does the plasma membrane control what enters and leaves the cell?

Q7 Give the function(s) of the following membrane components:

    a) cholesterol,

    b) glycoproteins and glycolipids.

Q8 Describe and explain what happens to the plasma membrane at temperatures above 45 °C.

Exam Tip
Not all diagrams of the fluid mosaic model look the same, so don't just memorise the pictures — make sure you learn what all the different components actually are, what they do and how they fit together.

- Understand the role of membranes as sites of cell communication (cell signalling).

- Understand the role of membrane-bound receptors as sites where hormones and drugs can bind.
  Specification Reference 2.1.5

2. Cell Membranes and Signalling

The cells in your body all need to work together — and to do that, they need to communicate. The cell membrane plays a key role in this communication.

Cell signalling

Cells need to communicate with each other to control processes inside the body and to respond to changes in the environment. Cells communicate with each other by cell signalling, which uses messenger molecules.

Cell signalling starts when one cell releases a messenger molecule (e.g. a hormone). This molecule travels to another cell (e.g. in the blood). The messenger molecule is detected by the cell because it binds to a receptor on its cell membrane. The binding then triggers a change in the cell, e.g. a series of chemical signals is set off.

Membrane receptors

The cell membrane is important in the signalling process. Proteins in the cell membrane act as receptors for messenger molecules. These receptor proteins are called 'membrane-bound receptors'.

Receptor proteins have specific shapes — only messenger molecules with a complementary shape can bind to them. Different cells have different types of receptors — they respond to different messenger molecules. A cell that responds to a particular messenger molecule is called a **target cell**. Figure 1 shows how messenger molecules are able to bind to target cells but not to non-target cells.

Tip: Complementary shapes fit together, e.g.

Tip: Non-complementary shapes don't fit together, e.g.

Tip: You don't just get a single type of receptor on each cell. Every cell type has a specific combination of many different receptors.

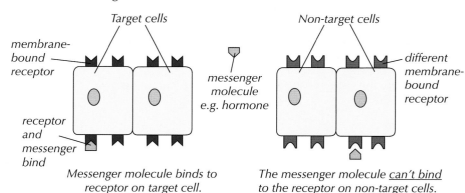

Messenger molecule binds to receptor on target cell.

The messenger molecule <u>can't bind</u> to the receptor on non-target cells.

Figure 1: *Messenger molecules and membrane-bound receptors.*

Hormones as messenger molecules

Many messenger molecules are hormones. Hormones work by binding to receptors in cell membranes and triggering a response in the cell.

┌─ **Example 1 — Glucagon** ──────────────

Glucagon is a hormone that's released when there isn't enough glucose in the blood. It binds to receptors on liver cells, causing the liver cells to break down stores of glycogen to glucose.

Example 2 — FSH

FSH is a hormone that's released by the pituitary gland during the menstrual cycle. It binds to receptors on cells in the ovaries, causing an egg to mature ready for ovulation.

Tip: A hormone can trigger different responses in different cells. For example, in men, FSH binds to cells in the testes and initiates the production of sperm.

The role of drugs

Many drugs work by binding to receptors in cell membranes. They either trigger a response in the cell, or block the receptor and prevent it from working. Understanding how cells communicate using membrane-bound receptors is important in the development of medicinal drugs — the receptors can be used as sites for targeted action.

Example 1 — Morphine

The body produces chemicals called endorphins, to relieve pain. Endorphins bind to opioid receptors in the brain and reduce the transmission of pain signals. Morphine is a drug used to relieve pain. It works by binding to the same opioid receptors as endorphins, also triggering a reduction in pain signals.

Example 2 — Antihistamines

Cell damage causes the release of a chemical called histamine. Histamine binds to receptors on the surface of other cells and causes inflammation. Antihistamines work by blocking histamine receptors on cell surfaces. This prevents histamine from binding to the cell and stops inflammation.

Practice Questions — Application

The diagrams below show a messenger molecule, its membrane-bound receptor and a molecule of an antagonistic drug. The drug inhibits the action of the messenger molecule.

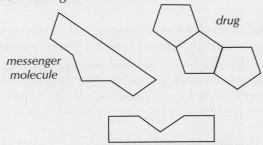

drug

messenger molecule

membrane-bound receptor

Tip: Don't worry if you're not sure what antagonistic means — all the information you need is given in the question. (But just so you know, an antagonistic molecule blocks the action of another molecule.)

Q1 Using the information in the diagrams and your own knowledge, explain how the drug works.

Q2 The diagram on the right shows a mutated version of the membrane-bound receptor. Explain why cells with only the mutated version of the receptor can't respond to the messenger molecule.

mutated receptor

Q3 The messenger molecule is only able to produce a response in liver cells. Suggest why this is the case.

Learning Objectives:

- Understand the movement of molecules across membranes by diffusion (a passive method).

- Know how to carry out practical investigations into the factors affecting diffusion rates in model cells (PAG8).

- Understand that osmosis is the movement of water across a partially permeable membrane down a water potential gradient.

- Understand the effects that solutions of different water potential can have on plant and animal cells.

- Know how to carry out practical investigations into the effects of solutions of different water potential on plant and animal cells (PAG8).

Specification Reference 2.1.5

Tip: Particles are constantly moving about randomly using their own kinetic energy — this is how they are able to diffuse from one side of the membrane to the other.

Tip: Large molecules, ions and most polar substances need help to cross the plasma membrane — see pages 131-133.

3. Diffusion and Osmosis

There are many ways substances move in and out of cells across the membrane. First up, diffusion and osmosis.

Diffusion

Diffusion is the net movement of particles (molecules or ions) from an area of higher concentration to an area of lower concentration — see Figure 1. Molecules will diffuse both ways, but the net movement will be to the area of lower concentration. This continues until particles are evenly distributed throughout the liquid or gas. The concentration gradient is the path from an area of higher concentration to an area of lower concentration. Particles diffuse down a concentration gradient.

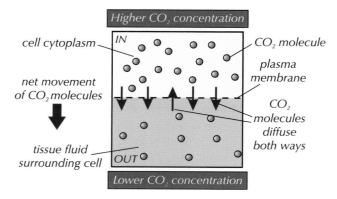

Figure 1: *Diffusion of carbon dioxide across the plasma membrane.*

Diffusion is a passive process — no energy is needed for it to happen. Particles can diffuse across plasma membranes, as long as they can move freely through the membrane.

Examples

- Small, non-polar molecules such as oxygen and carbon dioxide are able to diffuse easily through spaces between phospholipids.

- Water is also small enough to fit between phospholipids, so it's able to diffuse across plasma membranes even though it's polar. The diffusion of water molecules like this is called osmosis (see p. 126).

Factors affecting the rate of diffusion

There are four main factors that affect the rate of diffusion:

- The concentration gradient — the higher it is, the faster the rate of diffusion.

- The thickness of the exchange surface — the thinner the exchange surface (i.e. the shorter the distance the particles travel), the faster the rate.

- The surface area — the larger the surface area (e.g. of the plasma membrane), the faster the rate of diffusion.

- The temperature — the warmer it is, the faster the rate of diffusion because the particles have more kinetic energy so they move faster.

Investigating diffusion

You can investigate diffusion using model cells — these are materials that are used to represent real cells. Agar jelly is commonly used as a model cell because it has a similar consistency to the cytoplasm of a real cell.

PRACTICAL ACTIVITY GROUP 8

Phenolphthalein is a chemical that can be used to investigate diffusion. It's a pH indicator — it's pink in alkaline solutions and colourless in acidic solutions. If you place cubes of agar jelly containing phenolphthalein and an alkali, such as sodium hydroxide, in an acidic solution and leave them for a while they'll eventually turn colourless as the acid diffuses into the agar jelly and neutralises the sodium hydroxide.

The following three examples show you how you can use agar jelly and phenolphthalein to investigate factors that affect the rate of diffusion:

Example 1 — Concentration gradient

1. First, make up some agar jelly with phenolphthalein and dilute sodium hydroxide. This will make the jelly a lovely shade of pink.
2. Prepare 5 test tubes containing hydrochloric acid (HCl) in increasing concentrations, e.g. 0.2 M, 0.4 M, 0.6 M, 0.8 M, 1 M.
3. Using a scalpel, cut out 5 equal-sized cubes from the agar jelly.
4. Put one of the cubes into the first test tube and use a stopwatch to time how long it takes for the cube to turn colourless.
5. Then do the same for the rest of the test tubes of HCl using a new cube each time.

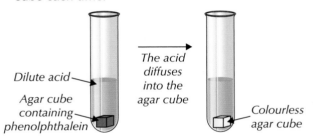

Dilute acid
Agar cube containing phenolphthalein
The acid diffuses into the agar cube
Colourless agar cube

Figure 2: *Using agar jelly cubes, phenolphthalein and acid to investigate diffusion.*

You would expect the cube in the highest concentration of HCl to go colourless fastest, because the concentration gradient is the greatest (see previous page).

Example 2 — Surface area

Prepare the agar jelly as in Example 1. Then cut it into different sized cubes and work out their surface area to volume ratio (see page 158). Time how long it takes each cube to go colourless when placed in the same concentration of HCl. You would expect the cube with the largest surface area to volume ratio to go colourless fastest.

Example 3 — Temperature

Prepare the agar jelly as in Example 1 and cut into equal-sized cubes. Then prepare several boiling tubes containing the same concentration of HCl (and put the boiling tubes into water baths at different temperatures). When the HCl in each tube has reached the desired temperature, put a cube of the agar jelly into it and time how long it takes the cube to go colourless. You would expect the cube in the highest temperature to go colourless fastest.

Tip: Before you start your experiment, make sure you do a risk assessment and identify any hazards. You should wear safety goggles and a lab coat when working with acids.

Exam Tip
There are other ways to investigate diffusion in model cells. For example, a different substance could be used as the model cell (e.g. Visking tubing or gelatine cubes) and different pH indicators could be used (e.g. cresol red). Don't worry if you get a question in the exam that uses a different method or different equipment to what's used here — just apply what you know about diffusion to the context you're given.

Tip: Don't forget to repeat your experiment at least three times and calculate the mean of your results. This helps to reduce the effect of random errors, making your results more precise (see page 6).

Tip: Remember you only change the variable you are investigating — all the other variables should be kept constant (see page 5).

Tip: Don't increase the temperature above 65 °C or the agar jelly will start to melt.

Q1 The photograph on the right shows ink diffusing through a beaker of water. Explain what is happening to the ink molecules.

Q2 Carbon dioxide is a waste product of respiration and must be removed from cells. How will each of the following affect the rate of diffusion of carbon dioxide across a plasma membrane? Explain your answer in each case.

   a) Increasing the thickness of the cell membrane.

   b) Increasing the number of folds in the cell membrane.

   c) Reducing the concentration of carbon dioxide outside of the cell.

Q3 A student wants to carry out an experiment to investigate diffusion. Her teacher gives her some agar jelly dyed purple with potassium permanganate. Potassium permanganate turns colourless when it reacts with hydrochloric acid.

   a) Describe how the student could use the agar jelly to investigate the effect of temperature on diffusion.

   b) Describe what she should expect to see in the experiment.

Osmosis

Tip: Water can also move across a membrane through protein channels (see pages 131-132) called aquaporins.

Osmosis is the diffusion of water molecules across a partially permeable membrane down a **water potential gradient**. This means water molecules move from an area of higher water potential (i.e. higher concentration of water molecules) to an area of lower water potential (i.e. lower concentration of water molecules) — see Figure 3.

Exam Tip
You should always use the term <u>water potential</u> in the exam — never say water concentration.

Water potential is the potential (likelihood) of water molecules to diffuse out of or into a solution.

Pure water has a water potential of zero. Adding solutes to pure water lowers its water potential — so the water potential of any solution is always negative. The more negative the water potential, the stronger the concentration of solutes in the solution.

Tip: Another way of looking at it is that pure water has the highest water potential and all solutions have a lower water potential than pure water.

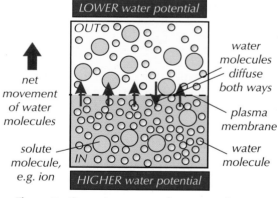

Figure 3: Osmosis across a plasma membrane.

Exam Tip
In the exam, you might get asked about experiments involving distilled water. Distilled water is water that's been purified, so it has a water potential of 0.

┌ **Example** ──────────────

Glass A contains pure water — it's got a water potential of zero. Glass B contains a solution of orange squash. The orange squash molecules are a solute. They lower the concentration of the water molecules. This means that the water potential of the orange squash is lower than the water potential of pure water.

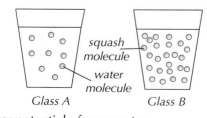

Glass A   *Glass B*

Water potential and cells

Cells are affected by the water potential of the surrounding solution. Water moves in or out of a cell by osmosis. How much moves in or out depends on the water potential of the surrounding solution compared to that of the cell. Animal and plant cells behave differently in different solutions.

Isotonic solutions

If two solutions have the same water potential they're said to be isotonic. Cells in an isotonic solution won't lose or gain any water — there's no net movement of water molecules because there's no difference in water potential between the cell and the surrounding solution. Both plant and animal cells will stay the same when placed in an isotonic solution — see Figure 4.

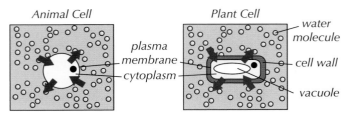

No net movement of water.

Figure 4: *Cells in isotonic solutions.*

Tip: A hypotonic solution would have a weaker concentration of solutes than the cell.

Hypotonic solutions

If a cell is placed in a solution that has a higher water potential, water will move into the cell by osmosis. Solutions with a higher water potential compared with the inside of the cell are called hypotonic. An animal cell in a hypotonic solution will swell and could eventually burst (see Figure 5).

If a plant cell is placed in a hypotonic solution, the vacuole will swell and the contents of the vacuole and cytoplasm will push against the cell wall (see Figure 5). This causes the cell to become **turgid** (swollen). The cell won't burst because the inelastic cell wall is able to withstand the increase in pressure.

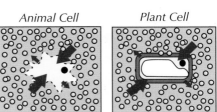

Net movement of water into the cell.

Figure 5: *Cells in hypotonic solutions.*

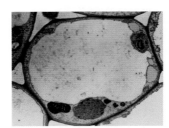

Figure 6a: *A turgid plant cell. The full vacuole (blue) is pushing against the cell wall.*

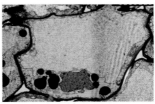

Figure 6b: *A flaccid plant cell. Water has left the vacuole.*

Hypertonic solutions

If a cell is placed in a solution that has a lower water potential, water will move out of the cell by osmosis. Solutions with a lower water potential than the cell are called hypertonic. If an animal cell is placed in a hypertonic solution it will shrink (see Figure 7). If a plant cell is placed in a hypertonic solution it will become

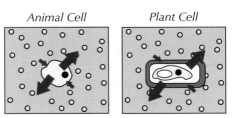

Net movement of water out of the cell.

Figure 7: *Cells in hypertonic solutions.*

flaccid (limp). The cytoplasm and plasma membrane will eventually pull away from the cell wall (again, see Figure 7). This is called **plasmolysis**.

Tip: A hypertonic solution would have a stronger concentration of solutes than the cell.

Tip: Before you start your investigation do a risk assessment so you are aware of any potential hazards.

Tip: You might also see M written as mol dm^{-3}.

Tip: You could also investigate the water potential of other plant cell types, such as carrot, using the same basic method.

Tip: See page 13 for more on calculating percentage change.

Investigating the effect of water potential on plant cells

PRACTICAL ACTIVITY GROUP **8**

You need to know how you could investigate the effect of solutions of different water potential on plant cells. The experiment described below is an example of an experiment you could do using potato cylinders and varying sucrose solutions. Remember, the higher the sucrose concentration, the lower the water potential.

Method for the experiment

1. Prepare sucrose solutions of the following concentrations: 0.0 M, 0.2 M, 0.4 M, 0.6 M, 0.8 M, 1.0 M.
2. Use a cork borer to cut potatoes into identically sized cylinders, about 1 cm in diameter. Divide the cylinders into groups of three and measure the mass of each group using a mass balance.
3. Place one group into each of your sucrose solutions and leave the cylinders in the solutions for at least 20 minutes (making sure that they all get the same amount of time).
4. Remove the cylinders and pat them dry gently with a paper towel. Weigh each group again and record your results.
5. Calculate the percentage change in mass for each group.

Examples — Maths Skills

To find the percentage change in mass, use the following formula:

$$\text{percentage change} = \frac{\text{final mass} - \text{initial mass}}{\text{initial mass}} \times 100$$

1. So, if you had a group of cylinders that weighed 13.2 g at the start of the experiment and 15.1 g at the end, the percentage change in mass would be...

$$\text{percentage change} = \frac{15.1 - 13.2}{13.2} \times 100 = \mathbf{14.4\%}$$

The positive result tells you the potato cylinders gained mass.

2. If you had another group of potato cylinders that weighed 13.3 g at the start of the experiment and 11.4 g at the end, the percentage change in mass would be...

$$\text{percentage change} = \frac{11.4 - 13.3}{13.3} \times 100 = \mathbf{-14.3\%}$$

The negative result tells you the potato cylinders lost mass.

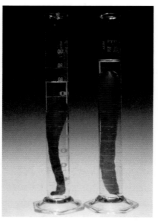

Figure 8: *Osmosis in carrot cells. The carrot on the left has been placed in salty water (low water potential) and the carrot on the right has been placed in pure water.*

Tip: If you could see the potato cells under a microscope, you'd see them becoming turgid as the cylinder gains mass and plasmolysed as the cylinder loses mass (see previous page).

The potato cylinders will gain water (and therefore mass) in solutions with a higher water potential than the cylinders, and lose water in solutions with a lower water potential.

Plotting a graph of your results

Next you can use your results to plot a graph. This helps you find the point at which the potato cells don't change in mass. At this point the cells must be in an isotonic solution, because the cells don't lose or gain water — so you can use your graph to find the water potential of the potato cells (see next page).

Example — Maths Skills

The table shows results from the experiment. You can use the data to draw a scatter graph.

concentration (M)	0	0.2	0.4	0.6	0.8	1.0
% change	20	5	-7	-14	-17	-18

1. Draw your axes — don't forget to label them, including the units.

2. Plot the points carefully. You then need to draw a line of best fit through your points. In this case, draw a smooth curve passing through as many points as possible.

This point is where the water potential of the sucrose solution is the same as the water potential of the potato cells.

3. The point where the line of best fit crosses the x-axis is the point where the sucrose solution has the same water potential as the potato cells. Here it's around 0.27 M. You can look up the water potential for this concentration of sucrose solution in, e.g. a textbook.

Tip: There's more about plotting graphs and lines of best fit on page 19.

Tip: Don't forget to use a sensible scale so that your graph takes up at least half of your graph paper.

Tip: Put the independent variable, the concentration, on the x-axis and the dependent variable, the percentage change in mass, on the y-axis.

Investigating the effect of water potential on animal cells

PRACTICAL ACTIVITY GROUP **8**

You can investigate the effect of water potential on animal cells using chickens' eggs that have had their shells dissolved. The remaining membrane is partially permeable, so it's a good model for showing the effects of osmosis in animal tissue.

Here's an example of how you could do it:

Example — Osmosis in chickens' eggs

1. Make up sodium chloride solutions of different concentrations, e.g. 0.2 M, 0.4 M, 0.6 M, 0.8 M, 1.0 M, and pour an equal volume into separate beakers.

2. Take your de-shelled eggs and carefully pat them with absorbent paper to remove any excess moisture.

3. Use a mass balance to weigh each egg, then record its mass in a table.

4. Place each egg in a different beaker, making sure that the sodium chloride solution is covering the whole egg (see Figure 9). Leave all the eggs for the same amount of time, e.g. 24 hours.

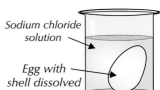

Sodium chloride solution

Egg with shell dissolved

Figure 9: *Investigating the effect of solutions of different water potential on animal cells.*

5. Remove the eggs, dry them and then weigh them again. Use your results to calculate the percentage change in mass for each egg (see previous page).

6. Plot a graph of your results (as shown above) and use it to see how solutions of different water potential (i.e. different sodium chloride solutions) affect the mass of the egg.

Tip: Before you start, make sure you think through any safety issues and work out how you are going to minimise the risks. You should wear safety goggles for this practical in case any of the solutions are splashed in your eyes.

Tip: Your teacher will dissolve the shells in hydrochloric acid so the eggs are ready for you to use.

Tip: Water potential is usually measured in kilopascals (or kPa). It's actually a unit of pressure.

Tip: Remember, a higher water potential is closer to 0 (the water potential of pure water).

Tip: Visking tubing is a partially permeable membrane — it's used a lot in osmosis and diffusion experiments.

Practice Questions — Application

Q1 Describe the net movement of water molecules in each of the following situations:

a) Human cheek cells with a water potential of –300 kPa are placed in a salt solution with a water potential of –325 kPa.

b) Apple slices with a water potential of –750 kPa are placed in a beaker of pure water.

c) Orange squash with a water potential of –450 kPa is sealed in a length of Visking tubing and suspended in a solution of equal water potential.

Q2 Potato cells with a water potential of –350 kPa are placed in sucrose solutions with varying water potentials. The water potential of each solution is shown in the table below.

Solution	Water potential
1	–250 kPa
2	–500 kPa
3	–1000 kPa

a) After 15 minutes, the potato cells in solution 1 have become turgid. Explain why this has happened.

b) Predict what will happen to the cells in solutions 2 and 3. Explain your answers.

Practice Questions — Fact Recall

Q1 What is diffusion?

Q2 Is diffusion an active or a passive process?

Q3 What types of molecules are able to diffuse through the plasma membrane of a cell?

Q4 Give four factors that affect the rate of diffusion.

Q5 What term is used to describe the diffusion of water molecules across a partially permeable membrane down a water potential gradient?

Q6 Define the term 'water potential'.

Q7 Describe and explain what will happen to each of the following:

a) an animal cell placed in a hypotonic solution,

b) a plant cell placed in a hypotonic solution,

c) a plant cell placed in a hypertonic solution.

Tip: A hypotonic solution has a higher water potential than the cell. A hypertonic solution has a lower water potential than the cell.

4. Facilitated Diffusion and Active Transport

The large size or charged nature of some molecules prevents them from being able to pass directly through a membrane. That's where facilitated diffusion and active transport come in...

Facilitated diffusion

Some larger molecules (e.g. amino acids, glucose) would diffuse extremely slowly through the phospholipid bilayer because they're so big. Charged particles, e.g. ions and polar molecules, would also diffuse slowly — that's because they're water soluble, and the centre of the bilayer is hydrophobic (see page 117). So to speed things up, large or charged particles diffuse through carrier proteins or channel proteins in the cell membrane instead — this is called facilitated diffusion.

Like diffusion, facilitated diffusion moves particles down a concentration gradient, from a higher to a lower concentration. It's also a passive process — it doesn't use energy. But unlike diffusion, there are two types of membrane protein involved — carrier proteins and channel proteins.

Carrier proteins

Carrier proteins move large molecules (including polar molecules and ions) into or out of the cell, down their concentration gradient. Different carrier proteins facilitate the diffusion of different molecules.

┌─ **Example** ───────────────────────────────────

GLUT1 is a carrier protein found in almost all animal cells. It specifically helps to transport glucose across the plasma membrane.

Here's how carrier proteins work:

- First, a large molecule attaches to a carrier protein in the membrane.
- Then, the protein changes shape.
- This releases the molecule on the opposite side of the membrane — see Figure 1.

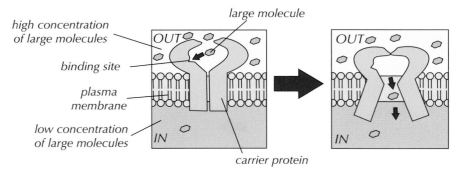

Figure 1: *Movement of a molecule by a carrier protein.*

Channel proteins

Channel proteins form pores in the membrane for smaller ions and polar molecules to diffuse through, down their concentration gradient (see Figure 3 — next page). Different channel proteins facilitate the diffusion of different charged particles.

Learning Objectives:

- Understand the movement of molecules across membranes by facilitated diffusion (a passive method).

- Understand the movement of molecules across membranes by active transport, endocytosis and exocytosis (all processes that require adenosine triphosphate, ATP, as an immediate source of energy).

Specification Reference 2.1.5

Tip: Remember — small, non-polar substances and water can diffuse directly through the membrane.

Exam Tip
Always say <u>down</u> the concentration gradient in the exam, not across or along — or you won't get the marks.

Tip: Carrier proteins are sometimes called transport proteins.

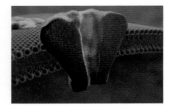

Figure 2: *Computer model showing a cross-section of a channel protein in the phospholipid bilayer.*

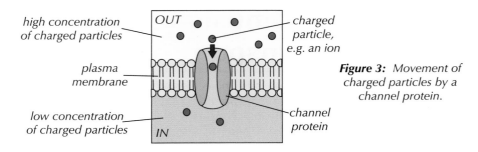

Figure 3: *Movement of charged particles by a channel protein.*

Tip: ATP stands for adenosine triphosphate (there's more about ATP on pages 81-82).

Tip: Most of the ATP in a cell is produced by aerobic respiration. Aerobic respiration takes place in the mitochondria and is controlled by enzymes.

Exam Tip
It's easy to get facilitated diffusion and active transport confused because they both use proteins to transport molecules. But active transport is the only one that uses energy (ATP) to do so.

Tip: Endocytosis and exocytosis (see next page) both require energy.

Active transport

Active transport uses energy to move molecules and ions across plasma membranes, against a concentration gradient. This process involves carrier proteins and is pretty similar to facilitated diffusion — see Figure 4. A molecule attaches to the carrier protein, the protein changes shape and this moves the molecule across the membrane, releasing it on the other side. The only difference is that energy is used (from ATP — a common source of energy used in the cell), to move the solute against its concentration gradient.

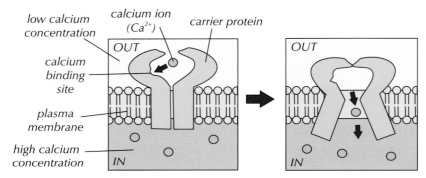

Figure 4: *The active transport of calcium ions.*

Endocytosis

Some molecules are way too large to be taken into a cell by carrier proteins, e.g. proteins, lipids and some carbohydrates. Instead a cell can surround a substance with a section of its plasma membrane. The membrane then pinches off to form a vesicle inside the cell containing the ingested substance — the substance has been taken in by endocytosis (see Figure 5).

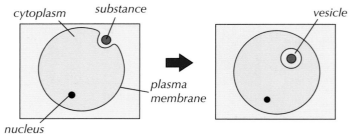

Figure 5: *The process of endocytosis.*

Some cells also take in much larger objects by endocytosis — for example, some white blood cells (mainly phagocytes, see page 222) use endocytosis to take in things like microorganisms and dead cells so that they can destroy them. Like active transport, this process uses ATP for energy.

Exocytosis

Some substances produced by the cell (e.g. digestive enzymes, hormones, lipids) need to be released from the cell — this is done by exocytosis (see Figure 6). Vesicles containing these substances pinch off from the sacs of the Golgi apparatus and move towards the plasma membrane. The vesicles fuse with the plasma membrane and release their contents outside the cell. Some substances (like membrane proteins) aren't released outside the cell — instead they are inserted straight into the plasma membrane. Exocytosis also uses ATP as an energy source.

Tip: It can be easy to confuse endocytosis and exocytosis — so try to remember that <u>ex</u>ocytosis is used for things <u>ex</u>iting the cell.

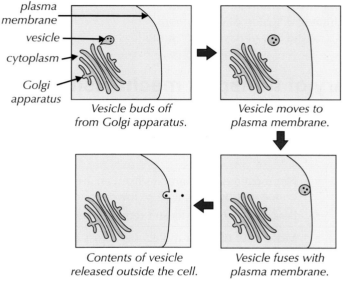

Vesicle buds off from Golgi apparatus.

Vesicle moves to plasma membrane.

Contents of vesicle released outside the cell.

Vesicle fuses with plasma membrane.

Figure 6: *The process of exocytosis.*

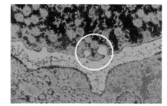

Figure 7: *Vesicles containing substances for secretion breaking through the plasma membrane (circled).*

Tip: There's more on vesicles and the Golgi apparatus on p. 33.

Practice Questions — Application

Q1 The diagram below shows a gap between two neurones. Each neurone is surrounded by a membrane. Chemical messengers are secreted from the membrane of neurone 1 and travel across the gap to the membrane of neurone 2, where they bind with cell surface receptors.

a) Name structure Z.

b) Describe what is happening in steps A to C on the diagram.

Once the chemical messengers bind to the receptors, they cause sodium ions (Na$^+$) to move across the membrane of neurone 2, down a concentration gradient.

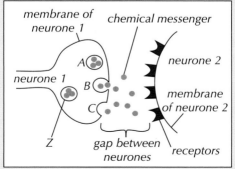

c) Suggest how the sodium ions might travel across the membrane.

Exam Tip
Always be specific about which membrane you're talking about in the exam — don't just say, 'fuses with the cell membrane', if what you mean is 'fuses with the cell surface (plasma) membrane'.

Q2 The overall equation for aerobic respiration can be written as:

glucose + oxygen → carbon dioxide + water + ATP

The graph below shows the relationship between the relative rates of oxygen consumption and the active transport of sodium ions across epithelial cells.

a) Describe the relationship shown by the graph and suggest an explanation for this relationship.

b) What effect would the rate of the facilitated diffusion of sodium ions have on the rate of oxygen consumption?

Rate of oxygen consumption

Rate of sodium ion active transport

Summary of transport mechanisms

You've covered a lot of different transport mechanisms in this section, so here's a handy table to help you remember the similarities and differences:

Tip: Understanding the different ways that substances are transported into our cells is really important in medicine. It helps scientists understand how different drugs get into our cells and could help them to develop new ways to administer drugs in the future.

Exam Tip
Make sure you know the definitions of each type of transport off by heart.

Exam Tip
Make sure you know what types of molecules (e.g. large/small, polar/non-polar/ionic) are moved by the different types of transport.

Type of transport:	Description
Diffusion (see p. 124)	▪ Net movement of particles from an area of higher concentration to an area of lower concentration. ▪ Passive process — doesn't require energy.
Osmosis (see pages 126-127)	▪ Movement of water molecules across a partially permeable membrane down a water potential gradient, from an area of higher water potential to an area of lower water potential. ▪ Passive process — doesn't require energy.
Facilitated diffusion (see pages 131-132)	▪ Net movement of particles from an area of higher concentration to an area of lower concentration. ▪ Uses carrier proteins to aid the diffusion of large molecules (including ions and polar molecules) through the plasma membrane. ▪ Uses channel proteins to aid the diffusion of smaller ions and polar molecules through the plasma membrane. ▪ Passive process — doesn't require energy.
Active transport (see p. 132)	▪ Movement of molecules against a concentration gradient. ▪ Uses carrier proteins to transport molecules. ▪ Active process — requires energy (ATP).
Endocytosis (see p. 132)	▪ Movement of large molecules (e.g. proteins) or objects (e.g. dead cells) into a cell. ▪ The plasma membrane surrounds a substance and then pinches off to form a vesicle inside the cell. ▪ Active process — requires energy (ATP).
Exocytosis (see p.133)	▪ Movement of molecules out of a cell. ▪ Vesicles fuse with the plasma membrane and release their contents. ▪ Active process — requires energy (ATP).

Practice Question — Application

Q1 Copy and complete the table to show which kind of transport could be used in each case. The first column has been done for you.

Transport system	A plant cell taking in water	Calcium ions moving into a cell against a concentration gradient	A muscle cell taking in polar glucose molecules	A white blood cell taking in anthrax bacteria
Osmosis	✓			
Facilitated diffusion using channel proteins	✓			
Facilitated diffusion using carrier proteins	✗			
Active transport using carrier proteins	✗			
Endocytosis	✗			
Exocytosis	✗			

Tip: Calcium ions are charged, but relatively small.

Tip: Glucose is a polar molecule, but it's also relatively large.

Tip: If you're struggling with this table, think carefully about the type of substance being transported in each case.

Practice Questions — Fact Recall

Q1 Describe the difference between simple diffusion through a plasma membrane and facilitated diffusion through a plasma membrane.

Q2 Summarise the similarities and differences between facilitated diffusion and active transport.

Q3 Describe how the following are used to transport substances across a cell membrane:

a) carrier proteins,   b) channel proteins.

Q4 Describe the process of endocytosis.

Q5 Give an example of a substance that might be transported across a cell membrane by exocytosis.

Section Summary

Make sure you know...

- That plasma membranes are partially permeable and have a range of functions including: controlling which substances enter and leave the cell, allowing recognition by other cells, and allowing cells to communicate.

- That membranes within cells are also partially permeable and have a range of functions including: surrounding an organelle and acting as a barrier between the organelle and the cytoplasm, controlling what substances enter and leave an organelle, acting as the site of chemical reactions, and (for membranes within organelles) acting as a barrier between the membrane contents and the rest of the organelle.

- The fluid mosaic model of cell membrane structure, including the roles of phospholipids (form a barrier to dissolved substances), cholesterol (gives the membrane stability), proteins (control what enters and leaves the cell, act as receptors), glycolipids and glycoproteins (stabilise the membrane, act as receptors/antigens).

- That some solvents, such as ethanol, dissolve the lipids in a cell membrane, causing it to lose its structure and become more permeable.

- That temperature influences how much the phospholipids in the bilayer of a cell membrane can move, affecting the membrane's structure and permeability.

- How to investigate the effect of a variable, such as solvent concentration or temperature, on cell membrane structure and permeability, e.g. by using cubes of beetroot.

- That cells communicate with each other through cell signalling using messenger molecules, and that messenger molecules bind to membrane-bound receptors on target cells.

- That membrane-bound receptors are sites where hormones and drugs bind.

- That diffusion is the passive movement of particles from an area of higher concentration to an area of lower concentration.

- That the rate of diffusion is affected by concentration gradient, thickness of the exchange surface, surface area and temperature.

- How to investigate the effect of a variable, such as concentration gradient, surface area or temperature, on the rate of diffusion in model cells, e.g. by using cubes of agar jelly and a pH indicator such as phenolphthalein.

- That osmosis is diffusion of water molecules across a partially permeable membrane down a water potential gradient, from an area of higher water potential to an area of lower water potential.

- How animal and plant cells behave in isotonic, hypotonic and hypertonic solutions.

- How to investigate the effect of water potential on plant and animal cells, e.g. by using potato cylinders or a chicken's egg with the shell dissolved and a range of sucrose or salt solutions.

- That facilitated diffusion (a passive process) uses carrier proteins and channel proteins to move large molecules and charged particles, e.g. ions and polar molecules, down a concentration gradient.

- That active transport uses carrier proteins and energy (from ATP) to actively move molecules against a concentration gradient.

- That cells can take in large substances by endocytosis using energy from ATP — the plasma membrane surrounds the substance and then pinches off, forming a vesicle inside the cell.

- That cells can secrete substances by exocytosis also using energy from ATP — vesicles containing substances for release outside the cell fuse with the plasma membrane, then release their contents.

Exam-style Questions

1   **Fig. 1.1** shows normal onion cells under a light microscope. The cytoplasm appears dark grey. **Fig. 1.2** shows the same onion cells after they have been placed in a **weak salt solution**. The solution has a lower water potential than the onion cells.

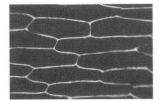

         Fig. 1.1   **Fig. 1.2**

(a) (i)   Explain what is meant by the term water potential.

(1 mark)

(ii)   Describe and explain the changes seen between **Fig. 1.1** and **Fig. 1.2**.

(3 marks)

(iii)   Describe what might happen if animal cells were placed in a solution with a lower water potential than the cell contents.

(1 mark)

(b)   In **Fig. 1.2** it is possible to see the cells' plasma membranes.
(i)   Describe the fluid mosaic structure of the plasma membrane.

(4 marks)

(ii)   State **two** functions of the plasma membrane.

(2 marks)

2   Glucose is a product of digestion. It is also a relatively large polar molecule. Once glucose has been digested, it must be absorbed into the bloodstream from the cells of the small intestine. Part of the absorption process happens by facilitated diffusion.

(a) (i)   Suggest why facilitated diffusion is necessary for glucose to cross the plasma membranes of the intestinal cells.

(3 marks)

(ii)   Does this process require energy? Explain your answer.

(1 mark)

(iii)   State the type of molecule that facilitates the diffusion of glucose across plasma membranes in the small intestine, and briefly describe how it does so.

(2 marks)

(b)   Another stage of the absorption process uses active transport. Explain what is meant by the term active transport.

(2 marks)

3   A group of students investigated the water potential of potato cells.

They cut cubes of potato of the same size and shape, weighed them and placed a single cube into each of four different concentrations of sucrose solution.
One cube was placed in pure water.

They re-weighed each of the cubes every hour, and after 12 hours the mass of all the cubes remained constant. The overall change in mass for each cube is shown in **Fig. 3.1**.

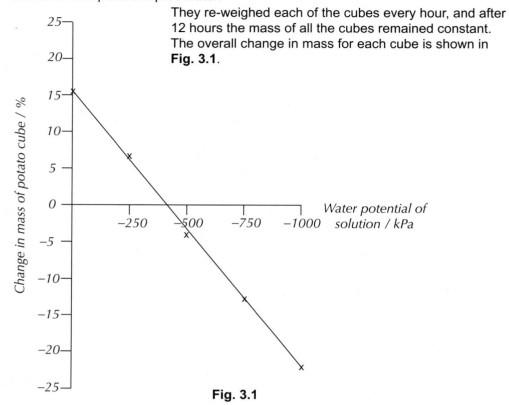

Fig. 3.1

(a)   The students recorded the difference in mass between the cubes at the start and end of the experiment in grams, but plotted the overall change as a percentage. Suggest why the graph was plotted in this way.

(1 mark)

(b)   What was the change in mass for the potato cube placed in pure water?

(1 mark)

(c) (i)   Explain why the cubes in the **–500, –750** and **–1000 kPa** solutions lost mass.

(2 marks)

(ii)   Use **Fig. 3.1** to estimate the water potential of the potato cells.

(1 mark)

(d)   Suggest how the students could make their results more precise.

(1 mark)

(e)   If the experiment was repeated with cubes that had a larger surface area, would you expect the mass of all the cubes to become constant before 12 hours, at 12 hours or after 12 hours? Explain your answer.

(2 marks)

1. The Cell Cycle and Mitosis

We need new cells for growth and to replace damaged tissue, so our body cells need to be able to make more of themselves. They do this during the cell cycle.

The cell cycle

The cell cycle is the process that all body cells in multicellular organisms use to grow and divide. It starts when a cell has been produced by cell division and ends with the cell dividing to produce two identical cells.

The cell cycle consists of a period of cell growth and DNA replication, called **interphase**, and a period of cell division, called M phase. M phase involves **mitosis** (nuclear division) and **cytokinesis** (cytoplasmic division). Interphase (cell growth) is subdivided into three separate growth stages. These are called G_1, S and G_2 — see Figure 1.

The cell cycle is regulated by checkpoints. Checkpoints occur at key points during the cycle to make sure it's OK for the process to continue.

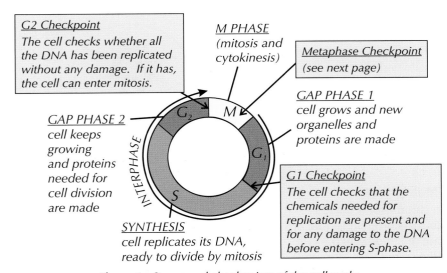

G2 Checkpoint
The cell checks whether all the DNA has been replicated without any damage. If it has, the cell can enter mitosis.

M PHASE
(mitosis and cytokinesis)

Metaphase Checkpoint
(see next page)

GAP PHASE 2
cell keeps growing and proteins needed for cell division are made

GAP PHASE 1
cell grows and new organelles and proteins are made

G1 Checkpoint
The cell checks that the chemicals needed for replication are present and for any damage to the DNA before entering S-phase.

SYNTHESIS
cell replicates its DNA, ready to divide by mitosis

Figure 1: *Stages and checkpoints of the cell cycle.*

Interphase

During interphase the cell carries out normal functions, but also prepares to divide. The cell's DNA is unravelled and replicated, to double its genetic content. The organelles are also replicated so it has spare ones, and its ATP content is increased (ATP provides the energy needed for cell division).

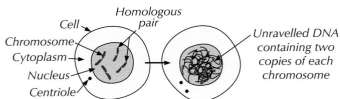

Cell
Chromosome
Cytoplasm
Nucleus
Centriole
Homologous pair
Unravelled DNA containing two copies of each chromosome

Learning Objectives:

- Understand the cell cycle, including the processes taking place during interphase (G_1, S and G_2), mitosis and cytokinesis, leading to genetically identical cells.

- Know how the cell cycle is regulated, including an outline of the use of checkpoints to control the cycle.

- Understand the significance of mitosis in life cycles, including growth, tissue repair and asexual reproduction in plants, animals and fungi.

- Know the main stages of mitosis, including the changes in the nuclear envelope, chromosomes, chromatids, centromere, centrioles, spindle fibres and cell membrane.

- Be able to recognise sections of plant tissue showing the cell cycle and stages of mitosis.

- Be able to prepare and examine stained sections and squashes of plant tissue, in order to produce labelled diagrams showing the cell cycle and stages of mitosis observed (PAG1).

Specification Reference 2.1.6

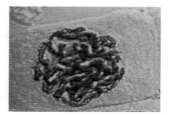

Figure 2: *Interphase in bluebell cells.*

Mitosis

There are two types of cell division — mitosis and meiosis (see p. 143 for more on meiosis). Mitosis is the form of cell division that occurs during the cell cycle. It's needed for the growth of multicellular organisms (like us) and for repairing damaged tissues. Some animals, plants and fungi also use it to reproduce asexually (without sex). Mitosis is really one continuous process, but it's described as a series of division stages — prophase, metaphase, anaphase and telophase.

The structure of chromosomes in mitosis

Before we go into the detail of mitosis, you need to know more about the structure of chromosomes. As mitosis begins, the chromosomes are made of two strands joined in the middle by a **centromere**. The separate strands are called **chromatids**. Two strands on the same chromosome are called **sister chromatids**. There are two strands because each chromosome has already made an identical copy of itself during interphase. When mitosis is over, the chromatids end up as one-strand chromosomes in the new daughter cells.

Tip: You could remember the order of the phases in mitosis (**p**rophase, **m**etaphase, **a**naphase, **t**elophase) by using, 'purple mice are tasty'.

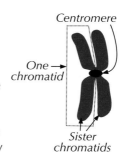

Centromere
One → chromatid
Sister chromatids

1. Prophase

The chromosomes condense, getting shorter and fatter. Tiny bundles of protein called **centrioles** start moving to opposite ends of the cell, forming a network of protein fibres across it called the **spindle**. The **nuclear envelope** (the membrane around the nucleus) breaks down and chromosomes lie free in the cytoplasm.

Figure 3: *Prophase in bluebell cells.*

Centrioles move to opposite ends of the cell
Nuclear envelope starts to break down
Centromere

2. Metaphase

The chromosomes (each with two chromatids) line up along the middle of the cell (at the spindle equator) and become attached to the spindle by their centromere. At the metaphase checkpoint, the cell checks that all the chromosomes are attached to the spindle before mitosis can continue.

Figure 4: *Metaphase in bluebell cells.*

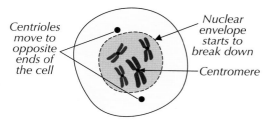

Spindle fibres
Centromeres on spindle equator

3. Anaphase

The centromeres divide, separating each pair of sister chromatids. The spindles contract, pulling chromatids to opposite ends of the cell, centromere first.

Figure 5: *Anaphase in bluebell cells.*

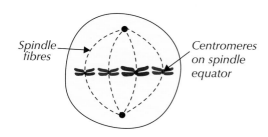

Sister chromatids moving to opposite ends of the cell

4. Telophase

The chromatids reach the opposite poles on the spindle. They uncoil and become long and thin again. They're now called chromosomes again. A nuclear envelope forms around each group of chromosomes, so there are now two nuclei.

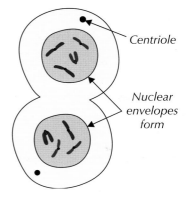

Centriole

Nuclear envelopes form

Figure 6: Telophase in bluebell cells.

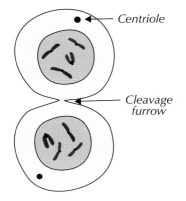

Centriole

Cleavage furrow

Cytokinesis

The cytoplasm divides. In animal cells, a cleavage furrow forms to divide the cell membrane. There are now two daughter cells that are genetically identical to the original cell and to each other. Cytokinesis usually begins in anaphase and ends in telophase. It's a separate process to mitosis.

Investigating mitosis

PRACTICAL ACTIVITY GROUP **1**

You can stain chromosomes so you can see them under a microscope. This means you can watch what happens to them during mitosis. To do this, you need to stain the specimen, put it on a microscope slide and examine it under a microscope — see pages 44-46 for more details of how to do these things.

Figure 7 shows some plant root tip cells on a 'squash' microscope slide, viewed under a light microscope. Squashes like this can be made by treating the very tips of growing roots in hydrochloric acid, then breaking them open and spreading the cells thinly on a microscope slide using a mounted needle. A few drops of stain are then added to the spread out cells before they are physically squashed beneath a coverslip. When you look at the slide under the light microscope, you should be able to see cells at different stages of the cell cycle and mitosis. You need to be able to recognise, draw and label each stage.

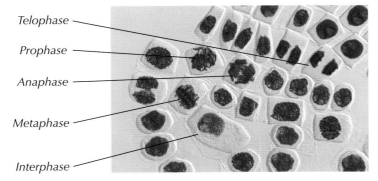

Telophase

Prophase

Anaphase

Metaphase

Interphase

Figure 7: Stained plant root cells on a squash microscope slide.

Tip: If you do carry out an experiment like this make sure you're wearing safety goggles and a lab coat before you start. You should also wear gloves when using stains.

Tip: Different stains you can use for this include toluidine blue O, ethano-orcein and Feulgen stain. Make sure you carry out a risk assessment (see p. 7) before you do this experiment, including assessing the specific risks for the particular staining technique you're using.

Tip: You can recognise cells in interphase because the chromosomes will be spread out and not condensed.

Practice Question — Application

Q1 Mitosis takes place during M phase of the cell cycle.

a) Copy and complete the table below to show the different stages involved in mitosis and the order that they occur in.

Stage of Mitosis	Step Number
	3
Prophase	1
Metaphase	

b) The images below show mitosis occurring in three onion cells.

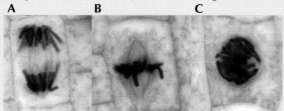

A   B   C

Which cell (A-C) is undergoing the following:

i) metaphase?

ii) prophase?

c) Describe the stage of mitosis shown by cell A.

Practice Questions — Fact Recall

Q1   What is the cell cycle?

Q2   During which period of the cell cycle does cell growth occur?

Q3   Why is DNA is checked during interphase?

Q4   Why is mitosis needed?

Q5   Describe what happens during prophase.

Q6   During which stage of mitosis do chromosomes line up along the centre of a cell?

Q7   During which stage of mitosis are chromatids pulled to opposite ends of the cell?

Q8   How does an animal cell divide by cytokinesis?

Q9   How many cells are produced during mitosis?

Q10 In mitosis, a parent cell divides to produce genetically different daughter cells. True or false?

2. Sexual Reproduction and Meiosis

Some organisms reproduce using mitosis. Other organisms produce offspring through sexual reproduction, so they need gametes (sex cells) — and these are made by meiosis. It's way less confusing than it sounds, promise...

Sexual reproduction

Gametes are the sperm cells in males and egg cells in females. In sexual reproduction two gametes join together at fertilisation to form a zygote, which divides and develops into a new organism.

Normal body cells have the **diploid number (2n)** of chromosomes — meaning each cell contains two of each chromosome (a pair), one from the mum and one from the dad. The chromosomes that make up each pair are the same size and have the same genes, although they could have different versions of those genes (called alleles). These pairs of matching chromosomes are called **homologous chromosomes**.

┌─ **Example** ───────────────

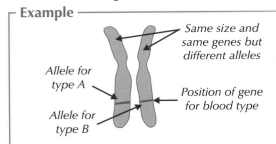

Same size and same genes but different alleles

Allele for type A

Position of gene for blood type

Allele for type B

Figure 1: *Diagram showing a pair of homologous chromosomes.*

Gametes have a **haploid (n) number** of chromosomes — there's only one copy of each chromosome. At fertilisation, a haploid sperm fuses with a haploid egg, making a cell with the normal diploid number of chromosomes. Half these chromosomes are from the father (the sperm) and half are from the mother (the egg). The diploid cell produced by fertilisation is called a zygote.

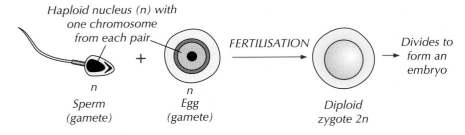

Haploid nucleus (n) with one chromosome from each pair

FERTILISATION

Divides to form an embryo

n
Sperm (gamete)

n
Egg (gamete)

Diploid zygote 2n

Figure 2: *Diagram to show fertilisation.*

What is meiosis?

Meiosis is a type of cell division that happens in the reproductive organs to produce gametes. Meiosis involves a reduction division. Cells that divide by meiosis are diploid to start with, but the cells that are formed from meiosis are haploid — the chromosome number halves. Cells formed by meiosis are all genetically different because each new cell ends up with a different combination of chromosomes.

Learning Objectives:

- Understand what homologous chromosomes are.

- Understand the significance of meiosis in life cycles, including the production of haploid cells.

- Know the main stages of meiosis, including:
  - interphase
  - prophase 1
  - metaphase 1
  - anaphase 1
  - telophase 1
  - prophase 2
  - metaphase 2
  - anaphase 2
  - telophase 2

- Understand the mechanisms of genetic variation by crossing over and independent assortment.

  Specification Reference 2.1.6

Exam Tip
Make sure you know what a homologous pair of chromosomes is for the exam.

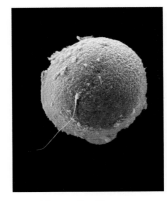

Figure 3: *Electron micrograph of a sperm fertilising an egg.*

Interphase

Tip: You've come across interphase before — it also takes place before mitosis (see page 139).

The whole of meiosis begins with interphase. During interphase, the cell's DNA unravels and replicates to produce double-armed chromosomes called sister chromatids (see p. 140).

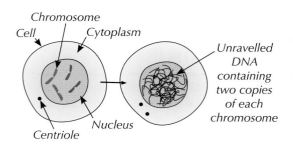

Meiosis 1

Meiosis involves two divisions — meiosis 1 and meiosis 2. After interphase, the cells enter meiosis 1. Meiosis 1 is the reduction division (it halves the chromosome number). There are four similar stages to each division in meiosis called prophase, metaphase, anaphase and telophase.

Here's what happens during each of those stages in meiosis 1:

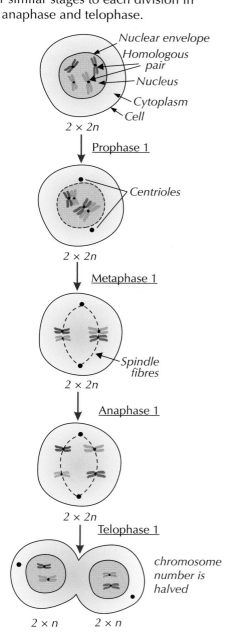

Prophase 1

Tip: If you need a reminder about what centrioles and spindle fibres are, take a look back at prophase in mitosis on page 140.

The chromosomes condense, getting shorter and fatter. **Homologous chromosomes** pair up — number 1 with number 1, 2 with 2, 3 with 3 etc. Crossing-over occurs (see next page). Just like in mitosis, centrioles start moving to opposite ends of the cell, forming the spindle fibres. The nuclear envelope (the membrane around the nucleus) breaks down.

Metaphase 1

The homologous pairs line up across the centre of the cell and attach to the spindle fibres by their centromeres.

Anaphase 1

The spindles contract, pulling the pairs apart (one chromosome goes to each end of the cell).

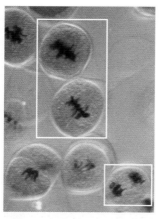

Figure 4: *Light micrograph of cells undergoing meiosis. The highlighted cells in the centre are in metaphase 1. The bottom right cell is in anaphase 1.*

Telophase 1

A nuclear envelope forms around each group of chromosomes. Cytokinesis (division of the cytoplasm) occurs and two haploid daughter cells are produced.

Tip: We've only shown 4 chromosomes here for simplicity. Humans actually have 46 (23 homologous pairs).

Meiosis 2

The two daughter cells undergo prophase 2, metaphase 2, anaphase 2, telophase 2 (and cytokinesis) — these are pretty much the same as the stages in meiosis 1, except with half the number of chromosomes. In anaphase 2, the sister chromatids are separated — each new daughter cell inherits one chromatid from each chromosome.

Four haploid daughter cells are produced.

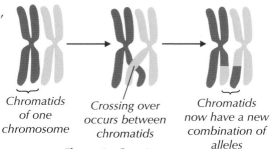

End of meiosis 1 = two haploid daughter cells

$2 \times n$ *STAGES OF MEIOSIS 2* $2 \times n$

n   *n*   *n*   *n*

End of meiosis 2 = four haploid daughter cells

Tip: Unlike in prophase 1, there is no pairing up of homologous chromosomes in prophase 2. This is because the pairs have already been split up by the end of meiosis 1.

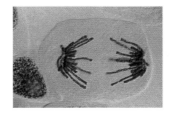

Figure 5: *Chromatids separating during meiosis 2.*

Genetic variation

Genetic variation is the differences that exist between individuals' genetic material. The reason meiosis is important is that it creates genetic variation — it makes gametes that are all genetically different. Then during fertilisation, any egg can fuse with any sperm, which also creates variation. This means new individuals have a new mixture of alleles, making them genetically unique.

Creating genetic variation in gametes

There are two main events during meiosis that lead to genetic variation:

1. Crossing over of chromatids

During prophase 1 of meiosis 1, homologous pairs of chromosomes come together and pair up. The chromatids twist around each other and bits of chromatids swap over. The chromatids still contain the same genes but now have a different combination of alleles — see Figure 6.

Chromatids of one chromosome   *Crossing over occurs between chromatids*   *Chromatids now have a new combination of alleles*

Figure 6: *Crossing over.*

Tip: Crossing over is also known as recombination.

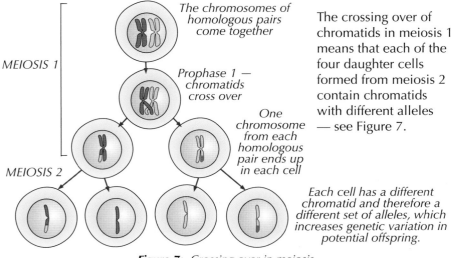

The chromosomes of homologous pairs come together

MEIOSIS 1

Prophase 1 — chromatids cross over

One chromosome from each homologous pair ends up in each cell

MEIOSIS 2

Each cell has a different chromatid and therefore a different set of alleles, which increases genetic variation in potential offspring.

Figure 7: *Crossing over in meiosis.*

The crossing over of chromatids in meiosis 1 means that each of the four daughter cells formed from meiosis 2 contain chromatids with different alleles — see Figure 7.

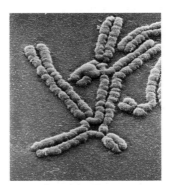

Figure 8: *Electron micrograph showing crossing over occurring in cells.*

2. Independent assortment of chromosomes

Remember that each homologous pair of chromosomes in your cells is made up of one chromosome from your mum (maternal) and one chromosome from your dad (paternal). When the homologous pairs line up in metaphase 1 and are separated in anaphase 1, it's completely random which chromosome from each pair ends up in which daughter cell, so the four daughter cells produced by meiosis have completely different combinations of those maternal and paternal chromosomes. This is called independent assortment (separation) of the chromosomes. This 'shuffling' of chromosomes leads to genetic variation in any potential offspring.

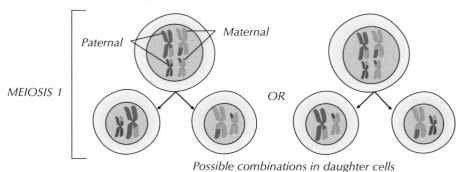

Possible combinations in daughter cells

Figure 9: *Independent assortment of chromosomes.*

Practice Questions — Application

Tip: To answer Q1 you need to look at the number of chromosomes as well as what is happening to them in each cell.

Q1 For each of the following cells, state which stage of meiosis 1 or 2 the cell is in (e.g. prophase 1).

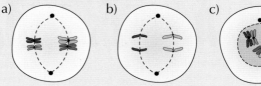

a)   b)   c)   d)

Q2 The diagram to the right shows two homologous chromosomes. The red cross marks a point at which crossing-over can occur. Draw the chromosomes as they would be if crossing-over occurred at this point.

Practice Questions — Fact Recall

Q1 Are the following haploid or diploid:
    a) normal body cells?   b) gametes?   c) zygotes?

Q2 During meiosis 1, describe what happens in:
    a) prophase,   b) metaphase,   c) anaphase,   d) telophase.

Q3 Briefly describe what happens during meiosis 2.

Q4 a) What are the two main events in meiosis that lead to genetic variation?

    b) Describe how each of these processes works.

3. Stem Cells and Differentiation

All multicellular organisms stem from, err, stem cells. Every cell in your body was produced from a stem cell. So was every cell in every other multicellular organism's body. So they're pretty important.

Stem cells

Multicellular organisms are made up of many different cell types that are **specialised** for their function, e.g. liver cells, muscle cells and white blood cells. All these specialised cell types originally came from stem cells. Stem cells are **unspecialised** cells — they can develop into different types of cell. All multicellular organisms have some form of stem cell.

┌─ **Example** ───
In humans, stem cells are found in early embryos and in a few places in adults. In the first few days of an embryo's life, any of its cells can develop into any type of human cell — they're all stem cells. In adults, stem cells are found in a few places (e.g. bone marrow), but they're not as flexible — they can only develop into a limited range of cells (see below).
└──

Differentiation

Stem cells divide to become new cells, which then become specialised. The process by which a cell becomes specialised for its job is called **differentiation** (see Figure 1). Stem cells are also able to divide to produce more undifferentiated stem cells, i.e. they can renew themselves.

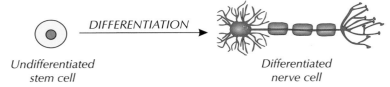

Undifferentiated stem cell — DIFFERENTIATION → *Differentiated nerve cell*

Figure 1: *Diagram showing stem cell differentiation.*

In animals, adult stem cells are used to replace damaged cells.

┌─ **Example** ───
Bones are living organs, containing nerves and blood vessels. The main bones of the body have marrow in the centres. Here, adult stem cells divide and differentiate to replace worn out blood cells — **erythrocytes** (red blood cells) and **neutrophils** (white blood cells that help to fight infection).

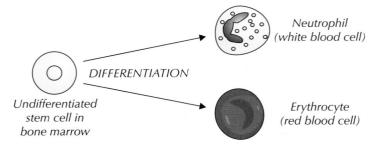

Undifferentiated stem cell in bone marrow — DIFFERENTIATION → *Neutrophil (white blood cell)* / *Erythrocyte (red blood cell)*

Figure 2: *Diagram showing how a stem cell in the bone marrow can differentiate into a neutrophil or erythrocyte.*
└──

Learning Objectives:

- Understand the features and differentiation of stem cells, including that they are a renewing source of undifferentiated cells.

- Know that erythrocytes and neutrophils are derived from stem cells in bone marrow.

- Know that xylem vessels and phloem sieve tubes are produced from meristems.

- Understand the potential uses of stem cells in research and medicine including:

  - the repair of damaged tissues,

  - the treatment of neurological conditions such as Alzheimer's and Parkinson's,

  - research into developmental biology.

- Know how cells of multicellular organisms are specialised for particular functions, including erythrocytes, neutrophils, squamous and ciliated epithelial cells, sperm cells, palisade cells, root hair cells and guard cells.

Specification Reference 2.1.6

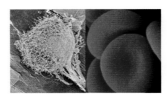

Figure 3: *Bone marrow stem cells (left) can differentiate into red blood cells (right).*

Plants are always growing, so stem cells are needed to make new shoots and roots throughout their lives. Stem cells in plants can differentiate into various plant tissues.

Exam Tip
Make sure you know the example from the previous page of bone marrow stem cells differentiating into blood cells and this example of meristem cells differentiating into xylem and phloem for the exam — you could be tested on them.

Tip: There's more about the function of xylem and phloem on p. 198.

┌─ **Example** ─────────────────────────

In plants, stem cells are found in the meristems (parts of the plant where growth can take place). In the root and stem, stem cells of the vascular cambium divide and differentiate to become **xylem vessels** and **phloem sieve tubes**.

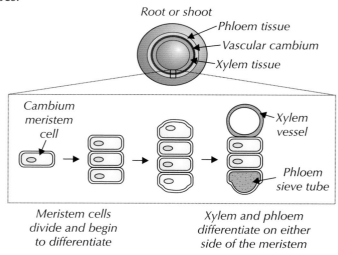

Figure 4: The differentiation of stem cells in the meristem into xylem and phloem.

└────────────────────────────────────

Stem cells and medicine

Stem cells can develop into different specialised cell types, so they have a huge potential for use in medicine. Scientists think they could be used to repair damaged tissues (like the heart) and treat neurological disorders (like **Alzheimer's** and **Parkinson's**).

┌─ **Examples** ─────────────────────────

- Heart disease is a big problem in many countries. If it results in heart tissue becoming damaged, the body is unable to sufficiently replace the damaged cells. Researchers are currently trying to develop ways of using stem cells to make replacement heart cells to repair the damaged tissue.

- With Alzheimer's, nerve cells in the brain die in increasing numbers. This results in severe memory loss. Researchers are hoping to use stem cells to regrow healthy nerve cells in people with Alzheimer's.

- Patients with Parkinson's suffer from tremors that they can't control. The disease causes the loss of a particular type of nerve cell found in the brain. These cells release a chemical called dopamine, which is needed to control movement. Transplanted stem cells may help to regenerate the dopamine-producing cells.

└────────────────────────────────────

Exam Tip
You could get asked about how stem cells can be used to repair all sorts of damaged tissues — you won't necessarily get asked about repairing heart tissue. Don't worry though — the principles for repairing different tissues are the same.

Stem cells are also used by scientists researching developmental biology, i.e. how organisms grow and develop. Studying stem cells can help us to understand more about things like developmental disorders and cancer.

Specialised cells

Once cells differentiate, they have a specific function. Their structure is adapted to perform that function. You need to know how the following cell types, found in multicellular organisms, are specialised for their functions:

Examples — Animal cells

Erythrocytes (red blood cells) carry oxygen in the blood. The biconcave disc shape provides a large surface area for gas exchange. They have no nucleus so there's more room for haemoglobin (see p. 191), the protein that carries oxygen.

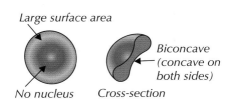

Large surface area

No nucleus

Cross-section

Biconcave (concave on both sides)

Neutrophils (a type of white blood cell) defend the body against disease. Their flexible shape allows them to engulf foreign particles or pathogens (see p. 222). The many lysosomes in their cytoplasm contain digestive enzymes to break down the engulfed particles.

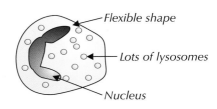

Flexible shape

Lots of lysosomes

Nucleus

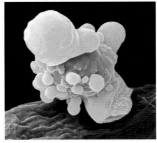

Figure 5: *A scanning electron micrograph of a white blood cell.*

Epithelial cells cover the surfaces of organs. The cells are joined by interlinking cell membranes and a membrane at their base. Ciliated epithelia (e.g. in the airways) have cilia that beat to move particles away. Other epithelia (e.g. in the small intestine) have microvilli — folds in the cell membrane that increase the cell's surface area. Squamous epithelia (e.g. in the lungs) are very thin to allow efficient diffusion of gases.

Tip: Cells that have cilia on them are called ciliated cells — the tissue is called ciliated epithelium.

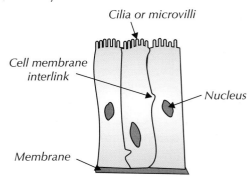

Cilia or microvilli

Cell membrane interlink

Nucleus

Membrane

Figure 6: *Epithelial cells (pinkish-brown) with cilia (yellow) in the airways.*

Sperm cells (male sex cells) have a flagellum (tail) so they can swim to the egg (female sex cell). They also have lots of mitochondria to provide the energy to swim. The acrosome contains digestive enzymes to enable the sperm to penetrate the surface of the egg.

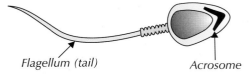

Flagellum (tail)

Acrosome

Figure 7: *Scanning electron micrograph of a sperm cell.*

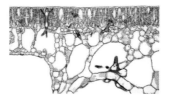

Figure 8: The band of green cells at the top of this water lily leaf are palisade mesophyll cells.

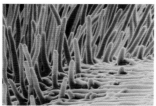

Figure 9: Scanning electron micrograph of the root hairs on a cress root.

Exam Tip
Any of the animal cell or plant cell examples on p. 149-150 could come up in the exam, so make sure you learn them.

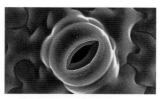

Figure 10: Turgid guard cells (red) open the stoma in a tobacco leaf.

Exam Tip
You could be given diagrams or photos of erythrocytes, neutrophils, epithelial cells, sperm cells, palisade mesophyll cells, root hair cells and guard cells in the exam. Don't worry if they don't look exactly like the ones on these pages — they will still have the same adaptations.

Examples — Plant cells

Palisade mesophyll cells in leaves do most of the photosynthesis. They contain many chloroplasts, so they can absorb a lot of sunlight. The walls are thin, so carbon dioxide can easily diffuse into the cell.

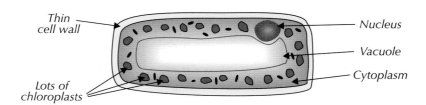

Thin cell wall — Nucleus — Vacuole — Cytoplasm — Lots of chloroplasts

Root hair cells absorb water and mineral ions from the soil. They have a large surface area for absorption and a thin, permeable cell wall, for entry of water and ions. The cytoplasm contains extra mitochondria to provide the energy needed for active transport (see p. 132).

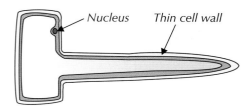

Nucleus — Thin cell wall

Guard cells are found in pairs, with a gap between them to form a stoma. This is one of the tiny pores in the surface of the leaf used for gas exchange. In the light, guard cells take up water (into their vacuoles) and become turgid. Their thin outer walls and thickened inner walls force them to bend outwards, opening the stomata. This allows the leaf to exchange gases for photosynthesis.

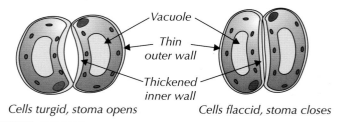

Vacuole — Thin outer wall — Thickened inner wall

Cells turgid, stoma opens   Cells flaccid, stoma closes

Practice Questions — Application

Q1 The cornea is the exposed transparent component that covers the front of the eye. The cornea has its own supply of stem cells known as limbal stem cells, which are located at its edge. As the outside of the cornea is exposed, it is quite susceptible to damage.

    a) Suggest the advantage of the cornea having its own supply of stem cells.

    b) Limbal stem cells are a type of adult stem cell. Suggest why most types of adult stem cell are unlikely to be suitable for the treatment of Alzheimer's.

Q2 The photograph below shows epithelial cells of the small intestine.

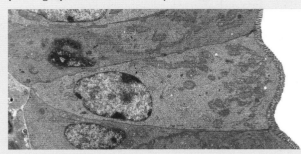

With reference to the photograph above, give one way in which epithelial cells are adapted to their function.

Practice Questions — Fact Recall

Q1 What is a stem cell?

Q2 Define the term differentiation.

Q3 a) What are:
   i) erythrocytes?
   ii) neutrophils?

b) Where in the body are the stem cells that differentiate into erythrocytes and neutrophils found?

Q4 Briefly describe the formation of xylem and phloem from stem cells in the root of a plant.

Q5 Describe how stem cells could be used to treat heart disease.

Q6 Describe how stem cells could be used to treat Parkinson's disease.

Q7 Describe one adaptation of the following to their function:
   a) erythrocytes,
   b) neutrophils.

Q8 What is the function of:
   a) palisade mesophyll cells?
   b) root hair cells?

Q9 Describe how guard cells are adapted to their function.

4. Tissues, Organs and Systems

As you saw on pages 149-150, there are loads of different types of specialised cells. These cells are grouped together to make up tissues, organs and organ systems, which perform particular functions. To understand how a whole organism operates, you need to understand how cells, tissues, organs and organ systems work together.

Tissues

A tissue is a group of cells (plus any extracellular material secreted by them) that are specialised to work together to carry out a particular function. A tissue can contain more than one cell type.

Animal tissues

You need to know the following examples of animal tissues:

Examples — Animal Tissues

Squamous epithelium tissue is a single layer of flat cells lining a surface. It's found in many places in the body, including the alveoli in the lungs, and provides a thin exchange surface for substances to diffuse across quickly.

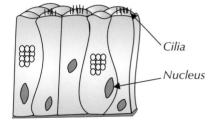

Nucleus

Basement membrane

Ciliated epithelium is a layer of cells covered in cilia (see p. 34). It's found on surfaces where things need to be moved — in the trachea for instance, where the cilia waft mucus along (see p. 163).

Cilia

Nucleus

Tip: Epithelium is a tissue that forms a covering or a lining.

Muscle tissue is made up of bundles of elongated cells called muscle fibres. There are three different types of muscle tissue: smooth (e.g. found lining the stomach wall), cardiac (found in the heart) and skeletal (which you use to move). They're all slightly different in structure.

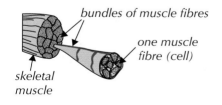

bundles of muscle fibres

one muscle fibre (cell)

skeletal muscle

Figure 1: Scanning electron micrograph of skeletal muscle, showing muscle fibres (shown in red).

Cartilage is a type of connective tissue found in the joints. It also shapes and supports the ears, nose and windpipe. It's formed when cells called chondroblasts secrete an extracellular matrix (a jelly-like substance containing protein fibres), which they become trapped inside.

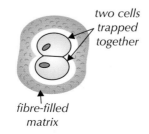

two cells trapped together

fibre-filled matrix

Plant tissues

You also need to know these two examples of plant tissues:

Examples — Plant Tissues

Xylem tissue is a plant tissue with two jobs — it transports water around the plant, and it supports the plant. It contains hollow xylem vessel cells (which are dead) and living parenchyma cells.

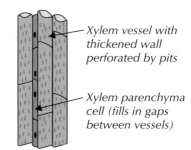

Xylem vessel with thickened wall perforated by pits

Xylem parenchyma cell (fills in gaps between vessels)

Phloem tissue transports sugars around the plant. It's arranged in tubes and is made up of sieve cells, companion cells, and some ordinary plant cells. Each sieve cell has end walls with holes in them, so that sap can move easily through them. These end walls are called sieve plates.

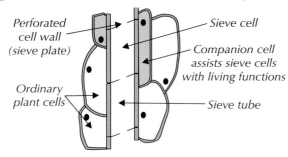

Perforated cell wall (sieve plate)

Sieve cell

Companion cell assists sieve cells with living functions

Ordinary plant cells

Sieve tube

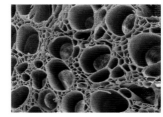

Figure 2: Xylem tissue in a small root. The xylem vessels are brown and the parenchyma cells green.

Exam Tip
Take a look at pages 198-200 for more on xylem and phloem.

Organs

An organ is a group of different tissues that work together to perform a particular function.

Examples

The **lungs** are an animal organ which carry out gas exchange. They contain squamous epithelium tissue (in the alveoli) and ciliated epithelium tissue (in the bronchi etc.). They also have elastic connective tissue and vascular tissue (in the blood vessels).

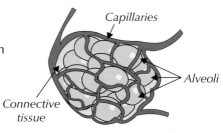

Capillaries

Alveoli

Connective tissue

Tip: Gas exchange is the exchange of gases (oxygen and carbon dioxide) between an organism and its environment. There's loads more about it on pages 163-170.

The **leaf** is a plant organ which carries out gas exchange and photosynthesis. It contains palisade tissue, as well as epidermal tissue (to prevent water loss from the leaf), and xylem and phloem tissues in the veins.

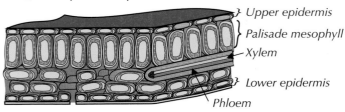

} Upper epidermis

Palisade mesophyll

Xylem

} Lower epidermis

Phloem

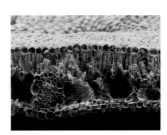

Figure 3: The cross section of a taro leaf. The palisade mesophyll is bright green and the xylem and phloem are grey.

Organ systems

Organs work together to form organ systems — each system has a particular function.

Examples

The **respiratory system** is made up of all the organs, tissues and cells involved in gas exchange. The lungs, trachea, larynx, nose, mouth and diaphragm are all part of the respiratory system.

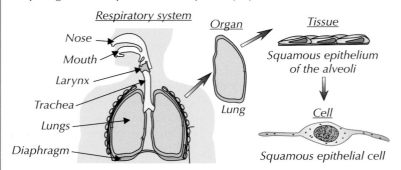

The **circulatory system** is made up of the organs involved in blood supply. The heart, arteries, veins and capillaries are all parts of this system.

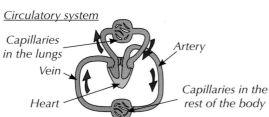

Exam Tip
Make sure you know the definition of tissues, organs and organ systems really well. You could be asked to apply your knowledge to lots of different examples in the exam — and it's easy marks if you've got the definitions straight in your head.

Tip: For more on the function of the circulatory system take a look at page 177.

Practice Question — Application

Q1 The picture below is a transmission electron micrograph of a type of plant tissue.

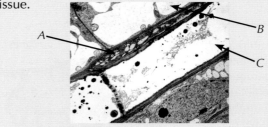

a) Name the cells labelled A - C.

b) What is this type of plant tissue called?

Practice Questions — Fact Recall

Q1 What is a tissue?

Q2 Tissues can't contain more than one type of cell. True or false?

Q3 Explain why the following are defined as tissues:

   a) squamous epithelium,

   b) ciliated epithelium.

Q4 Describe the basic structure of muscle tissue.

Q5 What is cartilage?

Q6 Give two examples of plant tissues.

Q7 What is an organ?

Q8 What is an organ system?

Q9 Give an example of an organ system and explain why it is classed as an organ system.

Section Summary

Make sure you know:

- That most of the cell cycle is taken up by interphase — a period of cell growth, consisting of G_1, S and G_2 phases, during which the cell's genetic material is copied and checked for DNA damage.
- That a small percentage of the cell cycle is taken up by mitosis and cytokinesis, which produce two genetically identical daughter cells.
- How the cell cycle is regulated by checkpoints.
- That mitosis is needed for the growth of multicellular organisms and tissue repair.
- That some animals, plants and fungi also use mitosis to reproduce asexually.
- The stages of mitosis — prophase (chromosomes condense, the spindle forms and the nuclear envelope breaks down), metaphase (chromosomes line up along the centre of the cell and attach to the spindle), anaphase (the spindles contract, pulling chromatids to opposite ends of the cell) and telophase (chromatids reach the opposite ends of the cell and uncoil and a nuclear envelope forms).
- That cytokinesis is where the cytoplasm of a cell divides.
- How to prepare and examine stained sections and squashes of plant tissue, in order to produce labelled diagrams of cells at different stages of the cell cycle and mitosis.
- That the term 'homologous pair of chromosomes' refers to a pair of matching chromosomes.
- That gametes are produced by meiosis (a type of cell division that produces four genetically different cells). These gametes are haploid (they only have one copy of each chromosome).
- That in sexual reproduction two haploid gametes join together at fertilisation to form a diploid zygote (it has two copies of each chromosome). This then divides and develops into a new organism.
- The main stages of meiosis — interphase, prophase 1, metaphase 1, anaphase 1, telophase 1, prophase 2, metaphase 2, anaphase 2 and telophase 2.
- How genetic variation can be caused by independent assortment of chromosomes and crossing over.
- That stem cells are unspecialised cells that can develop into different types of cell and can also replicate themselves, so are a renewing source of undifferentiated cells.
- That differentiation is the process by which a cell becomes specialised.
- That erythrocytes and neutrophils are derived from stem cells in bone marrow and xylem and phloem are produced from stem cells found in meristems.
- That stem cells have a huge potential in medicine and could be used to repair damaged tissues or treat neurological conditions such as Parkinson's and Alzheimer's. They're also used in developmental biology research.
- How erythrocytes, neutrophils, ciliated and squamous epithelial cells and sperm cells in animals, and palisade mesophyll cells, root hair cells and guard cells in plants are specialised for their functions.
- That a tissue is a group of cells (plus any extracellular material secreted by them) that are specialised to carry out a particular function.
- These examples of tissues — squamous epithelium, ciliated epithelium, muscle tissue, cartilage, xylem tissue and phloem tissue.
- That an organ is a group of different tissues that work together to perform a particular function and that organ systems are organs which work together for a particular function.
- How cells, tissues, organs and organ systems work together so multicellular organisms can function.

1   **Fig. 1.1** shows changes in the mass of a cell and its DNA during the cell cycle.

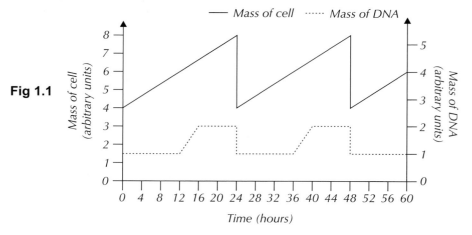

Fig 1.1

(a)   During which hours does synthesis take place? Explain your answer.

(2 marks)

(b)   At which hours does mitosis take place? Explain your answer.

(2 marks)

(c)   Describe what is happening within the cell between 0 and 24 hours.

(4 marks)

(d) (i)   How many cell divisions are shown on the graph? Explain your answer.

(2 marks)

     (ii)   At what time will the next cell division take place?

(1 mark)

(e) (i)   Telophase is a phase of mitosis. Describe what happens during telophase in animal cells.

(2 marks)

     (ii)   Give **three** reasons why mitosis is important for organisms.

(3 marks)

2   A doctor was studying a sperm sample using a microscope. He observed that a large proportion of the sperm cells in the sample had abnormally shaped tails.

(a)   Explain why the patient whose sample the doctor was studying may experience reduced fertility.

(2 marks)

(b)   Other than having a tail, give **two** other ways in which sperm cells are adapted for their function.

(2 marks)

3   Water enters the plant through its root hair cells and is transported around the plant in the xylem. **Fig. 3.1** on the right shows some root hair cells on the root of a plant.

Fig 3.1

(a)   Give **two** ways in which the structure of a root hair cell is specialised for its role.

(2 marks)

(b) (i)   Stem cells differentiate into xylem cells. Where are these stem cells found?

(1 mark)

(ii)   Explain why xylem can be considered a tissue.

(2 marks)

4   **Fig 4.1** shows the average DNA content of a group of cells that are undergoing meiosis:

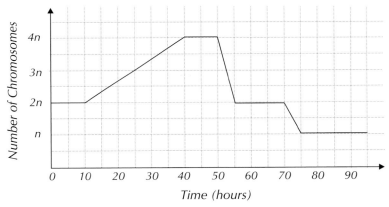

Fig 4.1

(a)   Explain what is happening:

(i)   between 10 hours and 40 hours.

(1 mark)

(ii)   between 40 hours and 50 hours.

(1 mark)

(iii)   between 50 hours and 55 hours.

(1 mark)

(iv)   between 70 hours and 75 hours.

(1 mark)

(b) (i)   Describe how daughter cells produced by meiosis differ to their parent cell.

(2 marks)

(ii)   Explain how crossing over during meiosis can give rise to genetic variation.

(3 marks)

Learning Objectives:

- Understand the need for specialised exchange surfaces, including the effects of metabolic activity, surface area to volume ratio (SA:V), and the different characteristics of single-celled and multicellular organisms.

- Know that surface area to volume ratio can be calculated using the formula: ratio = surface area ÷ volume.

- Know the features of an efficient exchange surface, including:
  - increased surface area – root hair cells
  - thin layer – alveoli
  - good blood supply/ventilation to maintain gradient – gills/alveolus.

Specification Reference 3.1.1

Figure 1: A hippo (top) has a small surface area : volume ratio. A mouse (bottom) has a large surface area : volume ratio.

1. Specialised Exchange Systems

Every organism has substances it needs to take in and others it needs to get rid of in order to survive. An organism's size and surface area affect how quickly this is done.

Exchange of substances with the environment

Every organism, whatever its size, needs to exchange things with its environment. Cells need to take in things like oxygen and glucose for aerobic respiration and other metabolic reactions. They also need to excrete waste products like carbon dioxide and urea. How easy the exchange of substances is depends on the organism's surface area to volume ratio.

Surface area : volume ratios

Before going into the effects of surface area : volume ratios, you need to understand a bit more about them. Smaller organisms have bigger surface area : volume ratios than larger organisms. This is shown in the example below.

Example — **Maths Skills**

A mouse has a bigger surface area relative to its volume than a hippo. This can be hard to imagine, but you can prove it mathematically.

Imagine these animals as cubes...

The mouse could be represented by a cube measuring 1 cm × 1 cm × 1 cm.

1 cm   1 cm   1 cm

"cube mouse"

Its volume is: $1 \times 1 \times 1 = 1$ cm³

Its surface area is: $6 \times 1 \times 1 = 6$ cm²

So the mouse has a surface area : volume ratio of <u>6 : 1</u>.

Compare this to a cube hippo measuring 2 cm × 4 cm × 4 cm.

4 cm   4 cm   2 cm

"cube hippo"

Its volume is: $2 \times 4 \times 4 = 32$ cm³

Its surface area is:

$2 \times 4 \times 4 = 32$ cm²
(top and bottom surfaces of cube)

$+ 4 \times 2 \times 4 = 32$ cm²
(four sides of the cube)

Total surface area = 64 cm²

So the hippo has a surface area : volume ratio of 64 : 32 or <u>2 : 1</u>.

The cube mouse's surface area is six times its volume, but the cube hippo's surface area is only twice its volume. Smaller animals have a bigger surface area compared to their volume.

To calculate the surface area to volume ratio (i.e. to express it as a single value rather than a ratio), you just divide the surface area by the volume.

Calculating volume and surface area

You might be asked to calculate volume or surface area in the exam. For example, you could be asked to calculate the volume or surface area of a cell.

Exam Tip
If you're asked to calculate a surface area to volume ratio in the exam, always give your answer in its simplest form, e.g. 2 : 1 rather than 64 : 32.

Example — **Maths Skills**

Bacillus are rod-shaped bacteria — as shown in Figure 2.

To calculate the volume of this cell, you need to split the bacterium into parts: the cylindrical centre and the hemispheres on either end.

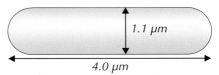

Figure 2: A Bacillus *cell.*

 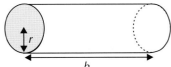

1. Start by calculating the volume of the cylinder. The formula you need is **πr²h** or **π × radius² × height**. First find the radius, then the height:

   radius (r) = 1.1 ÷ 2   height (h) = 4.0 – 0.55 – 0.55

           = **0.55 μm**   = **2.9 μm**

   Then use them to calculate the volume of the cylinder:
   Volume of a cylinder = $\pi r^2 h$
   = $\pi \times 0.55^2 \times 2.9$ = **2.755...**

2. Now find the volume of the two hemispheres.
   The formula for the volume of a sphere is $\frac{4}{3}\pi r^3$.

   A sphere is made of two hemispheres,
   so the total volume of the two hemispheres = $\frac{4}{3}\pi \times 0.55^3$

                           = **0.696...**

3. Finally, add the volume of the cylinder and the two hemispheres together to find the total volume of the cell:

   Total volume = 2.755... + 0.696...
   = **3.5 μm³** (2 s.f.)

Exam Tip
If an exam question requires you to calculate the surface area or volume of a sphere or cylinder, you'll be given the formula to use in the question. However, it's a good idea to learn the formulae for the area and circumference of a circle and the surface area and volume of other 3D shapes (e.g. cuboids), in case you're asked to calculate one in the exam.

Tip: The radius (r) of a circle is the distance from any point on the outer edge of the circle to its centre. It's half the diameter (d).

Tip: Remember that volume is given in units cubed (e.g. μm³) and surface area is given in units squared (μm²).

Tip: The formula for calculating the surface area of a sphere is 4πr².

Tip: A good way to compare two ratios (e.g. 7:2 and 3:1) is to get the last figure in each ratio to be 1 (e.g. 7:2 would become 3.5:1). Then you can easily see which ratio is the largest (e.g. 3.5:1 is a bigger ratio than 3:1).

Practice Question — Application

Q1 Below are three 3D shapes of different sizes (not drawn to scale).

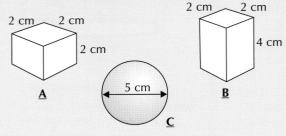

a) For each 3D shape work out its:

    i)   surface area.

    ii)   volume.

    iii)   surface area : volume ratio.

b) Which 3D shape has the greatest surface area : volume ratio?

Specialist exchange surfaces

An organism needs to supply every one of its cells with substances like glucose and oxygen (for respiration). It also needs to remove waste products from every cell to avoid damaging itself. Single-celled organisms exchange substances differently to multicellular organisms.

Tip: Remember, diffusion is the net movement of particles down a concentration gradient from an area of higher concentration to an area of lower concentration — see page 124 for more.

Single-celled organisms

In single-celled organisms, substances can diffuse directly into (or out of) the cell across the cell surface membrane. The diffusion rate is quick because of the short distances the substances have to travel and because single-celled organisms have a relatively high surface area : volume ratio.

Multicellular organisms

In multicellular organisms, diffusion across the outer membrane is too slow, for three reasons:

1.   Some cells are deep within the body — there's a big distance between them and the outside environment.

2.   Larger animals have a low surface area to volume ratio — it's difficult to exchange enough substances to supply a large volume of animal through a relatively small outer surface.

3.   Multicellular organisms have a higher metabolic rate than single-celled organisms, so they use up oxygen and glucose faster.

Tip: There's more on factors affecting the rate of diffusion on p. 124.

So rather than using straightforward diffusion to absorb and excrete substances, multicellular organisms need specialised **exchange surfaces** (like the alveoli in the lungs, see next page).

Special features of exchange surfaces

Exchange surfaces have special features to improve their efficiency, such as...

1. A large surface area

Most exchange surfaces have a large surface area to increase their efficiency.

┌ **Example — Root hair cells** ─────────────

The cells on plant roots grow into long 'hairs' which stick out into the soil. Each branch of a root will be covered in millions of these microscopic hairs.

This gives the roots a large surface area, which helps to increase the rate of absorption of water (by osmosis) and mineral ions (by active transport) from the soil.

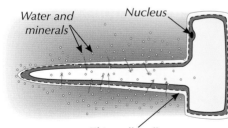

Figure 4: A root hair cell, showing the absorption of water and mineral ions from the soil.

Figure 3: An electron micrograph of a root tip from a poppy plant, showing how root hair cells (white) increase the surface area of the root.

2. They're thin

Exchange surfaces are usually thin to decrease the distance that the substances being exchanged have to travel over, and so improve efficiency. Some are only one cell thick.

The alveoli are the gas exchange surface in the lungs. Each alveolus is made from a single layer of thin, flat cells called the alveolar epithelium.

Oxygen (O_2) diffuses out of the alveolar space into the blood. Carbon dioxide (CO_2) diffuses in the opposite direction.

The thin alveolar epithelium helps to decrease the distance over which O_2 and CO_2 diffusion takes place, which increases the rate of diffusion (see p. 124).

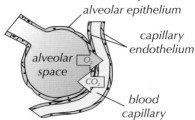

Figure 5: *Diagram of an alveolus, showing the thin alveolar epithelium.*

3. A good blood supply and/or ventilation

Another key feature of exchange surfaces is that they have a good blood supply and/or are well ventilated to increase efficiency.

Tip: For more on ventilation, see p. 166.

Example — Alveoli

The alveoli are surrounded by a large capillary network, giving each alveolus its own blood supply. The blood constantly takes oxygen away from the alveoli, and brings more carbon dioxide.

The lungs are also ventilated (you breathe in and out) so the air in each alveolus is constantly replaced.

These features help to maintain concentration gradients of O_2 and CO_2. Figure 7 sums this up nicely.

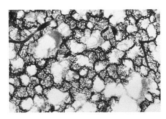

Figure 6: *A light micrograph of capillaries surrounding alveoli.*

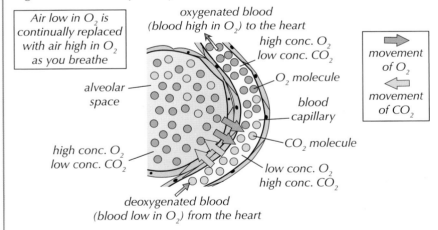

Figure 7: *Diagram showing how O_2 moves from an area of high concentration (inside the alveolus) to an area of low concentration (in the deoxygenated blood).*

Example — Gills

The gills are the gas exchange surface in fish. In the gills, O_2 and CO_2 are exchanged between the fish's blood and the surrounding water.

Fish gills contain a large network of capillaries — this keeps them well-supplied with blood. They're also well-ventilated — fresh water constantly passes over them.

These features help to maintain a concentration gradient of O_2 — increasing the rate at which O_2 diffuses into the blood.

Tip: There's more on how a concentration gradient is maintained in fish gills on p. 169.

Practice Questions — Application

Q1 A mountain climber is climbing at altitude, where there's less oxygen. Suggest how this will affect gas exchange in the alveoli.

Q2 One of the effects of severe obesity is that the sufferer cannot fully inhale. Suggest the effect this would have on the rate of diffusion of oxygen.

Q3 The pictures below show light micrographs of healthy lung tissue (top) and diseased lung tissue from a patient with emphysema (bottom). The alveoli appear white.

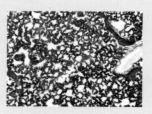

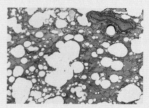

a) Describe the main difference between the healthy lung tissue and the diseased lung tissue.

b) Use your answer to part a) to explain why people with emphysema have a lower level of oxygen in the blood than normal.

Tip: To answer Q3 b) here, think about the factors that increase the efficiency of an exchange surface (see pages 160-161). Then decide what factor has been affected in the diseased lung tissue.

Practice Questions — Fact Recall

Q1 a) Name two substances an animal needs to take in from its environment.

b) Name two substances an animal needs to release into its environment.

Q2 Explain three reasons why diffusion is too slow in multicellular organisms for them to absorb and excrete substances in this way.

Q3 a) Describe an example where a large surface area increases the efficiency of an exchange system.

b) Other than having a large surface area, give two features that improve the efficiency of exchange surfaces.

Q4 Explain what makes fish gills efficient exchange surfaces.

2. Gas Exchange in Mammals

Multicellular organisms need a gaseous exchange system to survive. The gaseous exchange system in mammals is based around the lungs.

Gas exchange

In mammals, the lungs are gas exchange organs. They help to get oxygen into the blood (for respiration) and to get rid of carbon dioxide (made by respiring cells) from the body.

Structure of the gaseous exchange system

As you breathe in, air enters the trachea (windpipe). The trachea splits into two bronchi — one bronchus leading to each lung. Each bronchus then branches off into smaller tubes called bronchioles. The bronchioles end in small 'air sacs' called alveoli — see Figure 1. This is where gases are exchanged (see page 161). There are lots of alveoli in the lungs to provide a large surface area for diffusion. The ribcage, intercostal muscles and diaphragm all work together to move air in and out (see page 166).

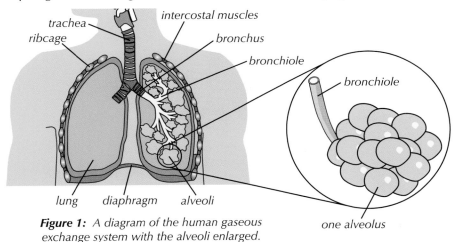

trachea *intercostal muscles* *ribcage* *bronchus* *bronchiole* *bronchiole* *lung* *diaphragm* *alveoli* *one alveolus*

Figure 1: *A diagram of the human gaseous exchange system with the alveoli enlarged.*

Learning Objective:

- Know the structures and functions of the components of the mammalian gaseous exchange system, including the distribution and functions of the following in the trachea, bronchi, bronchioles and alveoli:
  - cartilage,
  - ciliated epithelium,
  - goblet cells,
  - smooth muscle,
  - elastic fibres.

Specification Reference 3.1.1

Tip: There are actually three layers of intercostal muscles. You need to know about two of them (the internal and external intercostal muscles — see p. 166) for your exam. We've only shown one layer here for simplicity.

Key features of the gaseous exchange system

The gaseous exchange system is made up of different cells and tissues. These help it to exchange gases efficiently:

Goblet cells

Goblet cells (lining the airways) secrete mucus (see Figure 2). The mucus traps microorganisms and dust particles in the inhaled air, stopping them from reaching the alveoli.

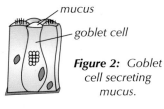

mucus *goblet cell*

Figure 2: *Goblet cell secreting mucus.*

Cilia

The cilia are hair-like structures on the surface of epithelial cells lining the airways. They beat the mucus secreted by the goblet cells — see Figure 3. This moves the mucus (plus the trapped microorganisms and dust) upward away from the alveoli towards the throat, where it's swallowed. This helps prevent lung infections.

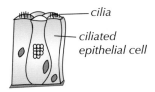

cilia *ciliated epithelial cell*

Figure 3: *Ciliated epithelium.*

Figure 4: *An electron micrograph of ciliated cells (pink) and goblet cells (green) in the bronchus.*

Tip: Blood vessels are also made up of elastic fibres and smooth muscle — see page 180.

Elastic fibres

Elastic fibres in the walls of the trachea, bronchi, bronchioles and alveoli help the process of breathing out (see page 166). On breathing in, the lungs inflate and the elastic fibres are stretched. Then, the fibres recoil to help push the air out when exhaling.

Smooth muscle

Smooth muscle in the walls of the trachea, bronchi and bronchioles (except the smallest bronchioles) allows their diameter to be controlled. During exercise the smooth muscle relaxes, making the tubes wider. This means there's less resistance to airflow and air can move in and out of the lungs more easily.

Cartilage

Rings of cartilage in the walls of the trachea and bronchi provide support. It's strong but flexible — it stops the trachea and bronchi collapsing when you breathe in and the pressure drops (see p. 166).

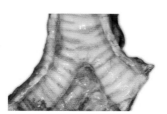

Figure 5: Cartilage rings (cream) in the trachea.

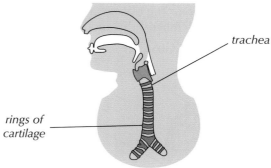

Figure 6: A diagram showing the rings of cartilage in the trachea.

Distribution of features in the gaseous exchange system

You need to know the distribution of the features described above and on the previous page for the exam. This is illustrated in Figure 8 and summarised in the table on the next page (Figure 9).

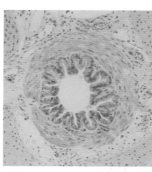

Figure 7: Cross-section of a bronchiole. The dark pink folds are ciliated epithelium. The pink ring around it is smooth muscle.

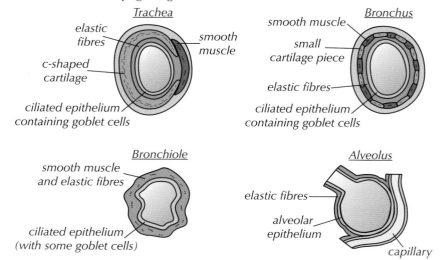

Figure 8: Cross-sections of structures in the mammalian gaseous exchange system.

Part of the lung	Cartilage	Smooth muscle	Elastic fibres	Goblet cells	Epithelium
Trachea	large C-shaped pieces	✓	✓	✓	ciliated
Bronchi	smaller pieces	✓	✓	✓	ciliated
Larger bronchiole	none	✓	✓	✓	ciliated
Smaller bronchiole	none	✓	✓	✗	ciliated
Smallest bronchiole	none	✗	✓	✗	no cilia
Alveoli	none	✗	✓	✗	no cilia

Figure 9: *Table summarising the distribution of features in the mammalian gaseous exchange system.*

Practice Question — Application

Q1 The light micrograph below shows a cross-section through part of the gaseous exchange system.

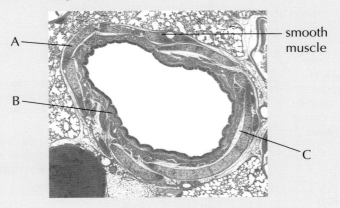

a) Name the part of the gaseous exchange system shown in the picture.

b) Name the components labelled A - C

Practice Questions — Fact Recall

Q1 In the mammalian gaseous exchange system, what is the function of:
a) goblet cells?   b) cilia?

Q2 Describe the function and distribution of elastic fibres in the gaseous exchange system of mammals.

Q3 Where in the airways is smooth muscle found?

Q4 Describe the difference between the distribution of cartilage in the trachea and in the bronchi.

3. Ventilation in Mammals

Breathing is pretty important, both for life and for the exam...

Learning Objectives:

- Understand the mechanism of ventilation in mammals, including the function of the ribcage, intercostal muscles (internal and external) and diaphragm.

- Understand the relationship between vital capacity, tidal volume, breathing rate and oxygen uptake, including analysis and interpretation of primary and secondary data, e.g. from a data logger or spirometer (PAG10).

Specification Reference 3.1.1

What is ventilation?

Ventilation consists of inspiration (breathing in) and expiration (breathing out). It's controlled by the movements of the diaphragm, intercostal muscles and ribcage.

Inspiration

- The external intercostal and diaphragm muscles contract.
- This causes the ribcage to move upwards and outwards and the diaphragm to flatten, increasing the volume of the thorax (the space where the lungs are).
- As the volume of the thorax increases the lung pressure decreases (to below atmospheric pressure).
- This causes air to flow into the lungs — see Figure 1.
- Inspiration is an active process — it requires energy.

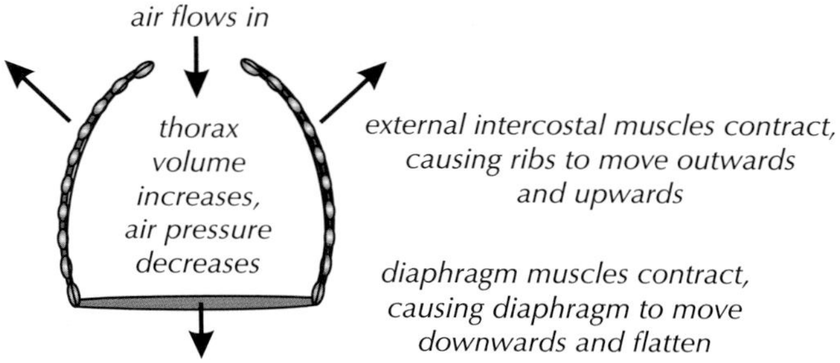

Tip: Air always flows from areas of <u>high</u> pressure to areas of <u>low</u> pressure.

Figure 1: Diagram showing what happens during inspiration.

air flows in

thorax volume increases, air pressure decreases

external intercostal muscles contract, causing ribs to move outwards and upwards

diaphragm muscles contract, causing diaphragm to move downwards and flatten

Expiration

- The external intercostal and diaphragm muscles relax.
- The ribcage moves downwards and inwards and the diaphragm becomes curved again.
- The thorax volume decreases, causing the air pressure to increase (to above atmospheric pressure).
- Air is forced out of the lungs — see Figure 2.
- Normal expiration is a passive process — it doesn't require energy.
- Expiration can be forced though (e.g. if you want to blow out the candles on your birthday cake). During forced expiration, the internal intercostal muscles contract, to pull the ribcage down and in.

Tip: It's the movement of the ribcage and diaphragm and the resulting change in lung pressure that causes air to flow in and out — not the other way round.

Tip: Remember, when the diaphragm contracts, it's flat. When it relaxes, it bulges upwards. Think of it like trying to hold your stomach in — you contract your muscles to flatten your stomach and relax to release it.

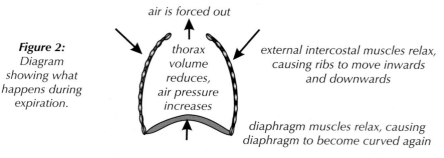

Figure 2: Diagram showing what happens during expiration.

air is forced out

thorax volume reduces, air pressure increases

external intercostal muscles relax, causing ribs to move inwards and downwards

diaphragm muscles relax, causing diaphragm to become curved again

Spirometers

A spirometer is a machine that can be used to investigate breathing.
It can give readings of:

- **Tidal volume** (TV) — the volume of air in each breath.
  This is usually about 0.4 dm³.
- **Vital capacity** — the maximum volume of air that can be breathed in or out.
- **Breathing rate** — how many breaths are taken per unit time
  (usually per minute).
- **Oxygen uptake** — the rate at which a person uses up oxygen
  (e.g. the number of dm³ used per minute).

Tip: dm³ is short for decimetres cubed — it's the same as litres.

How to use a spirometer

A spirometer has an oxygen-filled chamber with a movable lid (see Figure 4). The person using the spirometer breathes through a tube connected to the oxygen chamber. As the person breathes in and out, the lid of the chamber moves up and down. These movements are recorded by a pen attached to the lid of the chamber — this writes on a rotating drum, creating a **spirometer trace**. Or the spirometer can be hooked up to a motion sensor — this will use the movements to produce electronic signals, which are picked up by a **data logger**. The soda lime in the tube the subject breathes into absorbs carbon dioxide.

PRACTICAL ACTIVITY GROUP 10

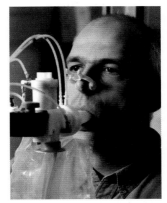

Figure 3: A person using a spirometer.

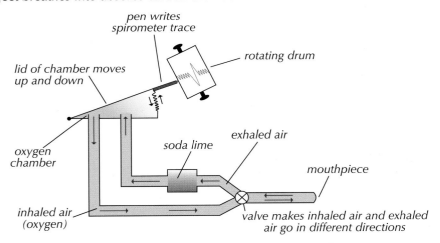

Figure 4: Diagram showing how a spirometer works.

pen writes spirometer trace

rotating drum

lid of chamber moves up and down

oxygen chamber

soda lime

exhaled air

mouthpiece

inhaled air (oxygen)

valve makes inhaled air and exhaled air go in different directions

The total volume of gas in the chamber decreases over time. This is because the air that's breathed out is a mixture of oxygen and carbon dioxide. The carbon dioxide is absorbed by the soda lime — so there's only oxygen in the chamber which the subject inhales from. As this oxygen gets used up by respiration, the total volume decreases.

To get a valid reading from a spirometer, the person using it must wear a nose clip — this ensures that they can only breathe in and out through their mouth (and so all the air they breathe goes through the spirometer). The machine must also be airtight.

Tip: Make sure you carry out a risk assessment before carrying out this experiment. E.g. using a spirometer can be dangerous as you're continually breathing in the same air that you just breathed out — so you need to make sure there's enough oxygen in the chamber.

Analysing data from spirometers

PRACTICAL ACTIVITY GROUP 10

In the exam, you might have to work out breathing rate, tidal volume, vital capacity and oxygen uptake from a spirometer trace. There's an example of how to do this on the next page.

Exam Tip
Sometimes, you'll see oxygen *consumption* written rather than oxygen *uptake*. They both mean the same thing.

Tip: A line sloping upwards on this spirometer trace indicates that the person using it is breathing out (and so the volume of gas in the spirometer is increasing).

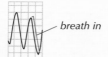

breath out

A line sloping down indicates that the person is breathing in.

breath in

The longer the line, the deeper the breath in or out.

Example — Maths Skills

The graph below shows a spirometer trace.

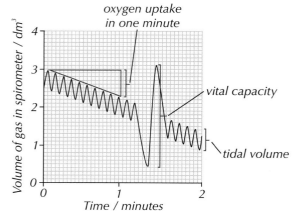

- In this trace, the breathing rate in the first minute is 10 breaths per minute (there are 10 'peaks' in the first minute).
- The tidal volume may change from time to time, but in this trace it's about 0.5 dm³.
- The graph shows a vital capacity of 2.65 dm³.
- Oxygen uptake is the decrease in the volume of gas in the spirometer chamber. It can be read from the graph by taking the average slope of the trace. In this case, it drops by 0.7 dm³ in the first minute — so oxygen uptake is 0.7 dm³/min.

Exam Tip
Make sure you look carefully at the axes of any graph you get in the exam. For example, it could be the volume of gas in the lungs, not the spirometer, that's plotted on the y-axis.

Practice Questions — Application

Look at the spirometer trace below.
It was recorded from a healthy 17 year old student at rest.

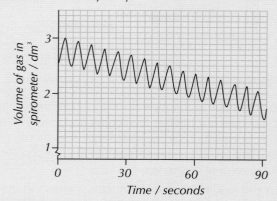

Q1 What is the student's tidal volume?

Q2 Work out the breathing rate of this student.
Give your answer in breaths per minute.

Q3 Explain why the volume of gas in the spirometer drops over time.

4. Gas Exchange in Fish and Insects

Gas exchange systems in fish and insects are quite different to those in mammals.

Gas exchange in fish

There's a lower concentration of oxygen in water than in air. So fish have special adaptations to get enough of it. In a fish, the gas exchange surface is the gills.

Structure of gills

Water, containing oxygen, enters the fish through its mouth and passes out through the gills. Each gill is made of lots of thin plates called **gill filaments** or **primary lamellae** which give a big surface area for exchange of gases (and so increase the rate of diffusion). The gill filaments are covered in lots of tiny structures called **gill plates** or **secondary lamellae**, which increase the surface area even more — see Figure 1. Each gill is supported by a gill arch. The gill plates have lots of blood capillaries and a thin surface layer of cells to speed up diffusion between the water and the blood.

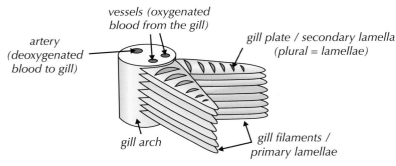

vessels (oxygenated blood from the gill)

artery (deoxygenated blood to gill)

gill plate / secondary lamella (plural = lamellae)

gill arch

gill filaments / primary lamellae

Figure 1: *A section of a fish's gill.*

The counter-current system

In the gills of a fish, blood flows through the gill plates in one direction and water flows over in the opposite direction — see Figure 3. This is called a counter-current system. The counter-current system means that the water with a relatively high oxygen concentration always flows next to blood with a lower concentration of oxygen. This in turn means that a steep concentration gradient is maintained between the water and the blood — so as much oxygen as possible diffuses from the water into the blood.

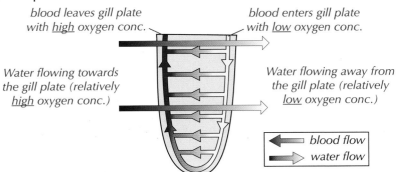

blood leaves gill plate with <u>high</u> oxygen conc.

blood enters gill plate with <u>low</u> oxygen conc.

Water flowing towards the gill plate (relatively <u>high</u> oxygen conc.)

Water flowing away from the gill plate (relatively <u>low</u> oxygen conc.)

blood flow
water flow

Figure 3: *The counter-current system across a gill plate.*

Learning Objective:

- Understand the mechanisms of ventilation and gas exchange in bony fish and insects, including:
  - bony fish – changes in volume of the buccal cavity and the functions of the operculum, gill filaments and gill lamellae (gill plates); countercurrent flow
  - insects – spiracles, trachea, thoracic and abdominal movement to change body volume, exchange with tracheal fluid.
  Specification Reference 3.1.1

Tip: You might've thought the slits on the side of a fish's head were its gills, but in fact the actual gills are inside the fish. Those slits just let out water that has flowed over the gills.

Figure 2: *The gills inside a mackerel.*

Ventilation in fish

You need to know how fish gills are ventilated in bony fish. First, the fish opens its mouth, which lowers the floor of the buccal cavity (the space inside the mouth). The volume of the buccal cavity increases, decreasing the pressure inside the cavity. Water is then sucked in to the cavity — see Figure 5. When the fish closes its mouth, the floor of the buccal cavity is raised again. The volume inside the cavity decreases, the pressure increases, and water is forced out of the cavity across the gill filaments.

Each gill is covered by a bony flap called the **operculum** (which protects the gill). The increase in pressure forces the operculum on each side of the head to open, allowing water to leave the gills.

Figure 4: Perch head showing operculum.

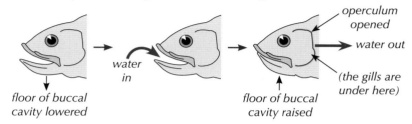

floor of buccal cavity lowered

water in

floor of buccal cavity raised

operculum opened

water out

(the gills are under here)

Figure 5: Diagram showing the mechanism of ventilation in fish.

Gas exchange and ventilation in insects

Terrestrial insects have microscopic air-filled pipes called tracheae which they use for gas exchange. Air moves into the tracheae through pores on the surface called spiracles. Oxygen travels down the concentration gradient towards the cells. Carbon dioxide from the cells moves down its own concentration gradient towards the spiracles to be released into the atmosphere. The tracheae branch off into smaller tracheoles which have thin, permeable walls and go to individual cells. The tracheoles also contain fluid, which oxygen dissolves in. The oxygen then diffuses from this fluid into body cells. Carbon dioxide diffuses in the opposite direction.

Insects use rhythmic abdominal movements to change the volume of their bodies and move air in and out of the spiracles. When larger insects are flying, they use their wing movements to pump their thoraxes too.

Figure 6: A spiracle on the surface of a garden tiger moth caterpillar.

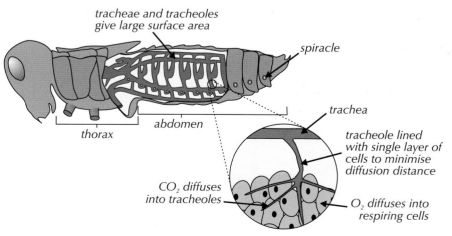

tracheae and tracheoles give large surface area

spiracle

thorax

abdomen

trachea

tracheole lined with single layer of cells to minimise diffusion distance

CO_2 diffuses into tracheoles

O_2 diffuses into respiring cells

Figure 7: Gas exchange across the tracheal system of an insect.

Practice Questions — Application

Q1 In polluted water the dissolved oxygen concentration is lower than it is in clean water. Explain how this would affect gas exchange across the gills of a fish.

Q2 The graph below shows how the relative oxygen concentrations of blood and water change with distance along a gill plate.

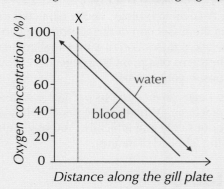

a) What happens to the oxygen concentration of blood as it moves along the gill plate?

b) What happens to the oxygen concentration of water as it moves along the gill plate?

c) What is the oxygen concentration of the blood at distance X on the graph?

d) Use evidence from the graph to explain why the oxygen concentration of the blood increases straight after point X.

Exam Tip
If you're asked to interpret data from a graph in the exam, use specific values in your answer where you can.

Practice Questions — Fact Recall

Q1 Describe the structure of fish gills.

Q2 Describe how the 'counter-current' system in fish aids gas exchange.

Q3 Describe how the gills of bony fish are ventilated.

Q4 What is an operculum?

Q5 What happens to the operculum during ventilation in fish?

Q6 How does air get into an insect's tracheae?

Q7 Describe how carbon dioxide moves out of an insect's cells into the atmosphere.

Q8 Give two ways in which larger insects can increase the movement of air in and out of their spiracles.

- Know how to dissect, examine and draw the gaseous exchange system of a bony fish and/or insect trachea (PAG2).
- Know how to examine microscope slides to show the histology of exchange surfaces.

Specification Reference 3.1.1

5. Dissecting Gas Exchange Systems

Here's your chance to see what gas exchange systems really look like inside...

Carrying out dissections

As part of your AS or A-Level in biology, you're expected to carry out some dissections, including the dissection of the gaseous exchange system in a bony fish and/or insect trachea, a dissection of a mammalian heart (see page 184) and a dissection of the stems of a plant (see page 201). You could also be asked about dissections in your exams.

The next two pages cover gaseous exchange system dissections in bony fish and insect tracheae. Whatever the dissection, you're expected to know how to carry it out safely and ethically. You might also need to record your observations using labelled diagrams.

Dissection tools

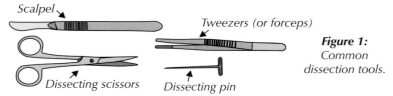

Scalpel

Tweezers (or forceps)

Figure 1: *Common dissection tools.*

Dissecting scissors *Dissecting pin*

Figure 1 shows some of the tools that you might need to use for your dissections. Scalpels have a very sharp detachable blade and can be used for making very fine cuts. Dissecting scissors are also used for precise cutting. They are safer to use than scalpels (because the blades are less likely to snap under pressure) and it can be easier to avoid damaging the tissue underneath when using scissors. Dissecting pins can be used with a wax-filled dissection tray (see Figure 2) to pin a specimen in place during the dissection. Tweezers are useful for holding and manipulating the smaller parts of the specimen.

Your dissecting tools (e.g. scalpels, dissecting scissors) should all be clean, sharp and free from rust — blunt tools don't cut well and can be dangerous.

Figure 2: *A wax-filled dissection tray.*

Tip: Always follow your teacher's safety instructions when working with dissection tools.

Dissecting fish gills

Fish dissection is messy, so make sure you're wearing an apron or lab coat, and gloves. Then follow these steps:

PRACTICAL ACTIVITY GROUP **2**

1) Place your chosen fish (something like a perch or salmon works well) in a dissection tray or on a cutting board.

2) Push back the operculum and use scissors to carefully remove the gills. Cut each gill arch through the bone at the top and bottom. They should look a bit like Figure 3.

3) If you look closely, you should be able to see the gill filaments.

4) Finish off by drawing the gill and labelling it.

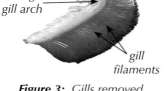

A single gill arch

gill filaments

Figure 3: *Gills removed from a bony fish*

Tip: Make sure that you assess all the risks involved in this dissection before you start.

Dissecting insects

Big insects like grasshoppers or cockroaches are usually best for dissecting because they're easier to handle. For dissection, you'll need to use an insect that's been humanely killed fairly recently.

PRACTICAL ACTIVITY GROUP 2

1. First fix the insect to a dissecting board. You can put dissecting pins through its legs to hold it in place.

2. To examine the tracheae, you'll need to carefully cut and remove a piece of exoskeleton (the insect's hard outer shell) from along the length of the insect's abdomen — see Figure 4.

3. Use a syringe to fill the abdomen with saline solution. You should be able to see a network of very thin, silvery-grey tubes — these are the tracheae. They look silver because they're filled with air.

4. You can mount the tracheae on a wet mount microscope slide and examine them under a light microscope (see pages 45-46). Again, the tracheae will appear silver or grey. You should also be able to see rings of chitin in the walls of the tracheae — these are there for support (like the rings of cartilage in a human trachea).

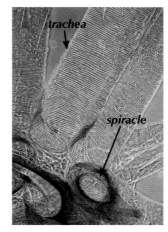

Figure 5: *Light microscope image of part of a silkworm showing the spiracles, chitin rings and silver/grey tracheae.*

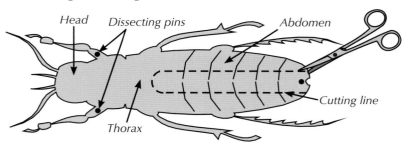

Figure 4: *How to remove a piece of exoskeleton from an insect abdomen.*

Practice Question — Application

Q1 A student was dissecting a grasshopper to examine the tracheae. As part of the protocol, she used scissors to remove a piece of exoskeleton from the insect's abdomen and then filled the abdomen with saline solution.

a) Give a possible reason for why she used scissors rather than a scalpel to remove the piece of exoskeleton.

b) Describe what the tracheae would look like when the abdomen was filled with saline solution.

c) When examining the tracheae under a light microscope, she noticed that the walls of the tracheae had lots of ring shaped structures along their length. What are these rings and what is their function?

Practice Questions — Fact Recall

Q1 What are dissection pins used for?

Q2 Why might you use tweezers when carrying out a dissection?

Q3 When carrying out a dissection on a bony fish, where would you expect to find the gills?

Section Summary

Make sure you know...

- How to work out the surface area : volume ratios of simple organisms, e.g. by using simple known shapes.
- That a value for a surface area to volume ratio can be calculated using the formula:
  ratio = surface area ÷ volume.
- That single-celled organisms exchange substances with their environment by direct diffusion through their cell surface membranes, and that the rate of diffusion is quick because of the organisms' high surface area : volume ratios.
- That multicellular organisms can't exchange substances by direct diffusion across their outer membranes because it would be too slow — some cells are deep within the body, larger animals have a low surface area : volume ratio and multicellular organisms have a higher metabolic rate, so need more oxygen and glucose faster. Instead, they have specialised exchange surfaces.
- That all exchange surfaces are adapted for efficient exchange including having a large surface area (e.g. root hair cells), being thin (often only one cell thick, e.g. alveoli) and having a good blood supply and/or ventilation to maintain a steep concentration gradient (e.g. alveoli, gills).
- The structures of the mammalian gaseous exchange system.
- The functions of parts of the mammalian gaseous exchange system, including:
    - that goblet cells lining the airways secrete mucus, and cilia sweep it away from the alveoli (removing trapped microorganisms and dust),
    - that elastic fibres in the walls of the airways and the alveoli stretch and recoil to help the process of breathing out,
    - that smooth muscle allows the diameter of the airways to be controlled,
    - that cartilage provides the trachea and bronchi with support.
- How to describe the distribution of goblet cells, ciliated epithelium, elastic fibres, smooth muscle and cartilage in the mammalian gaseous exchange system.
- How the ribcage, diaphragm and intercostal muscles all work together during ventilation.
- That tidal volume is the volume of air in each breath, vital capacity is the maximum volume of air that can be breathed in or out, breathing rate is how many breaths are taken per unit time (e.g. per minute) and oxygen uptake is the rate at which a person uses up oxygen.
- How a spirometer can be used to measure tidal volume, vital capacity, breathing rate and oxygen uptake, and how a data logger can be used to capture the information.
- How to interpret data from a spirometer trace.
- How gas exchange in bony fish works, including the structure of gills (gill filaments and gill plates) and the counter-current system (where blood flows through the gill plates in one direction and water flows over the gill plates in the opposite direction, to maintain a steep concentration gradient of oxygen between the water and blood).
- How ventilation works in bony fish — the changes in volume and pressure in the buccal cavity which cause water to be sucked in and then forced out, and the role of the operculum.
- How gas exchange works in insects — that air enters tracheae through spiracles and oxygen travels down its concentration gradient towards the cells, and carbon dioxide travels down its concentration gradient towards the spiracles.
- How insects use rhythmic abdominal movements and/or their wing movements during flying to change the volume of their bodies and pump air in and out for ventilation.
- How to carry out dissections of gaseous exchange systems in fish and insects and make labelled diagrams of your observations.
- How to observe dissected insect gaseous exchange systems under a light microscope, using a wet mount microscope slide.

Exam-style Questions

1   Breathing involves the processes of inspiration (breathing in) and expiration (breathing out).

(a)   Use the most appropriate terms to complete the passage on inspiration below.

During inspiration, the diaphragm and external .... muscles

.... This causes the .... to move upwards and outwards

and the diaphragm to flatten, increasing the .... of the thorax.

As this happens, lung .... decreases to below that of the atmosphere,

causing air to flow into the lungs.

(5 marks)

(b)   The volume of air in each breath is known as the tidal volume.
What is the **maximum volume** of air that can be breathed in or out known as?

(1 mark)

(c)   A spirometer is a machine used to investigate breathing.
A spirometer trace of a person at rest is shown in **Fig. 1.1**.

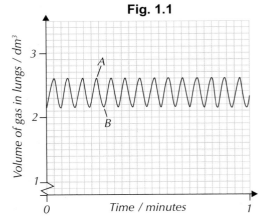

Fig. 1.1

(i)   What happened between points A and B?

(1 mark)

(ii)   Use **Fig. 1.1** to work out the person's breathing rate.

(1 mark)

(iii)   Suggest how the appearance of this trace would differ if the volume of gas in the spirometer was recorded instead of the volume of gas in the lungs. Explain your answer.

(4 marks)

(d)   Suggest **one** thing that could be done to obtain a more **precise** measurement of the person's tidal volume.

(1 mark)

2   **Fig. 2.1** shows a spherical bacterium with a radius of 0.7 μm.

(a)   Give the surface area to volume ratio of this bacterium.
Use the following formulae: surface area of a sphere = $4\pi r^2$,
volume of a sphere = $\frac{4}{3}\pi r^3$.

(1 mark)

Fig. 2.1

0.7 μm

(b)   Explain why this bacterium doesn't have a gaseous exchange system.

(3 marks)

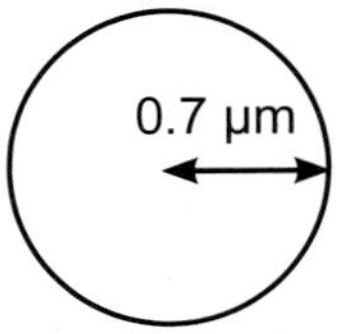

3   **Fig. 3.1** shows a scanning electron micrograph of alveoli in a healthy human lung (left) and in a diseased lung (right). The magnification is x 60.

Fig. 3.1

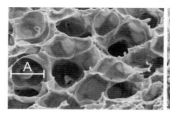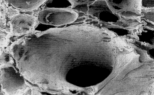

(a)   Calculate the actual width of the labelled alveolus, A.
Give your answer in µm.

(2 marks)

(b)   Describe **one** difference between the healthy alveoli and the diseased alveoli, and explain what effect this would have on gaseous exchange in the alveoli.

(3 marks)

(c)   Oxygen tents contain a higher percentage of oxygen than normal air.
Suggest how being in an oxygen tent might benefit a patient with emphysema.

(2 marks)

4   **Fig. 4.1** shows a cross section of the mammalian trachea.

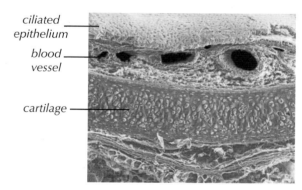

ciliated epithelium

blood vessel

cartilage

Fig. 4.1

(a)   Describe the function of the cilia on ciliated epithelial cells.

(1 mark)

(b) (i)   Give **one** function of cartilage in the trachea.

(1 mark)

(ii)   Where else in the mammalian gaseous exchange system is cartilage found?

(1 mark)

(c)   Give **one** other feature of the trachea **not** labelled in **Fig 4.1** and describe its function.

(2 marks)

1. Circulatory Systems

All multicellular organisms need to transport materials around the body. Transport systems can vary depending on the organism — we humans have a transport system called the circulatory system.

Why do multicellular organisms need a transport system?

As you saw on page 160, single-celled organisms can get substances that they need by diffusion across their outer membrane. If you're multicellular though, it's a bit harder to supply all your cells with everything they need — multicellular organisms are relatively big and they have a low surface area to volume ratio and a higher **metabolic rate** (the speed at which chemical reactions take place in the body). A lot of multicellular organisms (e.g. mammals) are also very active. This means that a large number of cells are all respiring very quickly, so they need a constant, rapid supply of glucose and oxygen. Carbon dioxide (a waste product of respiration) also needs to be removed from cells quickly.

To make sure that every cell has a good enough supply of useful substances and has its waste products removed, multicellular organisms need a transport system. The circulatory system in mammals uses blood to carry glucose and oxygen around the body. It also carries hormones, antibodies (to fight disease) and waste products (like CO_2).

Single and double circulatory systems

Not all organisms have the same type of circulatory system — some have a single circulatory system, e.g. fish, and others have a double circulatory system, e.g. mammals.

Single circulatory system

In a single circulatory system, blood only passes through the heart once for each complete circuit of the body.

Example

Fish have a single circulatory system. The heart pumps blood to the gills (to pick up oxygen) and then on through the rest of the body (to deliver the oxygen) in a single circuit.

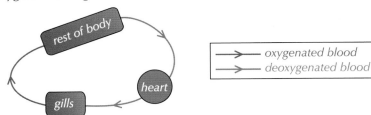

→ oxygenated blood
→ deoxygenated blood

Learning Objectives:

- Understand why multicellular animals need transport systems in terms of their size, surface area to volume ratio (SA:V) and metabolic rate.
- Know the different types of circulatory systems, including:
  - single (in fish)
  - double (in mammals)
  - closed (in fish and mammals)
  - open (in insects).
  Specification Reference 3.1.2

Exam Tip
Remember, multicellular organisms have a small <u>surface area to volume ratio</u> — just writing they have a small surface area won't get you full marks in the exam.

Exam Tip
You need to learn all the examples in this topic for your exams.

Double circulatory system

In a double circulatory system, the blood passes through the heart twice for each complete circuit of the body.

Example

Mammals have a double circulatory system. The heart is divided down the middle, so it's really like two hearts joined together. The right side of the heart pumps blood to the lungs (to pick up oxygen). From the lungs it travels to the left side of the heart, which pumps it to the rest of the body. When blood returns to the heart, it enters the right side again.

So, our circulatory system is really two linked loops. One sends blood to the lungs — this is called the pulmonary system, and the other sends blood to the rest of the body — this is called the systemic system.

The advantage of the mammalian double circulatory system is that the heart can give the blood an extra push between the lungs and the rest of the body. This makes the blood travel faster, so oxygen is delivered to the tissues more quickly.

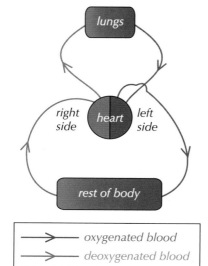

Closed and open circulatory systems

Some organisms have a closed circulatory system and some have an open circulatory system.

Closed circulatory system

All vertebrates (e.g. fish and mammals) have a closed circulatory system. In a closed circulatory system, the blood is enclosed inside blood vessels.

Example

In fish, the heart pumps blood into arteries. These branch out into millions of capillaries. Substances like oxygen and glucose diffuse from the blood in the capillaries into the body cells, but the blood stays inside the blood vessels as it circulates. Veins take the blood back to the heart.

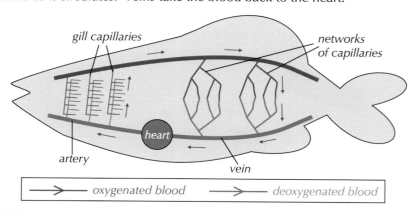

Open circulatory system

Some invertebrates (e.g. insects) have an open circulatory system. In an open circulatory system, blood isn't enclosed in blood vessels all the time. Instead, it flows freely through the body cavity.

Example

An insect's heart is segmented. It contracts in a wave, starting from the back, pumping the blood into a single main artery. That artery opens up into the body cavity. The blood flows around the insect's organs, gradually making its way back into the heart segments through a series of valves.

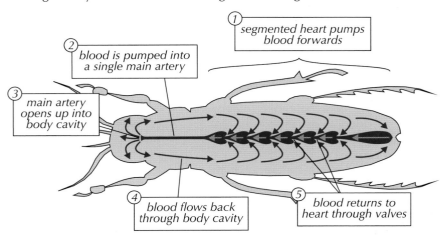

1. segmented heart pumps blood forwards
2. blood is pumped into a single main artery
3. main artery opens up into body cavity
4. blood flows back through body cavity
5. blood returns to heart through valves

The circulatory system supplies the insect's cells with nutrients, and transports things like hormones around the body. It doesn't supply the insect's cells with oxygen though — this is done by a system of tubes called the tracheal system.

Tip: Insects need to be relatively small to supply all their cells with the things they need. Useful substances in their blood have to diffuse through the whole body cavity — if they were bigger, they wouldn't be able to supply all their cells properly.

Tip: For more about the insect tracheal system see page 170.

Practice Questions — Fact Recall

Q1 Give two reasons why multicellular organisms need transport systems.

Q2 Name a group of animals that has a double circulatory system.

Q3 Explain why the circulatory system of a fish is described as:
   a) a single circulatory system,
   b) a closed circulatory system.

Q4 Explain why the insect circulatory system is described as an open circulatory system.

Exam Tip
Make sure you read the question properly — if you're asked what a closed circulatory system is, don't answer with the definition of a double circulatory system because you've misread the question.

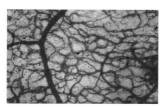

Figure 2: A light micrograph of capillaries.

Tip: Veins and some large venules contain valves. None of the other types of blood vessels do.

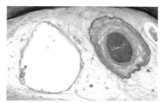

Figure 4:
A light micrograph of a cross-section through a vein (left) and an artery (right).

Tip: Arteries are the 'way art' (way out) of the heart, and veins are the 'vey in' (way in).

2. Blood Vessels

As you know, mammals have a closed circulatory system, which means our blood is enclosed in blood vessels (see p. 178). There are five different types of blood vessels...

Types of blood vessel

The five types of blood vessel that you need to know about are arteries, arterioles, capillaries, venules and veins.

Arteries

Arteries carry blood from the heart to the rest of the body. Their walls are thick and muscular and have elastic tissue to stretch and recoil as the heart beats, which helps maintain the high pressure. The inner lining (endothelium) is folded, allowing the artery to expand — this also helps it to maintain the high pressure. All arteries carry oxygenated blood except for the pulmonary arteries, which take deoxygenated blood to the lungs.

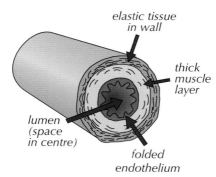

Figure 1: The structure of an artery.

Arterioles

Arteries branch into arterioles, which are much smaller than arteries. Like arteries, arterioles have a layer of smooth muscle, but they have less elastic tissue. The smooth muscle allows them to expand or contract, thus controlling the amount of blood flowing to tissues.

Capillaries

Arterioles branch into capillaries, which are the smallest of the blood vessels. Substances like glucose and oxygen are exchanged between cells and capillaries, so they're adapted for efficient diffusion, e.g. their walls are only one cell thick.

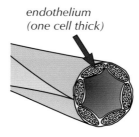

Figure 3: The structure of a capillary.

Venules

Capillaries connect to venules, which have very thin walls that can contain some muscle cells. Venules join together to form veins.

Veins

Veins take blood back to the heart under low pressure. They have a wider lumen than equivalent arteries, with very little elastic or muscle tissue. Veins contain valves to stop the blood flowing backwards (see p. 184). Blood flow through the veins is helped by contraction of the body muscles surrounding them. All veins carry deoxygenated blood (because oxygen has been used up by body cells), except for the pulmonary veins, which carry oxygenated blood to the heart from the lungs.

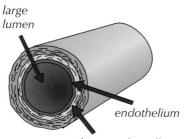

Figure 5: The structure of a vein.

Tissue fluid

Tissue fluid is the fluid that surrounds cells in tissues. It's made from substances that leave the blood plasma, e.g. oxygen, water and nutrients. (Unlike blood, tissue fluid doesn't contain red blood cells or big proteins, because they're too large to be pushed out through the capillary walls.) Cells take in oxygen and nutrients from the tissue fluid, and release metabolic waste into it. In a capillary bed (the network of capillaries in an area of tissue), substances move out of the capillaries, into the tissue fluid, by pressure filtration.

Pressure filtration

At the start of the capillary bed, nearest the arteries, the **hydrostatic pressure** inside the capillaries is greater than the hydrostatic pressure in the tissue fluid. This difference in hydrostatic pressure forces fluid out of the capillaries and into the spaces around the cells, forming tissue fluid. As fluid leaves, the hydrostatic pressure reduces in the capillaries — so the hydrostatic pressure is much lower at the end of the capillary bed that's nearest to the venules.

As water leaves the capillaries, the concentration of plasma proteins in the capillaries increases and the water potential decreases. Plasma proteins in the capillaries generate a form of pressure called **oncotic pressure** — so at the venule end of the capillary bed there's a high oncotic pressure and a low water potential. Because the water potential in the capillaries is lower than the water potential in the tissue fluid, some water re-enters the capillaries from the tissue fluid at the venule end by osmosis — see Figure 6.

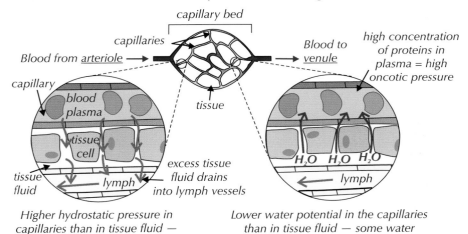

Higher hydrostatic pressure in capillaries than in tissue fluid — fluid is forced out of capillary.

Lower water potential in the capillaries than in tissue fluid — some water re-enters capillary by osmosis.

Figure 6: The movement of fluid between capillaries and tissue cells.

Lymph vessels

Not all of the tissue fluid re-enters the capillaries at the vein end of the capillary bed — some excess tissue fluid is left over. This extra fluid eventually gets returned to the blood through the **lymphatic system** — a kind of drainage system, made up of lymph vessels (see Figure 7 — next page).

The smallest lymph vessels are the lymph capillaries. Excess tissue fluid passes into lymph vessels. Once inside, it's called **lymph**. Valves in the lymph vessels stop the lymph going backwards (see Figure 8 — next page). Lymph gradually moves towards the main lymph vessels in the thorax (chest cavity). Here, it's returned to the blood, near the heart.

Exam Tip
Don't write in the exam that tissue fluid doesn't contain <u>any</u> proteins — it still contains some, just not big ones.

Tip: Hydrostatic pressure is the pressure exerted by a liquid.

Tip: Water potential is the likelihood of water molecules to diffuse out of or into a solution — see page 127.

Tip: Blood plasma is just the liquid that carries everything in the blood.

Tip: Pressure is highest at the start of a capillary bed nearest the arterioles — this is caused by the left ventricle contracting and sending the blood out of the heart, through the arteries and arterioles, at high pressure.

Tip: Don't get the effect of hydrostatic pressure and that of osmosis mixed up — at the arteriole end of a capillary bed, the fluid is forced out of the capillaries by hydrostatic pressure. However, at the venule end of a capillary bed, water moves into the capillaries by osmosis. See p. 126-127 for more on osmosis.

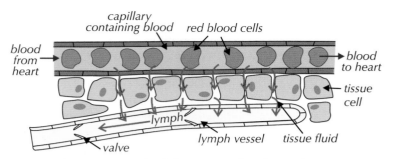

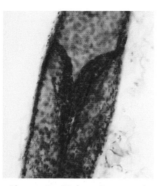

Figure 8: *Light micrograph of a lymph vessel containing a valve. Here the valve allows lymph to move from top to bottom only.*

Figure 7: *Tissue fluid draining into lymph vessels.*

Blood, tissue fluid and lymph

So, tissue fluid is formed from blood, and lymph is formed from tissue fluid — you need to know the differences in the composition of these three fluids.

	Blood	Tissue fluid	Lymph	Comment
Red blood cells	✓	✗	✗	Red blood cells are too big to get through capillary walls into tissue fluid.
White blood cells	✓	very few	✓	Most white blood cells are in the lymph system. They only enter tissue fluid when there's an infection.
Platelets	✓	✗	✗	Only present in tissue fluid if the capillaries are damaged.
Proteins	✓	very few	only antibodies	Most plasma proteins are too big to get through capillary walls.
Water	✓	✓	✓	Tissue fluid and lymph have a higher water potential than blood.
Dissolved solutes	✓	✓	✓	Solutes (e.g. salt) can move freely between blood, tissue fluid and lymph.

Practice Question — Application

Q1 Albumin is a protein found in the blood. Hypoalbuminemia is a condition where the level of albumin in the blood is very low. It causes an increase in tissue fluid, which can lead to swelling. Explain how hypoalbuminemia causes an increase in tissue fluid.

Practice Questions — Fact Recall

Q1 Explain how the structure of each of the following blood vessels is related to its function:

a) artery, b) capillary, c) vein.

Q2 Explain how the structure of an arteriole differs from an artery.

Q3 Which type of blood vessel connects capillaries to veins?

Q4 What is tissue fluid?

Q5 Explain the movement of fluid at the arteriole end of a capillary bed.

Q6 Where does excess tissue fluid drain into?

Q7 a) Give two differences between blood and tissue fluid.

b) Give one difference between tissue fluid and lymph.

3. Heart Basics

You've seen on p. 178 that mammals like you and I have a double circulatory system. Well, now you need to know about the pump that keeps the blood flowing nicely through the system. Introducing the mammalian heart...

External and internal structure of the heart

Figures 1 and 2 below show the external and internal structure of the heart. The heart consists of two muscular pumps. The right side of the heart pumps deoxygenated blood to the lungs and the left side pumps oxygenated blood to the rest of the body.

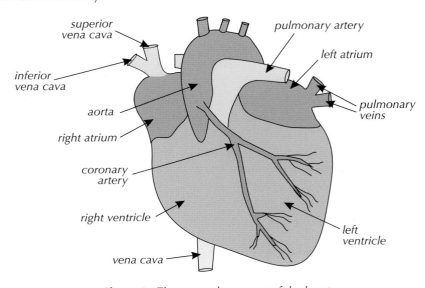

Figure 1: The external structure of the heart.

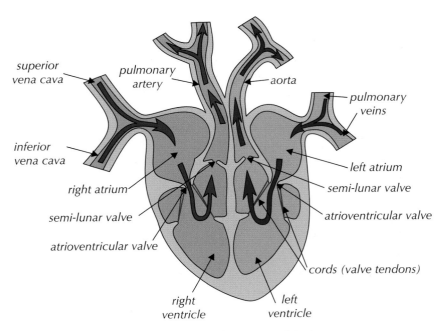

Figure 2: The internal structure of the heart.

Tip: The left ventricle wall is thicker and more muscular than the right, to push blood all the way round the body. Also, the ventricles have thicker walls than the atria because they have to push blood out of the heart.

Tip: There's more about how the atrioventricular valves and semi-lunar valves work on the next page.

Module 3: Section 2 Transport in Animals

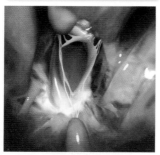

Figure 4: A heart valve.

Tip: Remember to carry
out a risk assessment
before you begin your
dissection. You need to
be very careful when
using scalpels — they're
really sharp.

Tip: See page 172 for
more information on
dissections and the tools
you might need to use.

*Figure 5: A heart before
dissection. The fat on the
outside may make it hard to
see the openings of the blood
vessels — you might have to
find them with your fingers.*

Heart valves

The **atrioventricular (AV) valves** link the atria to the ventricles, and the **semi-lunar (SL) valves** link the ventricles to the pulmonary artery and aorta — they all stop blood flowing the wrong way.

The valves only open one way — whether they're open or closed depends on the relative pressure of the heart chambers. If there's higher pressure behind a valve, it's forced open, but if pressure is higher in front of the valve it's forced shut — see Figure 3. This means that the flow of blood is unidirectional — it only flows in one direction.

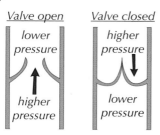

Figure 3: Diagram showing how heart valves open and close.

Heart dissection

You need to be able to dissect and examine a mammalian heart. You need to be able to draw the internal and external structure too. This is how you'd do it:

PRACTICAL ACTIVITY GROUP **2**

1. Make sure you are wearing an apron and lab gloves because heart dissections can be messy.

2. Place the heart you are given on your dissecting tray. You're likely to be given a pig or cow's heart.

3. Look at the outside of the heart and try to identify the four main vessels attached to it. Feel inside the vessels to help you — remember arteries are thick and rubbery, whereas veins are much thinner.

4. Identify the right and left atria, the right and left ventricles and the coronary arteries. Draw a sketch of the outside of the heart and label it.

5. Using a clean scalpel, carefully cut along the lines shown on Figure 6 to look inside each ventricle. You could measure and record the thickness of the ventricle walls and note any differences between them.

6. Next, cut open the atria and look inside them too. Note whether the atria walls are thicker or thinner than the ventricle walls.

7. Then find the atrioventricular valves, followed by the semi-lunar valves. Look at the structure of the valves and see if you can see how they only open one way. Draw a sketch to show the valves and the inside of the ventricles and atria.

8. Make sure you wash your hands and disinfect all work surfaces once you've completed your dissection.

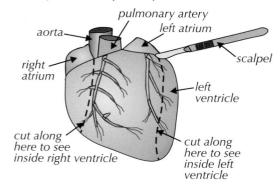

Figure 6: Diagram showing where to cut a heart to examine the ventricles.

The cardiac cycle

The cardiac cycle is an ongoing sequence of contraction and relaxation of the atria and ventricles that keeps blood continuously circulating round the body. The volumes of the atria and ventricles change as they contract and relax, altering the pressure in each chamber. This causes valves to open and close, which directs the blood flow through the heart. If you listen to a human heartbeat you can hear a 'lub-dub' sound. The first 'lub' sound is caused by the atrioventricular valves closing (see stage 2 below). The second 'dub' sound is caused by the semi-lunar valves closing (see stage 3 below). The cardiac cycle can be simplified into these three stages:

Tip: Cardiac contraction is also called systole, and relaxation is called diastole.

1. Ventricles relax, atria contract

The ventricles are relaxed. The atria contract, decreasing the volume of the chambers and increasing the pressure inside the chambers. This pushes the blood into the ventricles through the atrioventricular valves. There's a slight increase in ventricular pressure and chamber volume as the ventricles receive the ejected blood from the contracting atria.

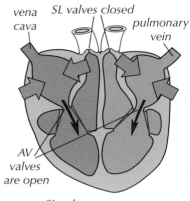

vena cava — SL valves closed — pulmonary vein

AV valves are open

Tip: Contraction of the atria or ventricles is a bit like squeezing a balloon — the size of the balloon decreases and the pressure inside it increases.

2. Ventricles contract, atria relax

The atria relax. The ventricles contract (decreasing their volume), increasing their pressure.
The pressure becomes higher in the ventricles than the atria, which forces the AV valves shut to prevent back-flow. The pressure in the ventricles is also higher than in the aorta and pulmonary artery, which forces open the SL valves and blood is forced out into these arteries.

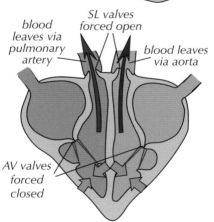

blood leaves via pulmonary artery — SL valves forced open — blood leaves via aorta

AV valves forced closed

Tip: Remember that if there's a higher pressure in front of a valve it's forced shut and if there's a higher pressure behind a valve it's forced open (see previous page).

3. Ventricles relax, atria relax

The ventricles and the atria both relax. The higher pressure in the pulmonary artery and aorta closes the SL valves to prevent back-flow into the ventricles.

Blood returns to the heart and the atria fill again due to the higher pressure in the vena cava and pulmonary vein. In turn this starts to increase the pressure of the atria. As the ventricles continue to relax, their pressure falls below the pressure of the atria and so the AV valves open. This allows blood to flow passively (without being pushed by atrial contraction) into the ventricles from the atria. The atria contract, and the whole process begins again.

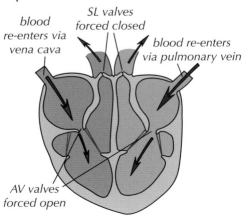

blood re-enters via vena cava — SL valves forced closed — blood re-enters via pulmonary vein

AV valves forced open

Exam Tip
When writing about the cardiac cycle in the exam, make sure you always name the valves. You should also make sure you name them in full at least once before abbreviating them.

Calculating cardiac output

In the exam you could be asked to calculate cardiac output. Cardiac output is the volume of blood pumped by the heart per minute (measured in cm³ min⁻¹). It's calculated using this formula:

> **cardiac output = heart rate × stroke volume**

- **Heart rate** — the number of beats per minute (bpm).
- **Stroke volume** — the volume of blood pumped during each heartbeat, measured in cm³.

Example — Maths Skills

Calculate your **cardiac output** if you have a stroke volume of 70 cm³ and a heart rate of 75 bpm.

cardiac output = heart rate × stroke volume
= 75 × 70 = **5250 cm³ min⁻¹**

Tip: You can rearrange this formula if you need to find the heart rate or stroke volume — a formula triangle like this might help:

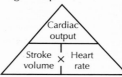

To use a formula triangle, put your finger over the bit of the triangle that corresponds to what you want to find, then read off the correct formula.

Practice Questions — Application

The diagram below shows pressure changes in one cardiac cycle.

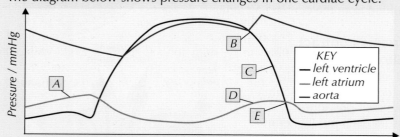

Tip: mmHg is a unit of measurement for pressure. It means millimetres of mercury.

Q1 Why is the atrial pressure increasing at point A?
Q2 Explain whether the semi-lunar valve is open or closed at point B.
Q3 Why is the ventricular pressure decreasing at point C?
Q4 Why is the atrial pressure increasing at point D?
Q5 Explain whether the atrioventricular valve is open or closed at point E.

Tip: To answer the questions on the right you need to be able to link the pressure changes in the left ventricle, left atrium and aorta to each of the three stages of the cardiac cycle.

Practice Questions — Fact Recall

Q1 Which side of the heart pumps deoxygenated blood?
Q2 The diagram on the right shows the external structure of the heart. Name the structures labelled A to H.
Q3 a) Name the valves that link the ventricles to the aorta and pulmonary artery.
    b) What is the function of these valves?
Q4 What is the cardiac cycle?
Q5 When the atria contract, describe the pressure and volume changes that take place in the atria.
Q6 What is the formula for calculating cardiac output?

Tip: Remember, as the volume in a chamber decreases, the pressure increases.

4. Electrical Activity of The Heart

You don't have to remember to send electrical impulses to your heart muscle to make it contract — it happens automatically. This electrical activity can be captured on electrocardiograms, which can help to diagnose heart problems.

Control of heartbeat

Cardiac muscle is 'myogenic' — this means that it can contract and relax without receiving signals from nerves. This pattern of contractions controls the regular heartbeat.

The process starts in the **sino-atrial node (SAN)**, which is in the wall of the right atrium. The SAN is like a pacemaker — it sets the rhythm of the heartbeat by sending regular waves of electrical activity over the atrial walls. This causes the right and left atria to contract at the same time. A band of non-conducting collagen tissue prevents the waves of electrical activity from being passed directly from the atria to the ventricles. Instead, these waves of electrical activity are transferred from the SAN to the **atrioventricular node (AVN)**.

The AVN is responsible for passing the waves of electrical activity on to the bundle of His. But, there's a slight delay before the AVN reacts, to make sure the ventricles contract after the atria have emptied. The **bundle of His** is a group of muscle fibres responsible for conducting the waves of electrical activity to the finer muscle fibres in the right and left ventricle walls, called the **Purkyne tissue**. The Purkyne tissue carries the waves of electrical activity into the muscular walls of the right and left ventricles, causing them to contract simultaneously, from the bottom up.

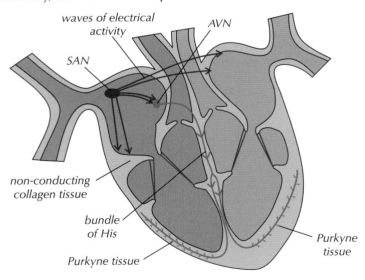

waves of electrical activity

AVN

SAN

non-conducting collagen tissue

bundle of His

Purkyne tissue

Purkyne tissue

Figure 1: *The pathway of electrical activity in the heart.*

Electrocardiographs

A doctor can check someone's heart function using an electrocardiograph — a machine that records the electrical activity of the heart. The heart muscle depolarises (loses electrical charge) when it contracts, and repolarises (regains charge) when it relaxes. An electrocardiograph records these changes in electrical charge using electrodes placed on the chest.

Learning Objectives:

- Know how heart action is initiated and coordinated, including the myogenic nature of cardiac muscle and the roles of the sino-atrial node (SAN), atrio-ventricular node (AVN) and Purkyne tissue.

- Understand the use of electrocardiograms (ECGs) and be able to interpret ECG traces for normal and abnormal heart activity, e.g. tachycardia, bradycardia, ectopic heartbeat and fibrillation.

  Specification Reference 3.1.2

Exam Tip
The waves of electrical activity initiated by the SAN are also called waves of excitation. Never write that they are 'signals', 'messages' or just 'electricity'.

Exam Tip
Make sure you learn where the different structures are in the heart — you could miss out on easy marks in the exam if you don't.

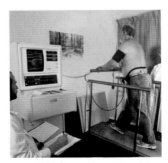

Figure 2: *A patient exercising whilst linked up to an electrocardiograph.*

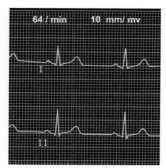

Figure 3: An ECG of a healthy heartbeat.

Electrocardiograms (ECGs)

The trace produced by an electrocardiograph is called an electrocardiogram, or ECG. A normal ECG looks like this:

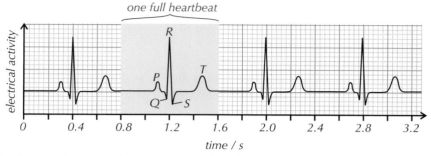

The **P wave** is caused by contraction (depolarisation) of the atria. The main peak of the heartbeat, together with the dips at either side, is called the **QRS complex** — it's caused by contraction (depolarisation) of the ventricles. The **T wave** is due to relaxation (repolarisation) of the ventricles. The height of the wave indicates how much electrical charge is passing through the heart — a bigger wave means more electrical charge, so (for the P and R waves) a bigger wave means a stronger contraction.

Calculating heart rate

Your heart rate is the number of beats per unit time — usually beats per minute (bpm). You can use an ECG to work out a person's heart rate by using the following equation:

heart rate (bpm) = 60 ÷ time taken for one heartbeat (s)

Examples — **Maths Skills**

1. To find out the heart rate shown on the ECG below, first you need to find the time taken for one heartbeat. You can do this by working out the time between one wave (e.g. the R wave) and the next.

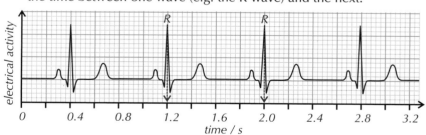

Here, one heartbeat lasts (2 − 1.2) = 0.8 s

Heart rate = 60 ÷ time taken for one heartbeat

= 60 ÷ 0.8 = **75 bpm**

2. Here, the time taken for one heartbeat is worked out using the time between one S wave and the next.

    One heartbeat lasts
    (0.92 − 0.34) = 0.58 s

    Heart rate = 60 ÷ 0.58 = **103 bpm**

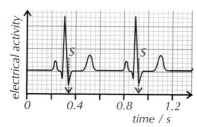

Diagnosing heart problems

Doctors compare their patients' ECGs with a normal trace. This helps them to diagnose any heart problems.

— Examples ——————————————————————————

Tachycardia

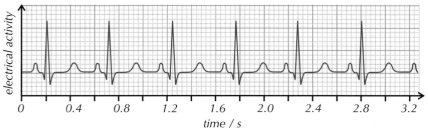

This heartbeat is too fast — around 120 beats per minute. It's called **tachycardia**. That might be OK during exercise, but at rest it shows that the heart isn't pumping blood efficiently.

Bradycardia

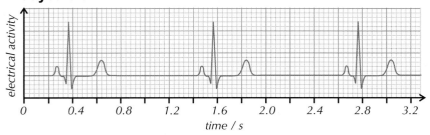

This heartbeat is too slow — 50 beats per minute. A heartbeat below 60 beats per minute is called **bradycardia**. A heart rate this slow is normal in some people (e.g. trained athletes) but in others it can indicate a problem with the electrical activity of the heart, e.g. there may be something preventing impulses from the SAN being passed on properly.

Ectopic heartbeat

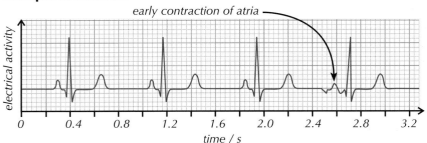

early contraction of atria

The 4th heartbeat on this ECG is an **ectopic heartbeat** — an 'extra' heartbeat that interrupts the regular rhythm. Here it's caused by an earlier contraction of the atria than in the previous heartbeats (you can see that the P wave is different and that it comes earlier than it should). However, it can be caused by early contraction of the ventricles too. Then you would see a taller and wider QRS complex, sometimes without the P wave before it. Occasional ectopic heartbeats in a healthy person don't cause a problem.

Exam Tip
Don't be thrown in the exam if you get shown an ECG that doesn't look exactly like one of these examples — they can look different depending on the exact nature of the heart problem. Just identify the different waves and apply your knowledge of how the heartbeat is coordinated to answer the question.

Exam Tip
In the exam the *y*-axis of an ECG may be labelled 'potential difference'. Don't let this put you off — just focus on what the question is asking you.

Exam Tip
You might be asked to find the differences between an ECG of normal heart activity and one of abnormal heart activity. To do this look for any differences between the P waves, QRS complexes and T waves, for example, look at their duration and height. Then relate this to what these waves are caused by. E.g. a longer T wave means the ventricles have a longer relaxation/rest period.

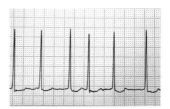

Figure 4: An ECG showing atrial fibrillation.

Fibrillation

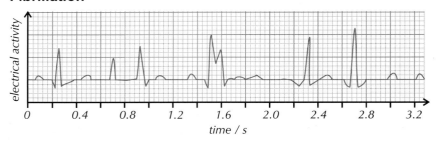

Fibrillation is a really irregular heartbeat. The atria or ventricles completely lose their rhythm and stop contracting properly. It can result in anything from chest pain and fainting to lack of pulse and death.

Practice Questions — Application

Below are an ECG of a person with a normal heart rate (A) and an ECG of a person with an abnormal heart rate (B).

Exam Tip
Always show your working for calculation questions — you can still pick up marks for correct working, even if you get the final answer wrong or misread values off a graph.

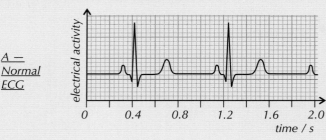

A —
Normal
ECG

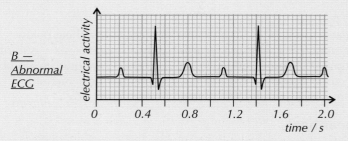

B —
Abnormal
ECG

Tip: Remember, the units for heart rate are usually beats per minute (bpm).

Q1 Work out the heart rate shown on: a) ECG A b) ECG B.
Q2 Describe two differences between the heartbeats shown by ECG A and ECG B.

Practice Questions — Fact Recall

Q1 a) What does SAN stand for, in relation to the heart?
   b) What is the function of the SAN?
Q2 Name the tissue that prevents electrical signals passing directly from the atria to the ventricles.
Q3 Describe the role of the bundle of His.
Q4 Describe the role of the Purkyne tissue.
Q5 a) What does ECG stand for?
   b) Give an example of a heart problem that an ECG can be used to diagnose.

5. Haemoglobin

Lots of organisms have haemoglobin in their blood to transport oxygen.

Haemoglobin and oxyhaemoglobin

Human haemoglobin is found in red blood cells — its role is to carry oxygen around the body. Haemoglobin is a large protein with a quaternary structure (see pages 63 and 64 for more) — it's made up of more than one polypeptide chain (four of them in fact). Each chain has a haem group which contains iron and gives haemoglobin its red colour (see Figure 1). Each molecule of human haemoglobin can carry four oxygen molecules.

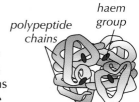

Figure 1: Human haemoglobin.

polypeptide chains   *haem group*

In the lungs, oxygen joins to the iron in haemoglobin to form **oxyhaemoglobin**. This is a reversible reaction — near the body cells, oxygen leaves oxyhaemoglobin and it turns back to haemoglobin (see Figure 2). When an oxygen molecule joins to haemoglobin it's referred to as **association** or **loading**, and when oxygen leaves oxyhaemoglobin it's referred to as **dissociation** or **unloading**.

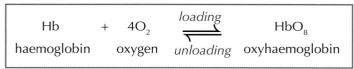

$$Hb + 4O_2 \underset{\text{unloading}}{\overset{\text{loading}}{\rightleftharpoons}} HbO_8$$

haemoglobin   oxygen   oxyhaemoglobin

Figure 2: The association and dissociation of oxyhaemoglobin.

Affinity for oxygen and pO_2

Affinity for oxygen means the tendency a molecule has to bind with oxygen. Haemoglobin's affinity for oxygen varies depending on the conditions it's in — one of the conditions that affects it is the **partial pressure of oxygen (pO_2)**.

pO_2 is a measure of oxygen concentration. The greater the concentration of dissolved oxygen in cells, the higher the partial pressure. As pO_2 increases, haemoglobin's affinity for oxygen also increases:

- Oxygen loads onto haemoglobin to form oxyhaemoglobin where there's a high pO_2.

- Oxyhaemoglobin unloads its oxygen where there's a lower pO_2.

Oxygen enters blood capillaries at the alveoli in the lungs. Alveoli have a high pO_2 so oxygen loads onto haemoglobin to form oxyhaemoglobin. When cells respire, they use up oxygen — this lowers the pO_2. Red blood cells deliver oxyhaemoglobin to respiring tissues, where it unloads its oxygen. The haemoglobin then returns to the lungs to pick up more oxygen. Figure 3 summarises this process.

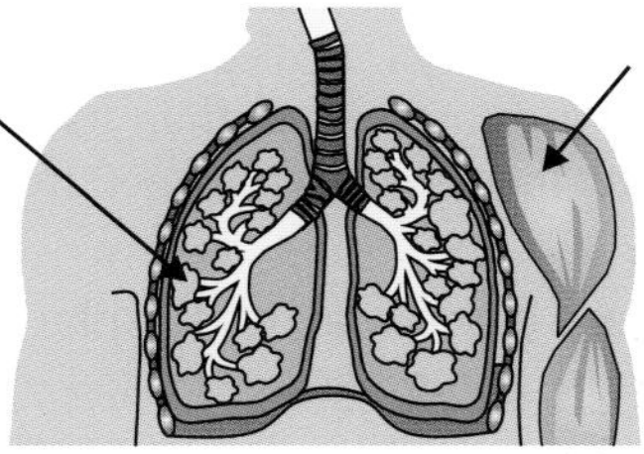

Alveoli in lungs
- *HIGH oxygen concentration*
- *HIGH pO_2*
- *HIGH affinity*
- *Oxygen LOADS*

Respiring tissue
- *LOW oxygen concentration*
- *LOW pO_2*
- *LOW affinity*
- *Oxygen UNLOADS*

Figure 3: Oxygen loading and unloading in the body.

Learning Objectives:

- Know the role of haemoglobin in the transportation of oxygen around the body.

- Understand that oxygen molecules bind reversibly to haemoglobin.

- Recognise the oxygen dissociation curves for human adult and fetal haemoglobin, and understand the significance of the different affinities for oxygen.

- Understand the changes to the dissociation curve at different carbon dioxide concentrations (the Bohr effect).

- Know the role of haemoglobin in the transportation of carbon dioxide to the lungs.

- Understand how carbonic anhydrase, haemoglobinic acid, HCO_3^- and the chloride shift are involved in the transport of oxygen and carbon dioxide by haemoglobin.

Specification Reference 3.1.2

Tip: Haemoglobin is sometimes shortened to Hb.

Tip: Red blood cells can also be called erythrocytes.

Dissociation curves

An oxygen dissociation curve shows how saturated the haemoglobin is with oxygen at any given partial pressure. The affinity of haemoglobin for oxygen affects how saturated the haemoglobin is:

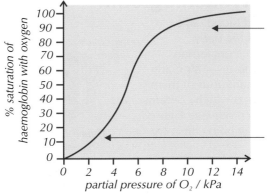

Where pO_2 is high (e.g. in the lungs), haemoglobin has a high affinity for oxygen, so it has a high saturation of oxygen.

Where pO_2 is low (e.g. in respiring tissues), haemoglobin has a low affinity for oxygen, so it has a low saturation of oxygen.

Figure 4: *Dissociation curve for adult haemoglobin.*

Weirdly, the saturation of haemoglobin can also affect the affinity — this is why the graph is 'S-shaped' and not a straight line. When haemoglobin combines with the first O_2 molecule, its shape alters in a way that makes it easier for other molecules to join too. But as the haemoglobin starts to become saturated, it gets harder for more oxygen molecules to join. As a result, the curve has a steep bit in the middle where it's really easy for oxygen molecules to join, and shallow bits at each end where it's harder — see Figure 5. When the curve is steep, a small change in pO_2 causes a big change in the amount of oxygen carried by the haemoglobin.

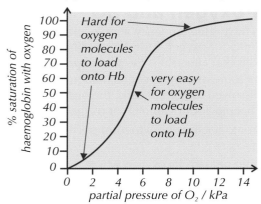

Figure 5: *The S-shaped dissociation curve for haemoglobin.*

Fetal haemoglobin

Adult haemoglobin and fetal haemoglobin have different affinities for oxygen. Fetal haemoglobin has a higher affinity for oxygen than adult haemoglobin (the fetus's blood is better at absorbing oxygen than its mother's blood). This is really important because the fetus gets oxygen from its mother's blood across the placenta.

By the time the mother's blood reaches the placenta, its oxygen saturation has decreased because some has been used up by the mother's body. The placenta has a low pO_2, so adult oxyhaemoglobin will unload its oxygen (adult oxyhaemoglobin will dissociate).

For the fetus to get enough oxygen to survive its haemoglobin has to have a higher affinity for oxygen than adult haemoglobin. This means fetal haemoglobin takes up oxygen (becomes more saturated) in lower pO_2 than adult haemoglobin — see Figure 6. If its haemoglobin had the same affinity for oxygen as adult haemoglobin, its blood wouldn't be saturated enough.

Tip: The placenta acts like a fetus's lungs — the fetal haemoglobin has a higher affinity for oxygen (than adult haemoglobin), so it becomes more saturated with O_2 at the placenta.

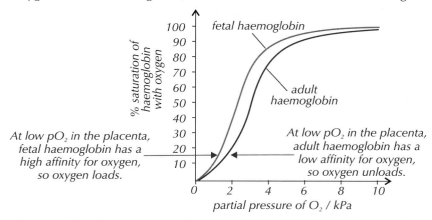

At low pO_2 in the placenta, fetal haemoglobin has a high affinity for oxygen, so oxygen loads.

At low pO_2 in the placenta, adult haemoglobin has a low affinity for oxygen, so oxygen unloads.

Figure 6: The dissociation curve for adult haemoglobin and fetal haemoglobin.

Exam Tip
If you're asked to draw a dissociation curve for feta**l** haemoglobin, make sure you draw it to the **l**eft of adult haemoglobin curve.

Carbon dioxide concentration

The **partial pressure of carbon dioxide (pCO_2)** is a measure of the concentration of CO_2 in a cell. To complicate matters, pCO_2 also affects oxygen unloading. Haemoglobin gives up its oxygen more readily at a higher pCO_2. It's a cunning way of getting more O_2 to cells during activity.

When cells respire they produce carbon dioxide, which raises the pCO_2. This increases the rate of oxygen unloading — the dissociation curve 'shifts' right (but it is still the same shape). The saturation of blood with oxygen is lower for a given pO_2, meaning that more oxygen is being released — see Figure 7. This is called the **Bohr effect**.

Tip: Active cells need more oxygen for aerobic respiration. The word equation for aerobic respiration is: glucose + oxygen → carbon dioxide + water + energy.

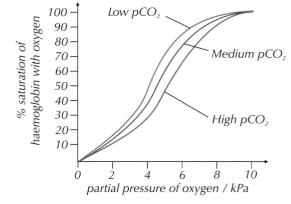

Figure 7: The Bohr effect.

Low pCO_2

Medium pCO_2

High pCO_2

Tip: When dissociation curves are being compared, the further left the curve is, the higher the haemoglobin's affinity for oxygen is.

Explanation of the Bohr effect

The reason for the Bohr effect is linked to how CO_2 affects blood pH. Most of the CO_2 from respiring tissues diffuses into red blood cells. Here it reacts with water to form **carbonic acid**, catalysed by the enzyme **carbonic anhydrase**. The rest of the CO_2, around 10%, binds directly to haemoglobin and is carried to the lungs. The carbonic acid dissociates (splits up) to give hydrogen ions (H^+) and hydrogencarbonate ions (HCO_3^-) — see Figure 8 on the next page.

Tip: The Boh**r** effect shifts the oxygen dissociation curve to the **r**ight.

Tip: Hydrogencarbonate ions can also be called bicarbonate ions.

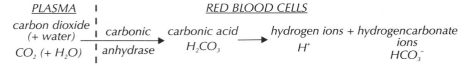

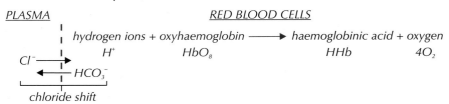

Figure 8: The formation and splitting of carbonic acid.

This increase in H^+ ions causes oxyhaemoglobin to unload its oxygen so that haemoglobin can take up the H^+ ions. This forms a compound called **haemoglobinic acid** — see Figure 9. (This process also stops the H^+ ions from increasing the cell's acidity — the haemoglobin 'mops up' the H^+ ions.) The HCO_3^- ions diffuse out of the red blood cells and are transported in the blood plasma. To compensate for the loss of HCO_3^- ions from the red blood cells, chloride ions (Cl^-) diffuse into the red blood cells (see Figure 9). This is called the **chloride shift** and it maintains the balance of charge between the red blood cell and the plasma.

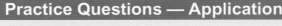

Figure 9: The chloride shift and the unloading of oxygen in red blood cells.

When the blood reaches the lungs the low pCO_2 causes some of the HCO_3^- ions and H^+ ions to recombine into CO_2 (and water). The CO_2 then diffuses into the alveoli and is breathed out.

Practice Questions — Application

The graph on the right shows a dissociation curve for adult haemoglobin.

Q1 Copy the graph and draw another dissociation curve to represent fetal haemoglobin.

Q2 Explain why you have drawn the dissociation curve for fetal haemoglobin in this way.

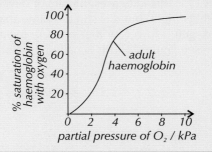

Practice Questions — Fact Recall

Q1 What does oxygen load onto haemoglobin to form?

Q2 Where in the body would you find cells with a high pO_2? Explain your answer.

Q3 What is shown on an oxygen dissociation curve?

Q4 State the main advantage of the Bohr effect.

Q5 Describe the shift that the Bohr effect would have on a dissociation curve for normal adult haemoglobin.

Q6 Name the enzyme that converts CO_2 to carbonic acid.

Q7 a) What happens to carbonic acid in red blood cells?

   b) How does this lead to the unloading of oxygen?

Q8 What is the chloride shift?

Section Summary

Make sure you know...

- That due to their large size, high metabolic rate and small surface area to volume ratio, multicellular organisms need a transport system to supply their cells with useful substances and to take away waste.
- That fish have a single circulatory system (blood only passes through the heart once for each complete circuit of the body) and that mammals have a double circulatory system (blood passes through the heart twice for each complete circuit of the body).
- That fish and mammals have a closed circulatory system (the blood is enclosed inside blood vessels) and that insects have an open circulatory system (the blood isn't always enclosed in blood vessels).
- The structures of arteries, arterioles, capillaries, venules and veins including the distribution of different tissues within the walls of the vessels.
- That the function of arteries and arterioles is to carry blood away from the heart (under high pressure), that capillaries are the site for the exchange of substances between the cells and the blood, and that venules and veins carry blood back to the heart under low pressure.
- How tissue fluid is formed — high hydrostatic pressure at the arteriole end of the capillary bed forces water and small molecules out of the capillaries into the spaces around the tissues.
- That the high oncotic pressure (and low water potential) at the venule end of the capillary bed causes some water to be reabsorbed back into the capillaries from the tissue fluid.
- That tissue fluid is formed from blood, and lymph is formed from tissue fluid, and the differences in the composition of blood, tissue fluid and lymph.
- The external and internal structure of the heart, including the superior and inferior vena cava, pulmonary artery, aorta, pulmonary vein, right atrium, left atrium, semi-lunar valves, atrioventricular valves, cords, right ventricle, left ventricle and coronary artery.
- How to safely dissect and examine a mammalian heart and draw the external and internal structure.
- The stages of the cardiac cycle, including the roles of the semi-lunar and atrioventricular valves and the pressure changes that occur in the heart and associated vessels during the cycle.
- That cardiac output is the volume of blood pumped by the heart per minute and is calculated using the formula: cardiac output = heart rate × stroke volume.
- That cardiac muscle is myogenic and the roles of the following structures in controlling the heartbeat: sino-atrial node, atrioventricular node, bundle of His, Purkyne tissue.
- How to interpret and explain electrocardiogram (ECG) traces of normal and abnormal heart activity, such as tachycardia, bradycardia, ectopic heartbeat and fibrillation.
- That the role of haemoglobin is to carry oxygen around the body.
- That oxygen binds reversibly with haemoglobin forming oxyhaemoglobin.
- That a dissociation curve shows how saturated haemoglobin is at any given partial pressure.
- That the fetal dissociation curve is shifted left from the adult dissociation curve — fetal haemoglobin has a higher affinity for oxygen than adult haemoglobin, allowing it to pick up the oxygen from adult oxyhaemoglobin at the placenta.
- That an increase in carbon dioxide concentration (pCO_2) increases the rate of oxygen unloading and the dissociation curve shifts right — this is called the Bohr effect.
- That some of the CO_2 that enters red blood cells is transported to the lungs by haemoglobin.
- The explanation behind the Bohr effect — CO_2 in red blood cells is converted to carbonic acid by carbonic anhydrase, carbonic acid splits into hydrogen ions (H^+) and hydrogencarbonate ions (HCO_3^-), and this increase in hydrogen ions causes oxyhaemoglobin to unload oxygen so that haemoglobin can take up the hydrogen ions (forming haemoglobinic acid).
- That the chloride shift is the movement of chloride ions (Cl^-) from the plasma into red blood cells to compensate for the loss of HCO_3^-.

Exam-style Questions

1 Which of the following statements about ECG traces is/are correct?

Statement 1: A longer QRS complex may indicate a problem with the Purkyne tissue.

Statement 2: A higher P wave indicates a stronger contraction of the atria.

Statement 3: The T wave is caused by contraction of the ventricles.

A 1, 2 and 3   **C** Only 2 and 3

B Only 1 and 2   **D** Only 1

(1 mark)

2 **Fig. 2.1** is a diagram of the internal structure of the mammalian heart. The valves are shown but not labelled.

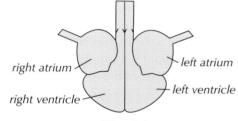

Fig. 2.1

(a) Describe and explain where the blood is flowing **into** in **Fig. 2.1**.

(3 marks)

(b) Name the valves that connect the atria to the ventricles and describe their function.

(2 marks)

(c) Mammals have a double circulatory system, which is why the heart is divided down the middle.

(i) Explain what is meant by a double circulatory system.

(1 mark)

(ii) Describe how the mammalian double circulatory system works and suggest the advantage to mammals of having this system.

(3 marks)

3 **Fig. 3.1** shows two oxygen dissociation curves for the same man.

One curve was produced based on blood tests when he was watching television and the other was produced based on blood tests immediately after a bike ride.

(a) Which curve was produced after the bike ride? Explain your answer.

(2 marks)

(b) What name is given to the effect shown on the graph?

(1 mark)

(c) Explain why more HCO_3^- ions would have been released from the man's red blood cells following his bike ride compared to when he was watching television.

(3 marks)

4 Some people suffer from a disease called third-degree atrioventricular block — the waves of electrical activity from the sino-atrial node (SAN) are not relayed to the atrioventricular node (AVN). A pacemaker can be fitted to take over this role. **Fig. 4.1** shows a heart with a pacemaker attached.

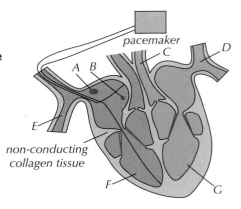

Fig. 4.1

(a) From **Fig. 4.1**, identify which labels correspond to the following structures by writing a letter from A to G in the table.

AVN	
Right ventricle	
Pulmonary vein	

(3 marks)

(b) What is the purpose of the non-conducting collagen tissue shown on the diagram?

(1 mark)

(c) Explain why the pacemaker must be programmed to have a delay between receiving waves of electrical activity from the SAN and activating the AVN.

(1 mark)

(d) Describe the passage of the waves of electrical activity from the AVN to rest of the heart, causing the ventricles to contract.

(3 marks)

5 **Fig 5.1** shows part of the circulatory system of a mammal. The arrows show the direction of blood flow.

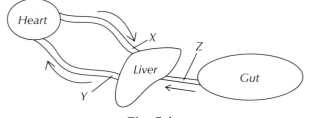

Fig. 5.1

(a) (i) Which vessel in **Fig 5.1**, **X**, **Y** or **Z**, transports blood at the highest pressure? Explain your answer.

(1 mark)

(ii) State **three** ways in which the structure of blood vessel **X** differs from the structure of blood vessel **Y**.

(3 marks)

(b) The liver is surrounded by a capillary bed and tissue fluid. Describe how tissue fluid is formed.

(2 marks)

(c) State **two** ways in which blood is different from lymph.

(2 marks)

- Understand why multicellular plants need transport systems in terms of their size, surface area to volume ratio (SA:V) and metabolic rate.

- Know the structure and function of the vascular system in the roots, stems and leaves of herbaceous dicotyledonous plants, including the structure and function of xylem vessels, sieve tube elements and companion cells.

- Be able to examine and draw stained sections of plant tissue to show the distribution of xylem and phloem (PAG1).

- Be able to dissect stems, both longitudinally and transversely, and examine them to demonstrate the position and structure of xylem vessels (PAG2).

Specification Reference 3.1.3

Tip: Plants also need carbon dioxide, but this enters at the leaves (where it's needed).

Tip: These diagrams all show the xylem and phloem in 'herbaceous dicotyledonous plants' — flowering plants without a woody stem.

1. Xylem and Phloem

Humans have one transport system — the circulatory system. Plants go one better and have two transport systems — the xylem and the phloem...

Why do plants need transport systems?

Plants need substances like water, minerals and sugars to live. They also need to get rid of waste substances. Like animals, plants are multicellular so have a small surface area to volume ratio (SA:V, see page 158). They are also relatively big so have a high metabolic rate. Exchanging substances by direct diffusion (from the outer surface to the cells) would be too slow to meet their metabolic needs. So plants need transport systems to move substances to and from individual cells quickly.

Location of xylem and phloem tissues

There are two types of tissue involved in transport in plants. **Xylem tissue** transports water and mineral ions in solution. These substances move up the plant from the roots to the leaves. **Phloem tissue** mainly transports sugars (also in solution) both up and down the plant.

Xylem and phloem make up a plant's vascular system. They are found throughout a plant and they transport materials to all parts. Where they're found in each part is connected to the xylem's other function, which is support. The position of the xylem and phloem in the root, stem and leaf are shown in the transverse cross-sections below (see Figures 1-3). Transverse means the sections are cut through each structure at a right angle to its length.

Roots

In a root, the xylem and phloem are in the centre to provide support for the root as it pushes through the soil — see Figure 1.

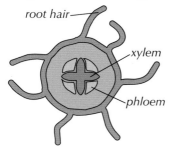

Figure 1: Transverse cross-section of a root.

Stem

In the stems, the xylem and phloem are near the outside to provide a sort of 'scaffolding' that reduces bending — see Figure 2.

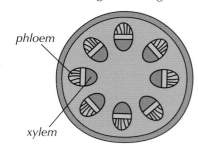

Figure 2: Transverse cross-section of a stem.

Leaves

In a leaf, xylem and phloem make up a network of veins which support the thin leaves — see Figure 3.

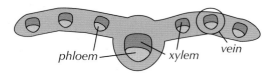

Figure 3: Transverse cross-section of a leaf.

You can also get longitudinal cross-sections. These are taken along the length of a structure. For example, Figure 4 shows where the xylem and phloem are located in a typical stem.

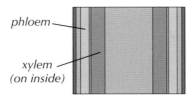

phloem

xylem
(on inside)

Figure 4: *Longitudinal cross-section of a stem.*

Adaptations of xylem vessels

Xylem is a tissue made from several different cell types (see page 153). You need to learn about xylem vessels — the part of xylem tissue that actually transports the water and ions.

Xylem vessels are very long, tube-like structures formed from cells (vessel elements) joined end to end — see Figure 5. There are no end walls on these cells, making an uninterrupted tube that allows water to pass up through the middle easily. The cells are dead, so they contain no cytoplasm.

The cell walls are thickened with a woody substance called **lignin**, which helps to support the walls and stops them collapsing inwards. Lignin can be deposited in xylem walls in different ways, e.g. in a spiral or as distinct rings. Being deposited in these patterns allows flexibility and prevents the stem from breaking. The amount of lignin increases as the cell gets older.

Water and mineral ions move into and out of the vessels through small **pits** in the walls where there's no lignin. This is how other types of cells are supplied with water.

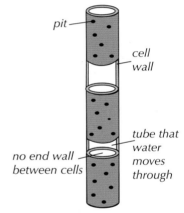

pit

cell wall

tube that water moves through

no end wall between cells

Figure 5: *A xylem vessel with internal detail showing.*

Exam Tip
Remember to write that lignin supports the xylem <u>walls</u>, not the whole plant.

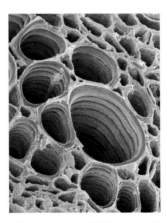

Figure 6: *An SEM image of xylem vessels — the lignin that supports the vessels is clearly visible (orange).*

Adaptations of phloem tissue

Phloem tissue transports **solutes** (dissolved substances), mainly sugars like sucrose, round plants. Like xylem, phloem is formed from cells arranged in tubes. But, unlike xylem, it's purely a transport tissue — it isn't used for support as well. Phloem tissue contains phloem fibres, phloem parenchyma, sieve tube elements and companion cells. Sieve tube elements and companion cells are the most important cell types in phloem for transport (see Figures 8 and 9 — next page).

Sieve tube elements

These are living cells that form the tube for transporting sugars through the plant. They are joined end to end to form sieve tubes. The 'sieve' parts are the end walls, which have lots of holes in them to allow solutes to pass through. Unusually for living cells, sieve tube elements have no nucleus, a very thin layer of cytoplasm and few organelles. The cytoplasm of adjacent cells is connected through the holes in the sieve plates.

Tip: Phloem tissue also transports small amounts of amino acids, certain ions and plant hormones — but mainly sugars.

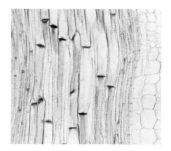

Figure 7: *Phloem vessels in a Cucurbita plant. The sieve cells are stained blue and the sieve plates are dark green.*

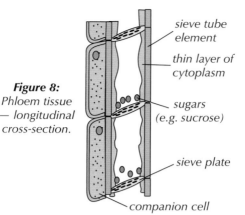

Figure 8: *Phloem tissue — longitudinal cross-section.*

- sieve tube element
- thin layer of cytoplasm
- sugars (e.g. sucrose)
- sieve plate
- companion cell

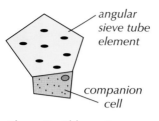

- angular sieve tube element
- companion cell

Figure 9: *Phloem tissue — transverse view.*

Tip: The active transport of solutes requires energy — see page 132 for more details.

Companion cells

The lack of a nucleus and other organelles in sieve tube elements means that they can't survive on their own. So there's a companion cell for every sieve tube element (see Figures 8 and 9). Companion cells carry out the living functions for both themselves and their sieve cells. For example, they provide the energy for the active transport of solutes.

Tip: You could look at a section of plant tissue you've prepared yourself — there's more on this on the next page.

Examination of stained plant tissue

PRACTICAL ACTIVITY GROUP **1**

You might have to look at stained sections of plant tissue under a light microscope and examine them to identify the distribution of the xylem and phloem tissue. The distribution of these tissues will depend on the part of the plant you are looking at. Look back at Figures 1-3 on page 198 to see how the distribution changes in the root, stem and leaf. Be aware that when you look at real plant tissue, the distribution won't be as clear cut as in the diagrams and you'll be able to see lots of other plant cells as well — it might take you a little while to figure out what you're looking at.

The cells will look different depending on what stain has been used on the sample. For example, staining with toluidine blue O (TBO) will make the lignin in the walls of the xylem cells blue-green. The phloem cells and the rest of the tissue will generally appear varying shades of pink and purple.

You need to be able to draw the sections you examine. Make your drawings as clear as possible — think about the relative size and position of the structures you draw and add clear labels to show what you've identified. You should also include the magnification you viewed the sample at.

Tip: With a light microscope you won't be able to see all of the organelles in your sample — you might see some of the bigger ones in some cells (e.g. nuclei, chloroplasts) depending on the magnification and the stain you are using.

┌─ **Example** ─────────────────

The picture on the right shows a transverse cross-section of a buttercup root viewed under a light microscope. As you can see, the xylem vessels are arranged in a rough cross shape. You might also notice that most of the xylem vessels have a wider diameter than the phloem vessels (you'll probably find this is the case for many cross-sections you look at).

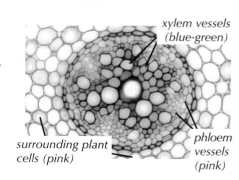

- xylem vessels (blue-green)
- surrounding plant cells (pink)
- phloem vessels (pink)

Plant dissection

PRACTICAL ACTIVITY GROUP **2**

You need to know how to dissect a plant stem and prepare the tissue in order to examine the position and the structure of the xylem vessels under a light microscope.
You can do this using the following method:

Example

1. Use a scalpel (or razor blade) to cut a cross-section of the stem (transverse or longitudinal). Cut the sections as thinly as possible — thin sections are better for viewing under a microscope. You might need to use tweezers to hold the stem still whilst you are cutting.

2. Use tweezers to gently place the cut sections in water until you come to use them. This stops them from drying out.

3. Add a drop of water to a microscope slide, add the plant section and carefully add one or two drops of a stain, e.g. toluidine blue O (TBO), and leave for about one minute.

4. Carefully apply a cover slip so you have created a wet mount (see page 45).

5. View the specimen under a light microscope and draw a labelled diagram of what you observe (see previous page).

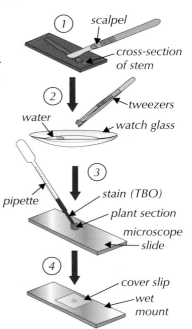

Tip: As with all practicals you do, make sure you have carried out a risk assessment before you begin. Pay particular attention to safety when working with sharp blades and remember you should wear gloves and eye protection when working with stains.

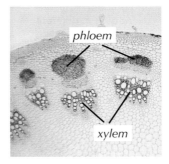

Figure 10: Light micrograph of a transverse cross-section through a stem showing xylem and phloem tissue.

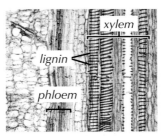

Figure 11: Light micrograph of a longitudinal cross-section through a stem showing xylem and phloem tissue.

Practice Questions — Application

Q1 The photo on the right is a light micrograph of a transverse cross-section through a leaf. The labels are pointing to the xylem and phloem tissue.

Which label, W or X, is pointing to phloem tissue? Give a reason for your answer.

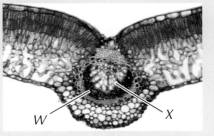

Q2 Figure A below is an SEM image of phloem tissue in a plant stem. Figure B below is an SEM image of xylem vessels in an ash tree.

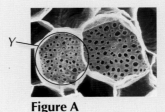

Figure A

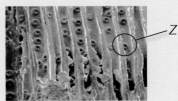

Figure B

a) Name structure Y in Figure A.
b) Name structure Z in Figure B and describe its function.

Tip: Microscopes pop up everywhere in Biology — SEM stands for scanning electron microscope. (You learnt about these on page 41.)

Q1 Explain why plants can't exchange substances by direct diffusion.

Q2 The outline below represents a transverse cross-section of a plant's stem. Copy the outline and draw in the position of the xylem and phloem.

Q3 The diagram below shows the cross-section of a root.

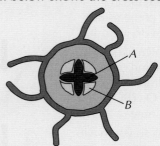

Name the structures labelled A and B.

Q4 What do xylem vessels transport?

Q5 Name the substance present in the xylem vessel walls that prevents them collapsing.

Q6 What is the main substance phloem tissue transports?

Q7 a) Are sieve tube elements living cells or dead cells?

   b) Give two ways that sieve tube elements differ from normal plant cells.

Q8 Briefly describe the function of companion cells.

Q9 Briefly describe how you could dissect and examine a plant stem.

2. Water Transport

Plants are pretty clever when it comes to transporting water. They can take it up from their roots to their leaves against the force of gravity. Let's see how they manage that...

Learning Objectives:

- Know how water is transported into a plant, through the plant and to the air surrounding the leaves in terms of water potential.
- Know details of the pathways taken by water as it is transported through a plant.
- Understand the mechanisms of water movement in a plant, in terms of the transpiration stream, cohesion and adhesion.

Specification Reference 3.1.3

How does water enter a plant?

Water has to get from the soil, through the root and into the xylem to be transported around the plant. Water enters through root hair cells and then passes through the root **cortex**, including the **endodermis**, to reach the xylem — see Figure 1.

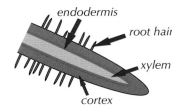

Figure 1: Cross-section of a root.

Water is drawn into the roots via **osmosis**. Water always moves from areas of higher water potential to areas of lower water potential — it goes down a water potential gradient. The soil around roots generally has a high water potential (i.e. there's lots of water there) and leaves have a lower water potential (because water constantly evaporates from them). This creates a water potential gradient that keeps water moving through the plant in the right direction, from roots (high) to leaves (low) — see Figure 2.

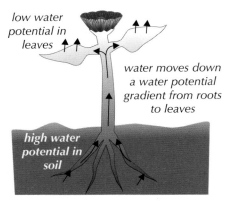

Figure 2: Water potential gradient up a plant.

Tip: Remember, osmosis is the diffusion of water molecules across a partially permeable membrane, from an area of higher water potential to an area of lower water potential — see p. 126.

Water transport through the root

Water travels through the roots (via the root cortex) into the xylem by two different pathways:

The symplast pathway

The symplast pathway (see Figure 3) goes through the living parts of cells — the cytoplasm. The cytoplasm of neighbouring cells connects through **plasmodesmata** (small channels in the cell walls). Water moves through the symplast pathway via osmosis.

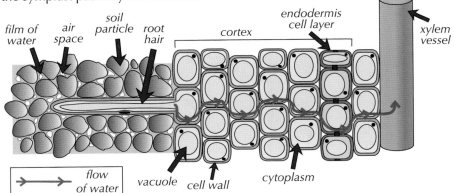

Figure 3: The symplast pathway.

Figure 4: Root hairs on a cress root.

The apoplast pathway

The apoplast pathway (see Figure 5) goes through the non-living parts of the cells — the cell walls. The walls are very absorbent and water can simply diffuse through them, as well as passing through the spaces between them. The water can carry solutes and move from areas of high hydrostatic pressure to areas of low hydrostatic pressure (i.e. along a pressure gradient). This is an example of mass flow (see page 210).

When water in the apoplast pathway gets to the endodermis cells in the root, its path is blocked by a waxy strip in the cell walls, called the **Casparian strip**. Now the water has to take the symplast pathway. This is useful, because it means the water has to go through a plasma (cell-surface) membrane. Cell membranes are partially permeable and are able to control whether or not substances in the water get through (see p. 116). Once past this barrier, the water moves into the xylem.

Tip: Both pathways are used, but the main one is the apoplast pathway because it provides the least resistance.

Exam Tip
If you're asked to identify the endodermis from a diagram, look for which layer of cells has the Casparian strip.

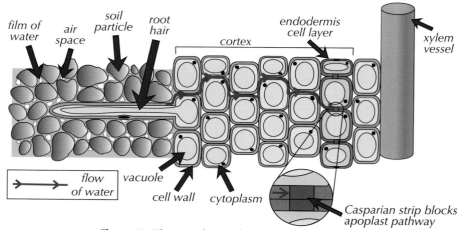

Figure 5: The apoplast pathway.

Water transport through the leaves

Xylem vessels transport the water all around the plant. At the leaves, water leaves the xylem and moves into the cells mainly by the apoplast pathway. Water evaporates from the cell walls into the spaces between cells in the leaf. When the **stomata** (tiny pores in the surface of the leaf) open, water evaporates — it diffuses out of the leaf (down the water potential gradient) into the surrounding air — see Figure 6. The evaporation of water from a plant's surface is called **transpiration** (see p. 206).

Tip: Water passes from the xylem into the leaf cells by osmosis (down its water potential gradient — see p. 126).

Tip: 'Stomata' is plural, 'stoma' is singular.

Exam Tip
Don't call stomata 'pores' in the exam — use the scientific term.

Exam Tip
Don't be put off in the exam if you come across the term 'mesophyll cells' — they're just a type of leaf cell.

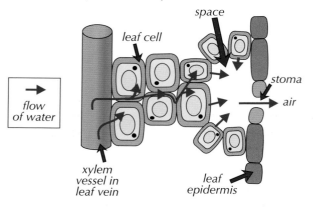

Figure 6: Water loss from a leaf.

Water movement up a plant

The movement of water from roots to leaves is called the **transpiration stream**. The mechanisms that move the water include cohesion, tension and adhesion.

Cohesion and tension

Cohesion and tension help water move up plants, from roots to leaves, against the force of gravity (see Figure 7).

1. Water evaporates from the leaves at the 'top' of the xylem (transpiration).

2. This creates a tension (suction), which pulls more water into the leaf.

3. Water molecules are cohesive (they stick together) so when some are pulled into the leaf others follow. This means the whole column of water in the xylem, from the leaves down to the roots, moves upwards.

4. Water enters the stem through the root cortex cells.

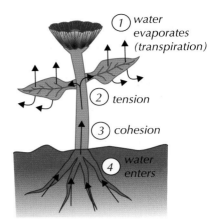

Figure 7: *Water movement up a plant.*

Adhesion

Adhesion is also partly responsible for the movement of water. As well as being attracted to each other, water molecules are attracted to the walls of the xylem vessels. This helps water to rise up through the xylem vessels.

Tip: Air bubbles can form in the xylem, which block the column of water, preventing water from reaching the cells. Without enough water the cells become flaccid (see page 127) and the plant wilts.

Tip: Water movement up a plant increases as the transpiration rate increases — see p. 206.

Tip: Cohesion and tension allow the mass flow of water over long distances up the stem.

Practice Questions — Application

The diagram below shows a section through a root.

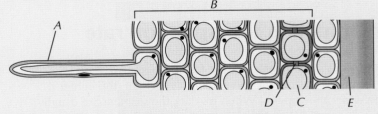

Answer the following questions about the diagram.

Q1 What type of cell is cell A?

Q2 Which cell layer is the endodermis — B or C?

Q3 Name structure D.

Q4 If structure E was blocked, suggest what effect this may have on the plant.

Practice Questions — Fact Recall

Q1 Briefly describe the pathway of water from the soil into the xylem.

Q2 Describe how water moves through the symplast and apoplast pathways.

Q3 What is transpiration?

Q4 What is the transpiration stream?

Q5 Explain adhesion in terms of water movement in the xylem.

Exam Tip
Don't get transpiration mixed up with the transpiration stream — they are two different processes.

3. Transpiration

Transpiration was introduced on the previous couple of pages, but unfortunately there's loads more you need to know about it...

Why does transpiration happen?

So you know that transpiration is the evaporation of water from a plant's surface, especially the leaves. But I bet you didn't know it happens as a result of **gas exchange**.

A plant needs to open its stomata to let in carbon dioxide so that it can produce glucose (by photosynthesis). But this also lets water out — there's a higher concentration of water inside the leaf than in the air outside, so water moves out of the leaf down the water potential gradient when the stomata open. So transpiration's really a side effect of the gas exchange needed for photosynthesis.

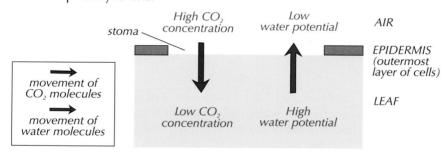

Figure 1: Simplified diagram to show gas exchange and water loss from a leaf.

Factors affecting transpiration rate

There are four main factors that affect transpiration rate:

1. **Light intensity** — the lighter it is the faster the transpiration rate. This is because the stomata open when it gets light (the lighter it gets, the wider they open). When it's dark the stomata are usually closed, so there's little transpiration.

2. **Temperature** — the higher the temperature the faster the transpiration rate. Warmer water molecules have more energy so they evaporate from the cells inside the leaf faster. This increases the water potential gradient between the inside and outside of the leaf, making water diffuse out of the leaf faster.

3. **Humidity** — the lower the humidity, the faster the transpiration rate. If the air around the plant is dry, the water potential gradient between the leaf and the air is increased, which increases transpiration rate.

4. **Wind** — the windier it is, the faster the transpiration rate. Lots of air movement blows away water molecules from around the stomata. This increases the water potential gradient, which increases the rate of transpiration.

Estimating transpiration rate — potometers

PRACTICAL ACTIVITY GROUP **5**

PRACTICAL ACTIVITY GROUP **11**

A potometer is a special piece of apparatus used to estimate transpiration rates. It actually measures water uptake by a plant, but it's assumed that water uptake by the plant is directly related to water loss by the leaves. You can use it to estimate how different factors affect the transpiration rate.

Using a potometer

The steps for using a potometer are listed below. As with all experiments you do, make sure you've carried out a risk assessment before you begin.

1. Cut a shoot underwater to prevent air from entering the xylem. Cut it at a slant to increase the surface area available for water uptake.

2. Assemble the potometer in water (see Figure 2) and insert the shoot under water, so no air can enter.

3. Remove the apparatus from the water but keep the end of the capillary tube submerged in a beaker of water.

4. Check that the apparatus is watertight and airtight.

5. Dry the leaves, allow time for the shoot to acclimatise and then shut the tap.

6. Remove the end of the capillary tube from the beaker of water until one air bubble has formed, then put the end of the tube back into the water.

7. Record the starting position of the air bubble.

8. Start a stopwatch and record the distance moved by the bubble per unit time, e.g. per hour. The rate of air bubble movement is an estimate of the transpiration rate.

9. Remember, only change one variable (e.g. temperature) at a time. All other conditions (e.g. light intensity, humidity) must be kept constant.

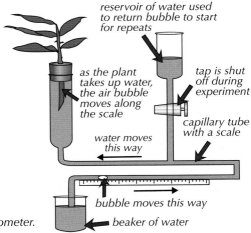

reservoir of water used to return bubble to start for repeats

as the plant takes up water, the air bubble moves along the scale

tap is shut off during experiment

capillary tube with a scale

water moves this way

bubble moves this way

beaker of water

Figure 2: A potometer.

> **Tip:** Transpiration rate isn't exactly the same as water uptake by a plant — some water is used for photosynthesis and to support the plant, and some water is produced during respiration.

> **Tip:** You can use a potometer to test the effect of different factors on transpiration rate, e.g. by using a fan to increase air movement or a lamp to increase light intensity etc. You could also investigate the role of stomata by preventing water from escaping from them (e.g. by coating the underside of the leaf with petroleum jelly).

> **Tip:** The air bubble is sometimes called the air-water meniscus.

> **Tip:** When estimating the rate of transpiration by measuring water uptake, you need to carry out repeats to improve the precision of your results and to help identify any anomalies in your data. (See pages 6 and 10 for more.)

Adaptations in xerophytic plants

Xerophytes are plants like cacti and marram grass (which grows on sand dunes). They're adapted to live in dry climates. Their adaptations prevent them losing too much water by transpiration.

┌─ **Example — Cacti** ─

- Cacti have a thick, waxy layer on the epidermis — this reduces water loss by evaporation because the layer is waterproof (water can't move through it).

- They have spines instead of leaves — this reduces the surface area for water loss.

- Cacti also close their stomata at the hottest times of the day when transpiration rates are the highest.

> **Tip:** The thick, waxy layer on the epidermis of a plant is called a cuticle.

Figure 3: Cacti spines.

Figure 4: Marram grass.

- Marram grass has stomata that are sunk in pits, so they're sheltered from the wind. This traps moist air in the pits and helps to slow transpiration down by lowering the water potential gradient.

- It also has a layer of 'hairs' on the epidermis — this also traps moist air round the stomata, which reduces the water potential gradient between the leaf and the air, slowing transpiration down.

- In hot or windy conditions marram grass plants roll their leaves — again this traps moist air, slowing down transpiration. It also reduces the exposed surface area for losing water and protects the stomata from wind.

- Like cacti, marram grass has a thick, waxy layer on the epidermis to reduce water loss by evaporation.

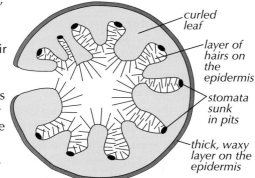

Figure 5: Cross-section through a marram grass leaf.

Adaptations in hydrophytic plants

Hydrophytes are plants like water lilies, which live in aquatic habitats. As they grow in water, they don't need adaptations to reduce water loss (like xerophytes), but they do need adaptations to help them cope with a low oxygen level. Here are some adaptations of hydrophytes...

Figure 6: Water lilies.

- Air spaces in the tissues help the plants to float and can act as a store of oxygen for use in respiration. For example, water lilies have large air spaces in their leaves (see Figure 8). This allows the leaves to float on the surface of the water, increasing the amount of light they receive. Air spaces in the roots and stems allow oxygen to move from the floating leaves down to parts of the plant that are underwater.

- Stomata are usually only present on the upper surface of floating leaves. This helps maximise gas exchange.

- Hydrophytes often have flexible leaves and stems — these plants are supported by the water around them, so they don't need rigid stems for support. Flexibility helps to prevent damage by water currents.

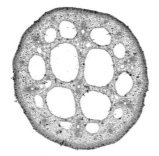

Figure 7: Light micrograph of a transverse cross-section through a water lily stem showing large air spaces (white circles).

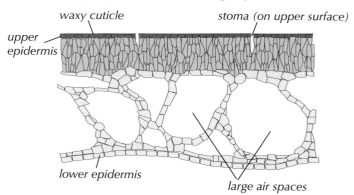

Figure 8: Transverse cross-section through a leaf from a water lily.

Practice Questions — Application

Q1 The photographs below show sections of leaves from two different plants.

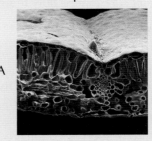 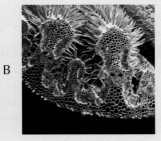

A   B

Which leaf belongs to a xerophyte? Explain your answer.

Q2 A potometer was used to test the effect of temperature on transpiration rate. The test was repeated 3 times. The results are shown in the table.

Temperature (°C)	Distance moved by the bubble in 10 minutes (mm)		
	Test 1	Test 2	Test 3
10	15	12	14
20	19	16	19
30	25	22	23

a) Calculate the mean result for each temperature. Give your answers to one decimal place.

b) Plot a graph of the mean results and use it to estimate the distance the bubble would move in ten minutes at 25 °C.

c) Describe and explain the results of the experiment.

Q3 The plant *Eichhornia crassipes* is causing problems in many parts of the world as, left uncontrolled, it can completely cover the surface of large bodies of water where it grows.

a) Suggest whether *Eichhornia crassipes* is a xerophyte or a hydrophyte. Give a reason for your answer.

b) With reference to the stems and leaves, suggest and explain how *Eichhornia crassipes* may be adapted to its habitat.

Exam Tip
If you're asked in the exam to give your answer to one decimal place, make sure you round it up or down correctly — otherwise you won't get the marks.

Practice Questions — Fact Recall

Q1 What process is transpiration a consequence of?

Q2 Explain how wind affects transpiration rate.

Q3 Other than wind, give three factors that affect transpiration rate.

Q4 When using a potometer to estimate transpiration rate, what assumption is made?

Q5 Describe and explain three adaptations that cacti have to reduce water loss.

Q6 Give an example of a hydrophyte.

- Understand the mechanism of translocation as an energy-requiring process transporting assimilates, especially sucrose, between sources (e.g. leaves) and sinks (e.g. roots and meristems).

- Know how assimilates are removed at the sink.

- Know the details of active loading at the source.

Specification Reference 3.1.3

Tip: Assimilates are substances that become incorporated into the plant tissue.

Exam Tip
Make sure you learn what the terms 'source' and 'sink' mean — you could be tested on them in the exam.

Tip: Sugars are transported as sucrose because sucrose is both soluble and metabolically inactive — so it doesn't get used up during transport.

Tip: The phloem transports solutes up and down a plant, from sources to sinks. (See pages 198-200 for more on the phloem.)

4. Translocation

The phloem transports dissolved substances (like sugars) around the plant to where they're needed. Scientists still aren't sure exactly how this movement works, but they do have a hypothesis...

What is translocation?

Translocation is the movement of dissolved substances (e.g. sugars like sucrose, and amino acids) to where they're needed in a plant. Dissolved substances are sometimes called **assimilates**. Translocation is an energy-requiring process that happens in the phloem.

Translocation moves substances from 'sources' to 'sinks'. The **source** of a substance is where it's made (so it's at a high concentration there). The **sink** is the area where it's used up (so it's at a lower concentration there).

┌ **Example** ────────────────────────────
The source for sucrose is usually the leaves (where it's made following photosynthesis), and the sinks are the other parts of the plant, e.g. food storage organs and meristems (areas of growth) in the roots, stems and leaves.

Some parts of a plant can be both a sink and a source.

┌ **Example** ────────────────────────────
Sucrose can be stored in the roots. During the growing season, sucrose is transported from the roots to the leaves to provide the leaves with energy for growth. In this case, the roots are the source and the leaves are a sink.

Enzymes maintain a concentration gradient from the source to the sink by changing the dissolved substances at the sink (e.g. by breaking them down or making them into something else). This makes sure there's always a lower concentration at the sink than at the source.

┌ **Examples** ────────────────────────────
In potatoes, sucrose is converted to starch in the sink areas, so there's always a lower concentration of sucrose at the sink than inside the phloem. This makes sure a constant supply of new sucrose reaches the sink from the phloem.

In other sinks, enzymes such as invertase break down sucrose into glucose (and fructose) for use by the plant — again this makes sure there's a lower concentration of sucrose at the sink.

The mass flow hypothesis

Scientists still aren't certain exactly how the dissolved substances (solutes) are transported from source to sink by translocation. The best supported theory is the mass flow hypothesis:

1. Source

Active transport is used to actively load the solutes (e.g. sucrose from photosynthesis) into the sieve tubes of the phloem at the source (e.g. the leaves). There's more on this on the next two pages. This lowers the water potential inside the sieve tubes, so water enters the tubes by osmosis from the xylem and companion cells. This creates a high pressure inside the sieve tubes at the source end of the phloem — see Figure 1 on the next page.

2. Sink

At the sink end, solutes are removed from the phloem to be used up. This usually happens by diffusion (a passive process) because the solutes are at a higher concentration in the phloem than they are in the surrounding tissue at the sink. The removal of solutes increases the water potential inside the sieve tubes, so water also leaves the tubes by osmosis. This lowers the pressure inside the sieve tubes — see Figure 1.

3. Flow

The result is a pressure gradient from the source end to the sink end. This gradient pushes solutes along the sieve tubes towards the sink. When they reach the sink the solutes will be used (e.g. in respiration) or stored (e.g. as starch).

The higher the concentration of sucrose at the source, the higher the rate of translocation.

Tip: There's more about sieve plates and companion cells on pages 199-200.

Tip: Once they've left the phloem cells, the solutes are transported to cells in the sink via the symplast or apoplast pathways (see pages 203-204).

Tip: Make sure you know the differences between transport in the xylem and phloem — transport in the phloem can take place in both directions, uses living cells and doesn't rely on cohesion or adhesion. Transport in the xylem happens in just one direction (from roots to leaves), in non-living cells and relies on cohesion and adhesion to move the column of water.

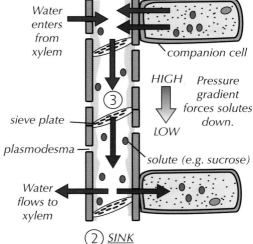

① SOURCE
low water potential, high pressure

Water enters from xylem

companion cell

HIGH   Pressure gradient forces solutes down.
LOW

sieve plate

plasmodesma

solute (e.g. sucrose)

Water flows to xylem

② SINK
high water potential, low pressure

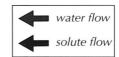

water flow

solute flow

Figure 1: How the mass flow hypothesis works.

Active loading

Active loading is used at the source to move substances into the companion cells from surrounding tissues, and from the companion cells into the sieve tubes, against a concentration gradient. The concentration of sucrose is usually higher in the companion cells than the surrounding tissue cells, and higher in the sieve tube cells than the companion cells (see Figure 2).

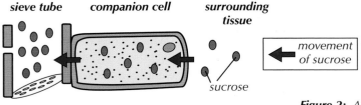

sieve tube   companion cell   surrounding tissue

movement of sucrose

sucrose

higher sucrose concentration

concentration gradient

lower sucrose concentration

Figure 2: Active loading of sucrose against its concentration gradient.

Tip: Active transport uses energy to move substances against their concentration gradient — see page 132.

Sucrose is moved to where it needs to go using active transport and co-transport proteins. Co-transport proteins are a type of carrier protein that bind two molecules at a time. The concentration gradient of one of the molecules is used to move the other molecule against its own concentration gradient. In active loading, H^+ ions are used to move sucrose against its concentration gradient. The steps and Figure 3 on the next page tell you how it works.

Tip: Carrier proteins are found in cell membranes — they're used to transport substances across the membrane (see page 131 for more).

1. In the companion cell, ATP is used to actively transport hydrogen ions (H⁺) out of the cell and into surrounding tissue cells (see Figure 3). This sets up a concentration gradient — there are more H⁺ ions in the surrounding tissue than in the companion cell.

2. An H⁺ ion binds to a co-transport protein in the companion cell membrane and re-enters the cell (down the concentration gradient). A sucrose molecule binds to the co-transport protein at the same time. The movement of the H⁺ ion is used to move the sucrose molecule into the cell, against its concentration gradient.

3. Sucrose molecules are then transported out of the companion cells and into the sieve tubes by the same process.

Tip: This diagram looks complicated but the process is really quite simple. Just remember an H⁺ ion is actively transported against its concentration gradient so it can be co-transported back again, this time down its concentration gradient and taking sucrose with it.

Tip: Companion cells contain many mitochondria, which means they can make lots of ATP for active loading.

Tip: Aphids are small insects that feed on the sap carried in the phloem of a plant.

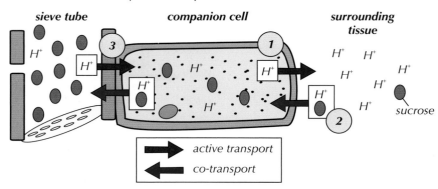

Figure 3: *Active transport and co-transport in the active loading of sucrose.*

ATP is one of the products of respiration. The breakdown of ATP supplies the initial energy needed for the active transport of the H⁺ ions.

Practice Questions — Application

Q1 An investigation into pressure in the phloem was carried out using aphids. The aphids were allowed to pierce the phloem of a plant, then their bodies were removed leaving the mouthparts behind, allowing the sap to run out. A higher pressure means that the sap flows out more quickly.

Would you expect sap to flow out more quickly when aphids were placed near the leaves or at the bottom of the stem? Explain your answer.

Q2 A scientist conducts an experiment in which a metabolic inhibitor (which stops ATP production) is introduced into a plant.

Explain how this would affect the active loading of sucrose into the phloem at the source and the process of translocation.

Practice Questions — Fact Recall

Q1 Define translocation.

Q2 What is the difference between a source and a sink in a plant?

Q3 Using the mass flow hypothesis:
   a) explain why water enters the sieve tubes in the roots,
   b) explain why water leaves the sieve tubes at the sink.

Q4 What is active loading?

Section Summary

Make sure you know...

- That plants are multicellular, have a small surface area to volume ratio and have a relatively high metabolic rate, so they need a transport system to move substances to and from individual cells — direct diffusion would be too slow to support their metabolic rate.

- That plants have two transport systems — the xylem (which transports water and mineral ions) and the phloem (which mainly transports sugars) and how they are distributed in the roots, stems and leaves of a plant.

- How xylem vessels are adapted for transporting water and mineral ions — they're made up of cells with no end walls (so water can easily pass up through the middle), the cells are dead (so they contain no cytoplasm), their walls are lignified (which helps to support the xylem walls and give flexibility) and they contain pits (which is how other types of cell are supplied with water).

- How sieve tube elements in phloem tissue are adapted for transporting solutes — they're joined end to end (to form sieve tubes), they have no nucleus, a thin layer of cytoplasm and few organelles, and they contain sieve plates with holes (which allow solutes to pass through from one cell to another).

- That companion cells in the phloem carry out the living functions for themselves and the sieve cells.

- How to examine and draw stained sections of plant tissue, showing the distribution of xylem and phloem.

- How to dissect stems, both longitudinally and transversely, and examine them to locate the position and structure of xylem vessels.

- That water is transported into, around and out of a plant by moving down a water potential gradient — from an area of high water potential in the soil surrounding the roots to an area of lower water potential in air surrounding the leaves.

- How water moves through a plant following the symplast pathway (via the cytoplasm of cells) and the apoplast pathway (via the cell walls).

- How water passes out of the leaves to the surrounding air — down a water potential gradient through the stomata.

- That the transpiration stream is the movement of water from roots to leaves and how cohesion and tension, and adhesion move water up the xylem.

- That transpiration is the evaporation of water from a plant's surface and occurs as a result of gas exchange — as stomata open to let carbon dioxide in, water is let out.

- How transpiration rate is affected by light, temperature, humidity and wind.

- How to use a potometer to estimate transpiration rates.

- How xerophytic plants (e.g. cacti and marram grass) are adapted to living in dry climates — cacti have a thick, waxy layer on the epidermis, spines instead of leaves and close their stomata at the hottest times of the day. Marram grass has stomata that are sunk in pits, a layer of hairs on the epidermis, can roll its leaves in hot or windy conditions and has a thick, waxy layer on the epidermis.

- How hydrophytes (e.g. water lilies) are adapted to live in aquatic habitats and cope with low oxygen levels — they have air spaces in their tissues, stomata on the upper surface of their leaves and flexible leaves and stems.

- That translocation is the movement of assimilates (e.g. sucrose) in a plant, from their source (where they're produced) to their sink (where they're used up).

- The mechanism of translocation — solutes are actively loaded into the sieve tubes at the source and diffuse out of the sieve tubes at the sink. This addition and removal of solutes affects the water potential inside the sieve tubes, which results in a pressure gradient from source to sink — this gradient pushes assimilates along the sieve tubes to where they're needed.

- How solutes are actively loaded from surrounding tissue cells into the phloem at the source — the process involves the active transport of H^+ ions and then the co-transport of H^+ ions and solutes.

1   **Fig 1.1** shows the passage of water through part of a plant's root. Which of the following statements about **Fig. 1.1** is correct?

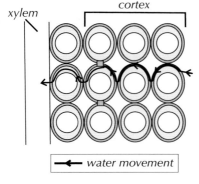

Fig. 1.1

A   ATP is required for the transport of water through the cells shown.

B   The water travels via the symplast pathway until it is stopped by the Casparian strip.

C   The rate of the water movement will decrease as it gets darker.

D   The cells shown have a lower water potential than cells in the leaves.

(1 mark)

2   **Fig. 2.1** and **Fig 2.2** show transverse cross-sections through two different plants. One is from *Potamogeton*, a plant found in ponds, and the other is from *Clematis*, a common garden plant.

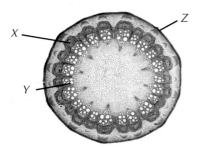
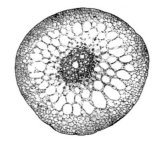

Fig. 2.1   **Fig. 2.2**

(a)   Which letter (X, Y or Z) on **Fig. 2.1** shows xylem tissue?

(1 mark)

(b)   From which region of the plant has the section shown in **Fig 2.1** been taken from? Give a reason for your answer.

(1 mark)

(c)   A longitudinal cross-section of the stem of a *Clematis* plant would reveal the presence of lignin. Explain the function of this substance in a plant stem.

(2 marks)

(d)   Which cross-section (**Fig 2.1** or **Fig 2.2**) shows the *Potamogeton*? Give a reason for your answer.

(1 mark)

(e)   Other than features that can be identified on the cross-section, suggest **one** way in which *Potamogeton* may be adapted to its environment.

(1 mark)

3 A student used a potometer to investigate the effect of light intensity on transpiration rate. Her results are shown in **Fig. 3.1**.

(a) (i) Using **Fig 3.1**, work out the rate of bubble movement for a light intensity of **1.5 arbitrary units**. Give your answer in mm min⁻¹.

(2 marks)

(ii) Using your knowledge of cohesion and tension, explain the results shown by the graph.

(4 marks)

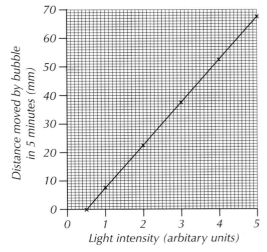

Fig. 3.1

(b) Suggest what negative control should be used for this investigation.

(1 mark)

(c) Explain how and why transpiration occurs.

(2 marks)

(d) The experiment was repeated in a more humid environment. Suggest how this would affect the results. Explain your answer.

(2 marks)

4 **Fig 4.1** shows a section of the phloem in a plant.

(a) (i) Name structure **A** and describe its function.

(2 marks)

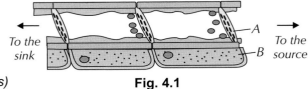

Fig. 4.1

(ii) Describe and explain the function of cell **B**.

(2 marks)

(b) Explain why lots of ATP is needed at the source end of the phloem.

(1 mark)

(c) Give **two** parts of plants that are common sinks.

(2 marks)

(d)* The mass flow hypothesis is the best supported theory to describe the mechanism of translocation.

Based on this mechanism, determine whether the pressure inside the phloem's sieve tubes would be greatest at the sink end or at the source end and explain the reason for the difference in pressure.

(6 marks)

*The quality of your response will be assessed in this question.

Learning Objectives:

- Know the different types of pathogen that can cause communicable diseases in plants and animals including:

  - bacteria: tuberculosis (TB), bacterial meningitis, ring rot,

  - viruses: HIV/AIDS, influenza, tobacco mosaic virus,

  - fungi: black sigatoka, ring worm, athlete's foot,

  - Protoctista: malaria, potato/tomato late blight.

- Understand the means of transmission of animal and plant communicable pathogens, including direct and indirect transmission, with reference to vectors, spores and living conditions (e.g. climate, social factors).

Specification Reference 4.1.1

Tip: You might have heard communicable diseases referred to as infectious diseases.

Exam Tip
Make sure you learn all the diseases on this page, what organisms they affect and the type of pathogen that causes each of them. You could get tested on them directly in the exam.

1. Pathogens and Communicable Diseases

There are many different types of pathogens that can cause diseases in plants or animals. Here are a few that you need to know about for your exams...

What is disease?

Disease is a condition that impairs the normal functioning of an organism. Both plants and animals can get diseases. A **pathogen** is an organism that causes disease. Types of pathogen include bacteria, viruses, fungi and protoctists (a type of single-celled eukaryotic organism).

Communicable diseases

A **communicable disease** is a disease that can spread between organisms. You need to learn all the communicable diseases in the table below, as well as the pathogens that cause them:

Disease:	Affects:	Pathogen Responsible:			
		Bacterium	Virus	Fungus	Protoctist
Tuberculosis (TB)	Animals, typically humans and cattle	✔			
Bacterial meningitis	Humans	✔			
Ring rot	Potatoes, tomatoes	✔			
HIV/AIDS	Humans		✔		
Influenza	Animals, including humans		✔		
Tobacco mosaic virus (TMV)	Plants		✔		
Black sigatoka	Banana plants			✔	
Ringworm	Cattle			✔	
Athlete's foot	Humans			✔	
Potato/tomato late blight	Potatoes/ tomatoes				✔
Malaria	Animals, including humans				✔

Transmission of disease

Communicable diseases can be spread from one organism to another by direct or indirect transmission.

Direct transmission

Direct transmission is when a disease is transmitted directly from one organism to another. Direct transmission can happen in several ways, including: droplet infection (coughing or sneezing tiny droplets of mucus or saliva directly onto someone), sexual intercourse, or touching an infected organism.

Examples
- HIV can be transmitted directly between humans via sexual intercourse. The virus can also be transmitted directly from a mother to her unborn child through the placenta.
- Athlete's foot can be spread via touch.

Figure 1: *Influenza can be directly transmitted by sneezing.*

Indirect transmission

Indirect transmission is when a disease is transmitted from one organism to another via an intermediate. Intermediates include air, water, food or another organism (known as a **vector**).

Examples
- Potato/tomato late blight is spread when spores are carried between plants — first in the air, then in water.
- Malaria is spread between humans (and other animals) via mosquitoes — insects that feed on blood. The mosquitoes act as vectors — they don't cause malaria themselves, they just spread the protoctists that cause it.

Tip: Spores are the cells that some organisms use to reproduce asexually, including some protoctists and all fungi.

Tip: A vector is an organism that spreads disease by carrying pathogens from one host to another.

Factors affecting transmission

Living conditions, social factors and climate affect the transmission of disease.

Living conditions

Overcrowded living conditions increase the transmission of many communicable diseases.

Example
Tuberculosis (TB) is spread directly via droplet infection (see above). It's also spread indirectly because the bacteria can remain in the air for long periods of time and infect new people. The risk of TB infection is increased when lots of people live crowded together in a small space.

Figure 2: *A mosquito feeding on human blood.*

Social factors

In humans, social factors (such as income, occupation and the area where a person lives) can also increase the transmission of communicable diseases.

Examples
The risk of HIV infection is high in places where there's limited access to:
- good healthcare — people are less likely to be diagnosed and treated for HIV, and the most effective anti-HIV drugs are less likely to be available, so the virus is more likely to be passed on to others.
- good health education — to inform people about how HIV is transmitted and how it can be avoided, e.g. through safe-sex practices like using condoms.

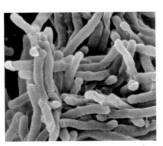

Figure 3: *An SEM of* Mycobacterium tuberculosis.

Figure 4: Tomatoes infected with late blight.

Climate

Climate can also affect the spread of communicable diseases.

Examples

- Potato/tomato late blight is especially common during wet summers because the spores need water to spread (see previous page).
- Malaria is most common in tropical countries, which are humid and hot. This is because these are the ideal conditions for mosquitoes (the malaria vectors) to breed.

Practice Questions — Application

Q1 Tobacco mosaic virus (TMV) is a virus that infects a wide range of plants, causing a characteristic mottled or mosaic effect on the leaves (see Figure 5). The virus enters plant cells through small wounds. It is present in the sap of infected plants, but can also contaminate seed coats (the protective coating on the seed).

    a) Suggest one way that TMV could be transmitted directly between plants.

    b) Suggest one way that TMV could be transmitted indirectly between plants.

Q2 Ringworm produces spores that can spread between cattle either directly or indirectly.

    a) Why might ringworm spread faster between cattle housed indoors rather than in a field?

    b) A farmer uses the same brush to groom all of his prize-winning cattle, which could transfer spores between cows. Is this an example of direct or indirect transmission?

    c) Ringworm can be transmitted to humans via direct contact. Suggest one way of minimising the risk of transmission from an infected cow to the farmer.

Q3 Tuberculosis (TB) usually affects the lungs. It's spread via droplet infection and through the air in poorly ventilated spaces. The disease can be treated with antibiotics but treatment takes several months and patients do not always finish the course.

Suggest two ways to prevent the spread of TB from a person with symptoms of TB infection to uninfected members of the public.

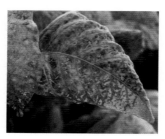

Figure 5: Leaf of a tobacco plant showing damage caused by the tobacco mosaic virus.

Practice Questions — Fact Recall

Q1 What is a pathogen?

Q2 What is a communicable disease?

Q3 What type of plant can be affected by black sigatoka?

Q4 What type of pathogen causes athlete's foot?

Q5 Give an example of a disease caused by a protoctist.

Q6 Give one way a disease can be transmitted directly.

Q7 What is a vector?

Q8 Why is transmission of HIV more likely in countries where there is limited access to good health care?

Q9 Why is malaria more common in countries with a hot, humid climate?

2. Defence Against Pathogens

Both animals and plants have several methods of protecting themselves against infection.

Barriers to infection

Pathogens need to enter an organism in order to cause disease. Animals and plants have evolved defences to protect themselves from pathogens gaining entry.

Animal defences

Most animals, including humans, have a range of primary, non-specific defences against pathogens. These include:

The skin

This acts as a physical barrier, blocking pathogens from entering the body. It also acts as a chemical barrier by producing chemicals that are antimicrobial (which destroy or slow the growth of microorganisms) and can lower pH, inhibiting the growth of pathogens.

> ### Examples
> - Skin cells secrete fatty acids, such as oleic acid, that can kill some bacteria. Fatty acids also lower the pH of the skin, creating an acidic environment that is difficult for pathogens to colonise.
> - Skin cells also secrete lysozyme, an enzyme which catalyses the breakdown of carbohydrates in the cell walls of some bacteria.

Mucous membranes

These protect body openings that are exposed to the environment (such as the mouth, nostrils, ears, genitals and anus). Some membranes secrete mucus — a sticky substance that traps pathogens and contains antimicrobial enzymes.

> ### Example — The gas-exchange system
> If you breathe in air that contains pathogens, most of them will be trapped in mucus lining the lung epithelium (the outer layer of cells in the passages to the lungs). These cells also have cilia (hair-like structures) that beat and move the mucus up the trachea to the throat and mouth, where it's removed — see Figure 2. There's loads more about this on page 163.
>
>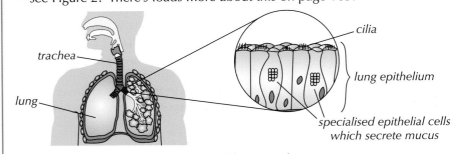
>
> *Figure 2: A diagram of the gas-exchange system.*

Blood clotting

A blood clot is a mesh of protein (fibrin) fibres. Blood clots plug wounds to prevent pathogen entry and blood loss. They're formed by a series of chemical reactions that take place when platelets (fragments of cells in the blood) are exposed to damaged blood vessels.

Learning Objectives:
- Recall the primary non-specific defences against pathogens in animals, including the skin, mucous membranes, blood clotting, inflammation, wound repair and expulsive reflexes.
- Recall plant defences against pathogens, including production of chemicals and plant responses that limit the spread of the pathogen (e.g. callose deposition).

Specification Reference 4.1.1

Tip: Non-specific means they work in the same way for all pathogens. There's more on non-specific and specific responses on page 222.

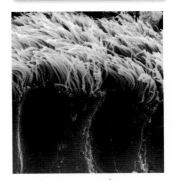

Figure 1: An electron micrograph of lung epithelium cells. The cilia are shown in blue.

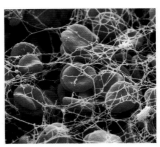

Figure 3: An electron micrograph of a blood clot.

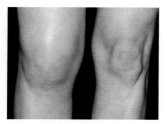

Figure 4: Swelling of the knee (on the left) due to a sports injury.

Figure 5: Woman coughing.

Figure 6: Waxy surface of a cabbage leaf.

Tip: Plasmodesmata connect the cytoplasm of neighbouring cells, so they can easily transfer substances between them (see page 203).

Inflammation

The signs of inflammation include swelling, pain, heat and redness. It can be triggered by tissue damage — the damaged tissue releases molecules which increase the permeability of the blood vessels, so they start to leak fluid into the surrounding area. This causes swelling and helps to isolate any pathogens that may have entered the damaged tissue. The molecules also cause vasodilation (widening of the blood vessels), which increases blood flow to the affected area. This makes the area hot and brings white blood cells to the area to fight off any pathogens that may be present.

Wound repair

The skin is able to repair itself in the event of injury and re-form a barrier against pathogen entry. The surface is repaired by the outer layer of skin cells dividing and migrating to the edges of the wound. The tissue below the wound then contracts to bring the edges of the wound closer together. It is repaired using collagen fibres — too many collagen fibres and you'll end up with a scar.

Expulsive reflexes

Expulsive reflexes include coughing and sneezing. A sneeze happens when the mucous membranes in the nostrils are irritated by things such as dust or dirt. A cough stems from irritation in the respiratory tract. Both coughing and sneezing are an attempt to expel foreign objects, including pathogens, from the body. They happen automatically.

If pathogens make it past these defences, they'll have the animal's immune system to deal with — see pages 222-224.

Plant defences

Like animals, plants have defences against infection by pathogens. These include:

Physical plant defences

Most plant leaves and stems have a waxy cuticle, which provides a physical barrier against pathogen entry. It may also stop water collecting on the leaf, which could reduce the risk of infection by pathogens that are transferred between plants in water.

Plant cells themselves are surrounded by cell walls. These form a physical barrier against pathogens that make it past the waxy cuticle.

Plants also produce a polysaccharide called callose. Callose gets deposited between plant cell walls and plasma membranes during times of stress, e.g. pathogen invasion. Callose deposition may make it harder for pathogens to enter cells. Callose deposition at the plasmodesmata (small channels in the cell walls) may limit the spread of viruses between cells — see Figure 7.

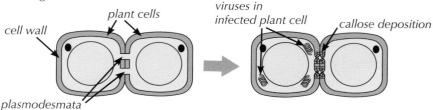

Figure 7: Callose deposition between two plant cells.

Chemical plant defences

Plants don't just rely on physical defences. They also produce antimicrobial chemicals (including antibiotics, see page 234) which kill pathogens or inhibit their growth.

Figure 8: Quinoa seeds coated in saponins (white).

┌─ **Examples** ─────────────────────────

- Some plants produce chemicals called saponins. These are thought to destroy the cell membranes of fungi and other pathogens.

- Plants also produce chemicals called phytoalexins, which inhibit the growth of fungi and other pathogens.

└

Other chemicals secreted by plants are toxic to insects — this reduces the amount of insect-feeding on plants and therefore reduces the risk of infection by plant viruses carried by insect vectors.

Practice Questions — Application

Q1 Tuberculosis is caused by the bacterium *Mycobacterium tuberculosis*, which can be spread through the air. Describe the non-specific defence that would be encountered by *M. tuberculosis* if it entered the lungs of a healthy person.

Q2 Patients with severe burns are susceptible to infection from usually harmless bacteria. Explain why this is the case.

Q3 Aphids are small insects that feed by sucking sap from a plant. Suggest why a plant that has an aphid infestation may be more susceptible to infection.

Practice Questions — Fact Recall

Q1 Describe how the skin acts as a chemical barrier against pathogens.

Q2 What is a blood clot?

Q3 What is the purpose of inflammation in the area surrounding damaged tissue?

Q4 Give an example of an expulsive reflex.

Q5 Name two physical defences that a plant cell has against pathogens.

Q6 a) Why might callose deposition occur in a plant cell?

b) State two places where callose deposition can occur.

Q7 What is the purpose of phytoalexins produced by plants?

3. The Immune System

The body's primary defences keep most pathogens away... but if any sneak through, the immune system is there to keep us safe.

Learning Objectives:

- Recall the structure and mode of action of phagocytes, including neutrophils and antigen-presenting cells and the roles of cytokines, opsonins, phagosomes and lysosomes.
- Be able to give an outline of the action of opsonins.
- Recall the structure, different roles and modes of action of T lymphocytes in the specific immune response, including clonal selection and clonal expansion, T helper cells, T killer cells and T regulatory cells.
- Recall the structure, different roles and modes of action of B lymphocytes in the specific immune response, including plasma cells.
- Understand the significance of cell signalling (reference to interleukins).
- Be able to examine and draw cells observed in blood smears.

Specification Reference 4.1.1

The immune response

If a pathogen gets past the primary defences and enters the body, the immune system will respond. An immune response is the body's reaction to a foreign **antigen**. Antigens are molecules (usually proteins or polysaccharides) found on the surface of cells. When a pathogen (like a bacterium) invades the body, the antigens on its cell surface are identified as foreign, which activates cells in the immune system.

The immune response involves specific and non-specific stages. The **non-specific response** happens in the same way for all microorganisms — whatever foreign antigens they have. The **specific response** is antigen-specific — it is aimed at specific pathogens. It involves white blood cells called T and B lymphocytes.

The main stages of the immune response

1. Phagocytosis

A **phagocyte** is a type of white blood cell that carries out phagocytosis (engulfment of pathogens). They're found in the blood and in tissues and carry out a non-specific immune response. Here's how they work:

- A phagocyte recognises the antigens on a pathogen.
- The cytoplasm of the phagocyte moves round the pathogen, engulfing it. This may be made easier by the presence of **opsonins** — molecules in the blood that attach to foreign antigens to aid phagocytosis.
- The pathogen is now contained in a **phagosome** (a type of vesicle, see page 33) in the cytoplasm of the phagocyte.
- A **lysosome** (an organelle that contains digestive enzymes) fuses with the phagosome. The enzymes break down the pathogen.
- The phagocyte then presents the pathogen's antigens. It sticks the antigens on its surface to activate other immune system cells. When a phagocyte does this it is acting as an **antigen-presenting cell** (APC).

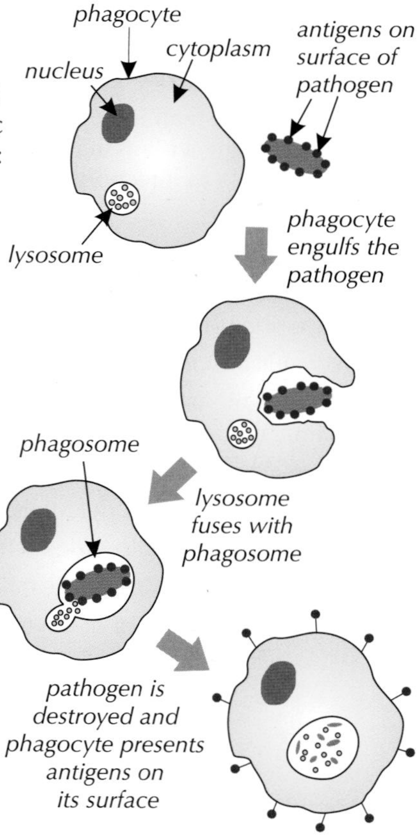

***Figure 1:** The process of phagocytosis and antigen presentation.*

Tip: Opsonins work in different ways. Some hide the negative charges on the membrane of the pathogen, making it easier for the negatively-charged phagocyte to get closer to the pathogen.

Neutrophils are a type of phagocyte. They're the first white blood cells to respond to a pathogen inside the body. Neutrophils move towards a wound in response to signals from **cytokines** (proteins that act as messenger molecules — see page 122). The cytokines are released by cells at the site of the wound.

2. T lymphocyte activation

A T lymphocyte is another type of white blood cell. Its surface is covered with receptors. The receptors bind to antigens presented by APCs (see Figure 3).

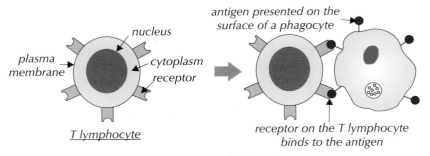

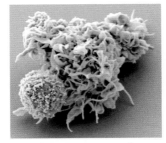

Figure 2: A SEM of a T lymphocyte (yellow) binding to a phagocytic cell (blue).

Figure 3: Activation of a T lymphocyte.

Each T lymphocyte has a different receptor on its surface. When the receptor on the surface of a T lymphocyte meets a complementary antigen, it binds to it — so each T lymphocyte will bind to a different antigen. This process activates the T lymphocyte and is known as **clonal selection**. The activated T lymphocyte then undergoes **clonal expansion** — it divides to produce clones of itself.

Tip: A complementary antigen means its shape fits into the shape of the receptor.

Different types of activated T lymphocytes carry out different functions:

- **T helper cells** release substances to activate B lymphocytes (see below) and T killer cells.

- **T killer cells** attach to and kill cells that are infected with a virus.

- **T regulatory cells** suppress the immune response from other white blood cells. This helps to stop immune system cells from mistakenly attacking the host's body cells.

Some activated T lymphocytes become **memory cells** (see page 228).

3. B lymphocyte activation and plasma cell production

B lymphocytes are also a type of white blood cell (see Figure 4). They're covered with **antibodies** — proteins that bind antigens to form an **antigen-antibody complex**.

Each B lymphocyte has a different shaped antibody on its membrane, so different ones bind to different shaped antigens (see Figure 5).

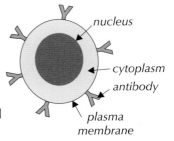

Figure 4: A B lymphocyte.

Tip: T lymphocytes and B lymphocytes are sometimes just called T cells and B cells.

Antibody A will bind to antigen A, as they have complementary shapes.

Antibody A will not bind to antigen B, as they don't have complementary shapes.

Figure 5: Complementary binding between antibodies and antigens.

Exam Tip
Never say that antigens and antibodies have the 'same shape' or a 'matching shape' — you need to use the phrase 'complementary shape'.

When the antibody on the surface of a B lymphocyte meets a complementary antigen, it binds to it — so each B lymphocyte will bind to a different antigen. This, together with substances released from helper T cells, activates the B lymphocyte. This process is another example of clonal selection. The activated B lymphocyte then divides, by mitosis, into plasma cells (see below) and memory cells (see p. 228). This is another example of clonal expansion.

4. Antibody production

Plasma cells are clones of the B lymphocyte (they're identical to the B lymphocyte). They secrete loads of the antibody, specific to the antigen, into the blood. These antibodies will bind to the antigens on the surface of the pathogen to form lots of antigen-antibody complexes. This is the signal for the immune system to attack and destroy the pathogen. There's lots more on the structure of antibodies and how they help to clear an infection in the next topic (pages 226-227).

Tip: The B lymphocyte divides by mitosis, so that all the cells produced are genetically identical. This means that they all produce identical antibodies specific to the pathogen.

Cell signalling and the immune response

Cell signalling is basically how cells communicate. A cell may release (or present) a substance that binds to the receptors on another cell — this causes a response of some kind in the other cell.

Tip: See page 122 for more on cell signalling.

Cell signalling is really important in the immune response because it helps to activate all the different types of white blood cells that are needed.

┌─ **Example** ───────────────────────────────────────

T helper cells release interleukins (a type of cytokine) that bind to receptors on B lymphocytes. This activates the B lymphocytes — the T helper cells are signalling to the B lymphocytes that there's a pathogen in the body.

Blood smears

Tip: See page 44 for more on staining microscope images.

As the name suggests, a blood smear is a sample of blood smeared over a microscope slide. Stains are added to the sample to make the different cells easy to see. You need to be able to examine and draw cells observed in a blood smear — see Figure 6. When looking at a blood smear you're likely to see red blood cells, white blood cells and platelets (tiny fragments of cells involved in blood clotting). Some types of white blood cell have granules in their cytoplasm (so they look grainy) and other types don't.

┌─ **Example** ───────────────────────────────────────

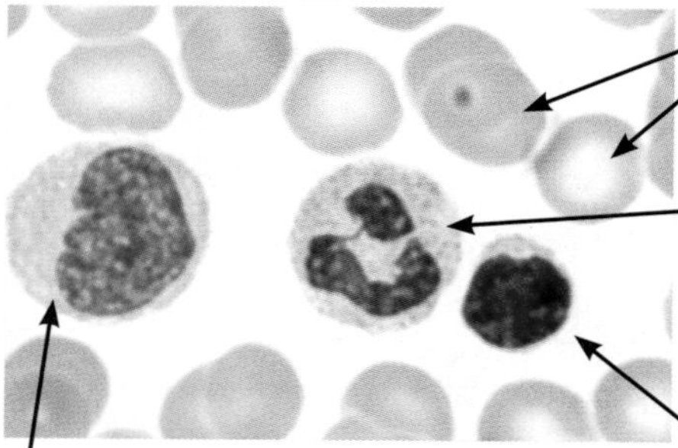

Most of the cells are red blood cells (see page 149). They're easy to spot because they don't have a nucleus.

This is a neutrophil. Its nucleus looks like three interconnected blobs — the posh way of saying this is that the nucleus is 'multi-lobed'. The cytoplasm of a neutrophil is grainy.

This is a lymphocyte. It's much smaller than the neutrophil. The nucleus takes up most of the cell and there's very little cytoplasm to be seen (it's not grainy either). You can't tell whether this is a T lymphocyte or a B lymphocyte under a light microscope.

This is a monocyte. It's the biggest white blood cell and a type of phagocyte. It has a kidney-bean shaped nucleus and a non-grainy cytoplasm.

Figure 6: *Light micrograph of a blood smear and how to interpret it.*

Q1 Look at the blood smear below.

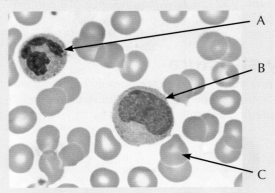

a) Name the cells A, B and C.

b) What is the role of cell A in a non-specific immune response?

Q2 AIDS is an immune system disorder caused by the human immunodeficiency virus. The virus infects and destroys T lymphocytes, so the number that work properly gradually falls. AIDS patients often suffer from opportunistic infections — infections that wouldn't normally cause too much of a problem in a healthy person. Common ones are tuberculosis, pneumonia and an infection of the brain called toxoplasmosis. Explain why AIDS patients suffer from opportunistic infections.

Q3 Rheumatic fever is a disease where the immune system attacks cells in the heart. It's often triggered by an infection with the bacterium *Streptococcus pyogenes*. Antigens on the surface of *S. pyogenes* have a very similar shape to antigens on the surface of heart cells. Suggest why *S. pyogenes* infection can lead to rheumatic fever.

Tip: Antigens aren't just found on pathogens — your body cells have antigens on them too.

Practice Questions — Fact Recall

Q1 What is an immune response?

Q2 What are antigens?

Q3 Define phagocytosis.

Q4 What is a phagosome?

Q5 What is the role of a lysosome during phagocytosis?

Q6 What proteins signal for neutrophils to move towards a wound?

Q7 Describe how a phagocyte that has captured a pathogen activates T lymphocytes.

Q8 What are the functions of T lymphocytes and plasma cells?

Q9 Draw a flow diagram showing the four main stages of the immune response.

Q10 Give an example of cell signalling being used during an immune response.

Learning Objectives:

- Recall the structure and general functions of antibodies.
- Be able to give an outline of the actions of agglutinins and anti-toxins.

Specification Reference 4.1.1

4. Antibodies

In the previous topic you saw how the presence of a pathogen in the body led to the production of antibodies by B lymphocytes. Now it's time to see how the production of antibodies leads to the destruction of the pathogen.

Antibody structure

Antibodies are proteins — they're made up of chains of amino acid monomers linked by peptide bonds (see pages 61-65 for more on proteins). You need to learn the structure of antibodies (see Figure 1).

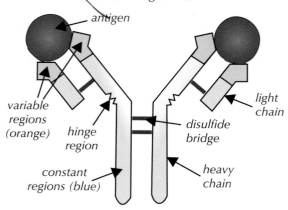

Figure 1: Antibody structure.

***Figure 2:** A molecular model of an antibody.*

Tip: Antibodies need variable regions so that they can recognise and bind to different antigens. If all antibodies recognised the same pathogen they wouldn't be very useful.

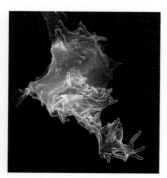

***Figure 3:** A phagocyte (yellow) engulfing a clump of bacteria that has been agglutinated by antibodies.*

The **variable regions** of the antibody form the antigen-binding sites. The shape of the variable region is complementary to a particular antigen. The variable regions differ between antibodies. The **hinge region** allows flexibility when the antibody binds to the antigen. The **constant regions** allow binding to receptors on immune system cells, e.g. phagocytes. The constant region is the same (i.e. it has the same sequence of amino acids) in all antibodies. Disulfide bridges (a type of bond) hold the polypeptide chains of the protein together.

The role of antibodies in clearing infections

Antibodies help to clear an infection in three main ways:

1. Agglutinating pathogens

Each antibody has two binding sites, so an antibody can bind to two pathogens at the same time — the pathogens become clumped together. Phagocytes then bind to the antibodies and phagocytose a lot of pathogens all at once (see Figure 4). Antibodies that behave in this way are known as **agglutinins**.

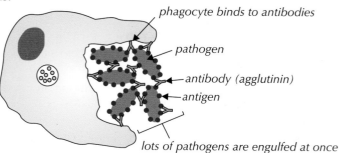

Figure 4: Agglutination of pathogens by antibodies.

2. Neutralising toxins

Like antigens, toxins have different shapes. Antibodies called **anti-toxins** can bind to the **toxins** produced by pathogens. This prevents the toxins from affecting human cells, so the toxins are neutralised (inactivated). The toxin-antibody complexes are also phagocytosed (see Figure 5).

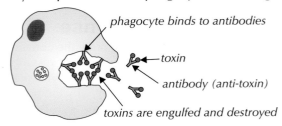

Figure 5: Neutralisation of toxins by antibodies.

3. Preventing the pathogen binding to human cells

When antibodies bind to the antigens on pathogens, they may block the cell-surface receptors that the pathogens need to bind to the host cells. This means the pathogen can't attach to or infect the host cells (see Figure 6).

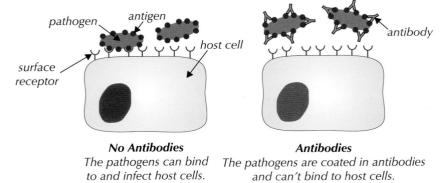

No Antibodies
The pathogens can bind to and infect host cells.

Antibodies
The pathogens are coated in antibodies and can't bind to host cells.

Figure 6: Antibodies preventing pathogens from binding to human cells.

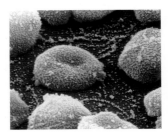

Figure 7: Flu virus particles (blue) attached to red blood cells (red). If these flu virus particles were bound by antibodies they would not be able to bind to the surface of the red blood cells.

Practice Question — Application

Q1 If someone is bitten by a poisonous snake or spider, they will be given antivenom. Antivenom contains anti-toxins against the toxins in the poison. Using your knowledge of antibodies, explain how antivenom works.

Practice Questions — Fact Recall

Q1 Give the functions of the following regions of an antibody:
   a) The variable region.
   b) The hinge region.
   c) The constant region.

Q2 How many binding sites do antibodies have, and why is it useful for them to have this number?

Q3 Give three ways in which antibodies can help defend the body against pathogens.

Learning Objective:

- Understand the primary and secondary immune responses, including the roles of T memory cells and B memory cells.

Specification Reference 4.1.1

5. Primary and Secondary Immune Responses

There's more than one type of immune response...

The primary immune response

When a pathogen enters the body for the first time, the antigens on its surface activate the immune system. This is called the primary response. The primary response is slow because there aren't many B lymphocytes that can make the antibody needed to bind to the pathogen. Eventually the body will produce enough of the right antibody to overcome the infection. Meanwhile the infected person will show symptoms of the disease.

After being exposed to an antigen, both T and B lymphocytes produce **memory cells**. These memory cells remain in the body for a long time. Memory T lymphocytes remember the specific antigen and will recognise it a second time around. Memory B lymphocytes record the specific antibodies needed to bind to the antigen. The person is now **immune** — their immune system has the ability to respond quickly to a second infection.

Tip: Being immune doesn't mean you'll never be infected by that pathogen again — it just means that if it gets into your body a second time your immune system quickly kills it before you get ill.

The secondary immune response

If the same pathogen enters the body again, the immune system will produce a quicker, stronger immune response — the secondary response (see Figure 1). Clonal selection happens faster. Memory B lymphocytes divide into plasma cells that produce the right antibody to the antigen. Memory T lymphocytes are activated and divide into the correct type of T lymphocytes to kill the cell carrying the antigen. The secondary response often gets rid of the pathogen before you begin to show any symptoms.

Tip: The secondary response only happens if it's the <u>same pathogen</u>. If it's a different pathogen you just get another primary response.

Tip: The secondary response is always faster than the primary response. This is shown by a steeper line in graphs of blood antibody concentration against time.

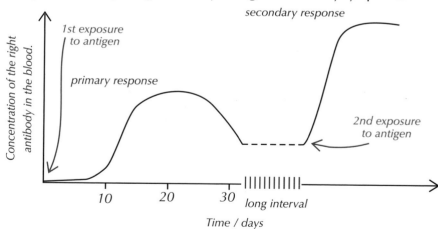

Figure 1: *A graph of antibody concentration against time since antigen exposure.*

Maintaining immunity

Memory B and T lymphocytes only have a limited lifespan. This means that someone who is immune to a particular pathogen won't always stay immune forever — once all of the memory B and T lymphocytes have died, that person may be susceptible to attack by the pathogen again. Immunity can be maintained by being continually exposed to the pathogen, so you continue to make more and more memory B and T lymphocytes.

Tip: This is why some vaccines require booster shots later on (e.g. after several years) — to maintain the numbers of memory T and B cells. See pages 230-232 for more on vaccines.

Example

People who live in malarial areas and who are constantly exposed to the malaria pathogen will build up a limited immunity to malaria. But if they move away from the malarial area, they'll have no further exposure to the pathogen and eventually they may lose the immunity they have. If they then returned to a malarial area, they would undergo a primary immune response when they encountered the malaria pathogen again.

Comparing the two responses

In the exam you might be asked to compare and contrast the primary and secondary immune response — basically say how they're similar and say how they're different. This is summarised in the table below:

	Primary response	Secondary response
Pathogen	Enters for 1st time	Enters for 2nd time
Speed of response	Slow	Fast
Cells activated	B and T lymphocytes	Memory cells
Symptoms	Yes	No

Exam Tip:
If you're asked to compare and contrast the primary and secondary responses in the exam, make sure you talk about similarities as well as differences. The similarities are, e.g. both are triggered by invasion of the body by a pathogen, both ultimately get rid of the pathogen and both involve the production of antibodies.

Practice Questions — Application

The graph below shows the immune responses of two mice exposed to a pathogen. Both mice were exposed on day 0 of the experiment.

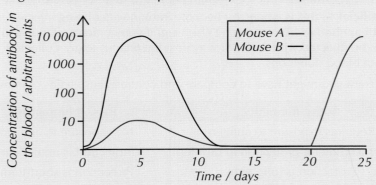

Q1 How much antibody did each mouse have in its blood on day 5?

Q2 Which mouse was already immune to the pathogen? Explain your answer.

Q3 a) On which day was Mouse A exposed to the pathogen again?

    b) Describe what happened to Mouse A's immune system after it was exposed again.

Tip: Don't get the primary response mixed up with primary defences (see pages 219-220).

Practice Questions — Fact Recall

Q1 Why is the primary immune response slower than a secondary immune response?

Q2 Why does immunity not always last forever?

Q3 Give three differences (other than the speed) between a primary and a secondary immune response.

After you've been infected once by a pathogen you'll be immune to it, but being infected in the first place can be pretty unpleasant. Vaccination can make you immune without the being ill part.

Active and passive immunity

Immunity can be active or passive:

Active immunity

This is the type of immunity you get when your immune system makes its own antibodies after being stimulated by an antigen. There are two different types of active immunity:

1. **Natural** — this is when you become immune after catching a disease. E.g. if you have measles as a child, you shouldn't be able to catch it again in later life.

2. **Artificial** — this is when you become immune after you've been given a vaccination containing a harmless dose of antigen (see next page).

Passive immunity

This is the type of immunity you get from being given antibodies made by a different organism — your immune system doesn't produce any antibodies of its own. Again, there are two types:

1. **Natural** — this is when a baby becomes immune due to the antibodies it receives from its mother, through the placenta and in breast milk.

2. **Artificial** — this is when you become immune after being injected with antibodies from someone else. E.g. if you contract tetanus you can be injected with antibodies against the tetanus toxin, collected from blood donations.

In the exam you might have to compare and contrast these types of immunity:

Active Immunity	Passive Immunity
Requires exposure to antigen	No exposure to antigen
It takes a while for protection to develop	Protection is immediate
Protection is long-term	Protection is short-term
Memory cells are produced	Memory cells aren't produced

Autoimmune diseases

Sometimes, an organism's immune system isn't able to recognise self-antigens — antigens present on the organism's own cells. When this happens, the immune system treats the self-antigens as foreign antigens and launches an immune response against the organism's own tissues. A disease resulting from this abnormal immune response is known as an **autoimmune disease**.

┌ **Example — Lupus**

Lupus is caused by the immune system attacking cells in the connective tissues. This damages the tissues and causes painful inflammation (see page 220). Lupus can affect the skin and joints, as well as organs such as the heart and lungs.

Learning Objectives:

- Understand the differences between active and passive immunity, and between natural and artificial immunity, and recall examples of each type of immunity.

- Understand autoimmune diseases, including an appreciation of the term 'autoimmune disease' and a named example, e.g. arthritis, lupus.

- Understand the principles of vaccination and the role of vaccination programmes in the prevention of epidemics, including routine vaccinations and reasons for changes to vaccines and vaccination programmes (including global issues).

Specification Reference 4.1.1

Tip: Don't get active and passive immunity mixed up. Just remember that in <u>active</u> immunity your body is <u>actively</u> doing something — it's producing antibodies.

Tip: T regulatory cells (p. 223) usually protect against autoimmune disease by suppressing any immune response to self-antigens.

⌐ Example — Rheumatoid arthritis ─────────────────

Rheumatoid arthritis is caused by the immune system attacking cells in the joints. Again, this causes pain and inflammation.

Autoimmune diseases are usually chronic (long-term). They can often be treated, but not cured.

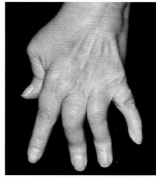

Figure 1: Inflamed joints in the hand caused by rheumatoid arthritis.

Vaccination

While your B lymphocytes are busy dividing to build up their numbers to deal with a pathogen (i.e. the primary response — see page 228), you suffer from the disease. Vaccination can help avoid this.

Vaccines contain antigens that cause your body to produce memory cells against a particular pathogen, without the pathogen causing disease. This means you become immune without getting any symptoms. These antigens may be free or attached to a dead or attenuated (weakened) pathogen.

Vaccines may be injected or taken orally. The disadvantages of taking a vaccine orally are that it could be broken down by enzymes in the gut or the molecules of the vaccine may be too large to be absorbed into the blood. Sometimes booster vaccines are given later on (e.g. after several years) to make sure that more memory cells are produced.

If most people in a community are vaccinated, the disease becomes extremely rare. This means that even people who haven't been vaccinated are unlikely to get the disease, because there's no one to catch it from. This is called **herd immunity** — see Figure 3. It helps to prevent epidemics — mass outbreaks of disease.

> **Tip:** Attenuated viruses have usually been genetically or chemically modified so that they can't produce toxins or attach to and infect host cells.

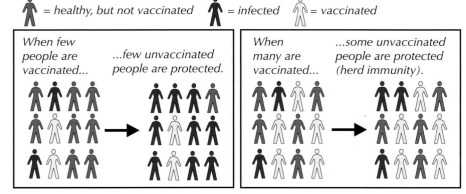

= healthy, but not vaccinated   = infected   = vaccinated

When few people are vaccinated... ...few unvaccinated people are protected.

When many are vaccinated... ...some unvaccinated people are protected (herd immunity).

Figure 3: Herd immunity

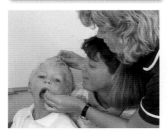

Figure 2: A boy being given an oral vaccination for polio.

> **Tip:** Herd immunity means not everyone needs to be vaccinated. As long as enough people get the vaccine, the pathogen won't be able to spread and even non-vaccinated people will be protected.

Vaccination is not the same as immunisation. Vaccination is the administration of antigens (in a vaccine) into the body. Immunisation is the process by which you develop immunity. Vaccination causes immunisation.

Routine vaccines

Routine vaccines are offered to everybody. They include:

- **the MMR** — protects against measles, mumps and rubella. The MMR is usually given to children as an injection at around a year old, and again before they start school. It contains attenuated measles, mumps and rubella viruses.

- **the meningitis C vaccine** — protects against the bacteria that cause meningitis C. It is first given as an injection to babies at 3 months. Boosters are then given to 1-year-olds and teenagers.

Changing vaccines and vaccination programmes

Vaccinating against a disease isn't always straightforward. For example, some sneaky pathogens can change their surface antigens. This means that when you're infected, the memory cells produced following a vaccination will not recognise the different antigens. So the immune system has to start from scratch and carry out a primary response against these new antigens. For this reason, a vaccine and vaccination programme may have to change regularly.

Exam Tip
You need to learn this example for the exam.

Tip: Pathogens of the same type that have different surface antigens are often referred to as <u>strains</u>.

Example — The influenza virus

The influenza (flu) vaccine changes every year. That's because the antigens on the surface of the influenza virus change regularly, forming new strains of the virus. Memory cells produced from vaccination with one strain of the flu will not recognise other strains with different antigens. The strains are immunologically distinct.

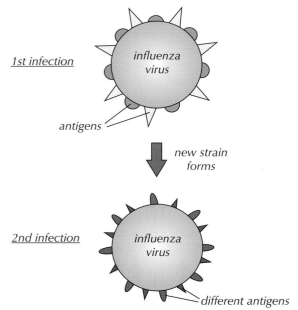

1st infection

influenza virus

antigens

new strain forms

2nd infection

influenza virus

different antigens

Figure 4: *Changing antigens in the influenza virus.*

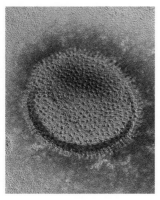

Figure 5: *A TEM of an influenza virus.*

Every year there are different strains of the influenza virus circulating in the population, so a different vaccine has to be made. Laboratories collect samples of these different strains, and organisations, such as the WHO (World Health Organisation) and CDC (Centre for Disease Control), test the effectiveness of different influenza vaccines against them.

New vaccines are developed and one is chosen every year that is the most effective against the recently circulating influenza viruses. Governments and health authorities then implement a programme of vaccination using this most suitable vaccine. This is a good example of how society uses science to inform decision making.

Sometimes people are given a vaccine that protects them from a strain causing an epidemic in another country — this helps stop the strain from spreading globally.

HOW SCIENCE WORKS

Q1 Which of the following is an example of artificial active immunity?

   A Becoming immune to chickenpox after receiving antibodies through the placenta.

   B Becoming immune to meningitis C after receiving a vaccine.

   C Becoming immune to swine flu after catching the disease.

   D Becoming immune to diphtheria after receiving an injection of antibodies against the diphtheria toxin.

Q2 Whooping cough is an infection of the respiratory system.
The graph below shows the number of cases of whooping cough in Scotland between 1960 and 1999, and the vaccine uptake from the 1970s to 1999.

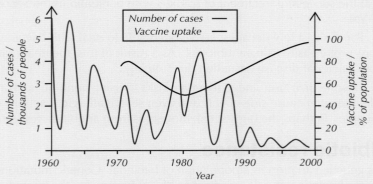

   a) What percentage of the population were vaccinated in 1990?

   b) How many cases of whooping cough were there in 1965?

   c) The whooping cough vaccine was introduced in Scotland in the 1950s. Describe and explain the overall trend in the number of cases of whooping cough from 1960 to 1975.

Exam Tip
Always pay attention to the units on the axes — on the graph on the left, the y-axis is number of cases in thousands of people, so in 1963 there weren't 6 cases — there were 6000.

Tip: When reading off graphs with multiple scales, double-check you've got the right one. If you're struggling to read off the answer, draw lines on the graph to help you.

Practice Questions — Fact Recall

Q1 Define the terms active and passive immunity.

Q2 a) What is an autoimmune disease?

   b) What causes this type of disease?

Q3 What causes the symptoms of lupus?

Q4 Other than lupus, give another example of an autoimmune disease.

Q5 How do vaccines give people immunity?

Q6 What is herd immunity?

Q7 Explain why a new vaccine against flu has to be developed every year.

7. Antibiotics and Other Medicines

Medical intervention, such as antibiotics, can be used to support the body's natural defences against pathogens.

Antibiotics

Antibiotics are chemicals that kill or inhibit the growth of bacteria. They're used by humans as drugs to treat bacterial infections. They're useful because they can usually target bacterial cells without damaging human body cells. Penicillin was the first antibiotic to be isolated (by Alexander Fleming, in 1928). Antibiotic use became widespread from the mid-twentieth century — partly thanks to the successful treatment of soldiers with penicillin in the Second World War.

For the past few decades, we've been able to deal with bacterial infections pretty easily using antibiotics. As a result of this, the death rate from infectious bacterial disease has fallen dramatically.

Despite their usefulness, there are risks to using antibiotics. For example, they can cause side effects and even severe allergic reactions in some people. Perhaps the biggest risk though, is from antibiotic resistance...

Antibiotic resistance

There is genetic variation in a population of bacteria. Genetic mutations make some bacteria naturally resistant to an antibiotic. For the bacterium, this ability to resist an antibiotic is a big advantage. It's better able to survive in a host who's being treated with antibiotics to get rid of the infection, and so it lives for longer and reproduces many more times. This leads to the **allele** for antibiotic resistance being passed on to lots of offspring. It's an example of natural selection — see Figure 1. This is how antibiotic resistance spreads and becomes more common in a population of bacteria over time.

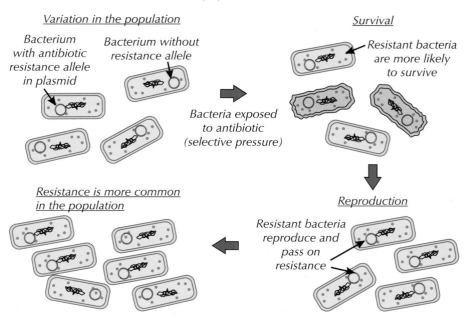

Figure 1: *Evolution of antibiotic resistance by natural selection.*

Problems with antibiotic resistance

Antibiotic resistance is a problem for people who become infected with these bacteria, because you can't easily get rid of them with antibiotics. Increased use of antibiotics means that antibiotic resistance is increasing. 'Superbugs' that are resistant to most known antibiotics are becoming more common. This means we are less able to treat some potentially life-threatening bacterial infections. You need to know about these antibiotic-resistant bacteria:

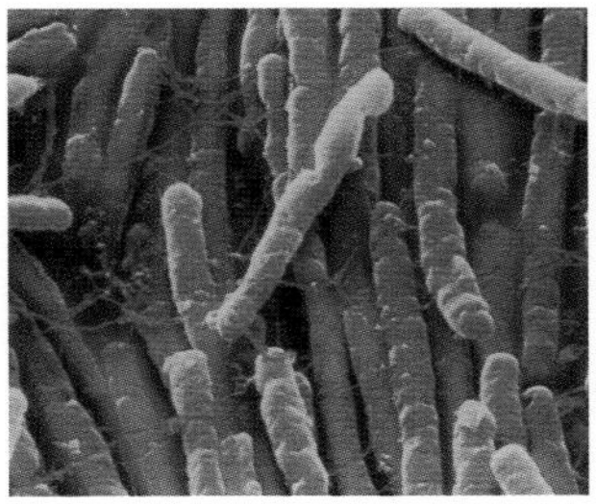

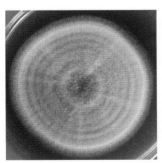

Figure 2: SEM of Clostridium difficile bacteria (rod-shaped cells).

Examples

- **MRSA** (meticillin-resistant *Staphylococcus aureus*) causes serious wound infections and is resistant to several antibiotics, including meticillin (which used to be called methicillin).

- ***Clostridium difficile*** infects the digestive system, usually causing problems in people who have already been treated with antibiotics. It is thought that the harmless bacteria that are normally present in the digestive system are killed by the antibiotics, which *C. difficile* is resistant to. This allows *C. difficile* to flourish. *C. difficile* produces a toxin, which causes severe diarrhoea, fever and cramps.

Preventing antibiotic resistance

Developing new antibiotics and modifying existing ones are two ways of overcoming the current problem of antibiotic resistance. This isn't easy though.

Tip: MRSA and *Clostridium difficile* infections are most common in hospitals, where many antibiotics are used and patients who are already ill have weakened immune systems.

To reduce the likelihood of antibiotic resistance developing in the first place, doctors are being encouraged to reduce their use of antibiotics, e.g. not to prescribe them for minor infections and not to prescribe them to prevent infections (except in patients with already weak immune systems, e.g. the elderly or people with HIV). Patients are advised to take all of the antibiotics they're prescribed to make sure the infection is fully cleared and all the bacteria have been killed (which reduces the likelihood of a population of antibiotic-resistant bacteria developing).

Sources of medicines

Scientists need to be constantly developing new drugs to target resistant strains of pathogens, as well as developing drugs for diseases that are currently incurable.

Many medicinal drugs are manufactured using natural compounds found in plants, animals or microorganisms.

Examples

- Penicillin is obtained from a fungus.
- Some cancer drugs are made using soil bacteria.
- Daffodils are grown to produce a drug used to treat Alzheimer's disease.

Only a small proportion of organisms have been investigated so far, so it's possible that plants or microorganisms exist that contain compounds that could be used to treat currently incurable diseases, such as AIDS. Others may produce new antibiotics.

Possible sources of drugs need to be protected by maintaining the **biodiversity** (the variety of different species) on Earth. If we don't protect them, some species could die out before we get a chance to study them. Even organisms that have already been studied could still prove to be useful sources of medicines as new techniques are developed for identifying, purifying and testing compounds.

Figure 3: A colony of Penicillium chrysogenum fungus growing on an agar plate. This fungus produces penicillin.

Future of medicine

The future of medicine looks very high-tech...

Personalised medicine

Your genes determine how your body responds to certain drugs. Different people respond to the same drug in different ways — which makes certain drugs more effective for some people than others. This is where personalised medicines come in.

Personalised medicines are medicines that are tailored to an individual's DNA. The theory is that if doctors have your genetic information, they can use it to predict how you will respond to different drugs and only prescribe the ones that will be most effective for you. Scientists hope that by studying the relationship between someone's genetic make-up and their responsiveness to drugs, more effective drugs can be produced in the future.

Synthetic biology

Synthetic biology involves using technology to design and make things like artificial proteins, cells and even microorganisms. It has applications in lots of different areas, including medicine.

> **Example**
>
> Scientists are looking at engineering bacteria to destroy cancer cells, while leaving healthy body cells intact.

Practice Questions — Application

Q1 When, approximately, did antibiotic use become widespread?

   A Mid-19th century

   B Late-19th century

   C Early-20th century

   D Mid-20th century

Q2 Transplant patients are more at risk of infection. Why might rising antibiotic resistance lead to high death rates in transplant patients?

Q3 In 2000, a strain of *Clostridium difficile* emerged that is resistant to fluoroquinolones, a widely used group of antibiotics.

   a) Outline how this strain of *C. difficile* may have evolved by natural selection.

   b) *C. difficile* infections are most common in hospitalised patients. Suggest why the bacteria are able to establish an infection in this case.

   c) Outline two strategies that are designed to reduce the likelihood of antibiotic resistance developing in populations of bacteria.

Tip: Drugs taken to prevent rejection of a transplanted organ can also make patients more at risk of infection by suppressing immune responses.

Practice Questions — Fact Recall

Q1 What are antibiotics?

Q2 What was the first antibiotic to be discovered?

Q3 Give an example of an antibiotic-resistant bacterium, other than *C. difficile*.

Q4 What type of microorganism is penicillin derived from?

Q5 What are personalised medicines?

Q6 What is synthetic biology?

Section Summary

Make sure you know...

- That a pathogen is an organism that can cause disease.
- That a communicable disease is a disease that can be spread between organisms.
- About the following communicable diseases (including the organisms they are caused by and affect):
  - Tuberculosis, bacterial meningitis and ring rot are caused by bacteria.
  - HIV/AIDS, influenza and tobacco mosaic virus are caused by viruses.
  - Black sigatoka, ring worm and athlete's foot are caused by fungi.
  - Malaria and potato/tomato late blight are caused by protoctists.
- How communicable diseases can be transferred between organisms by direct transmission (directly from one organism to another) or indirect transmission (from one organism to another via an intermediate, such as spores or a vector).
- How transmission of pathogens can be affected by living conditions, climate and social factors.
- The primary non-specific defences against pathogens in animals, including the skin, mucous membranes, blood clotting, inflammation, wound repair and expulsive reflexes.
- The primary non-specific defences against pathogens in plants, including waxy cuticles, cell walls and callose deposition (physical barriers) and the production of chemicals (against pathogens and vectors).
- The structure of phagocytes and the process of phagocytosis (engulfment of pathogens).
- The roles of opsonins, phagosomes, lysosomes, antigen-presenting cells (APCs), neutrophils and cytokines in phagocytosis.
- The structure of T lymphocytes, how they are activated (clonal selection) and divide to produce clones (clonal expansion), and the roles of different types — T helper cells, T killer cells and T regulatory cells in an immune response.
- The structure of B lymphocytes, and how they are activated and divide to produce plasma cells and memory cells.
- That cells communicate by signalling using substances such as interleukins.
- How to examine and draw cells observed in blood smears.
- The structure of antibodies (proteins that bind to antigens), including constant and variable regions.
- How antibodies clear infections by agglutinating pathogens, neutralising toxins and preventing pathogens from binding to cells.
- What the primary immune response and secondary immune response are and how they work, including the role of memory cells in secondary immune responses.
- The similarities and differences between active, passive, natural and artificial immunity, including examples of each type of immunity.
- What an 'autoimmune disease' is and a named example of one (e.g. lupus or rheumatoid arthritis).
- How vaccines make people immune to disease by stimulating memory cell production.
- The role of vaccines in preventing epidemics, by creating herd immunity.
- What routine vaccinations are and why vaccines or vaccination programmes may change.
- The benefits (reducing death rates from bacterial disease) and risks (side effects, allergic reactions and increasing antibiotic resistance) of using antibiotics to manage bacterial infection.
- That widespread use of antibiotics began in the mid-20th century, following the discovery of penicillin.
- How bacteria develop antibiotic resistance by natural selection, including *Clostridium difficile* and MRSA as examples of antibiotic-resistant bacteria.
- Possible sources for medicines, including microorganisms and plants.
- Why it's important, in terms of drug development, to maintain biodiversity.
- What personalised medicine and synthetic biology are, and their potential in the future.

Exam-style Questions

1   Which of the communicable diseases below is caused by a fungus?

     A   malaria

     B   tomato late blight

     C   ring rot

     D   ringworm

(1 mark)

2   Tuberculosis (TB) is an infectious disease. More than one million people worldwide die from tuberculosis every year.

  (a)   Identify the type of pathogen that causes TB.

(1 mark)

  (b)   **Fig. 1.1** shows the number of reported cases of TB in the UK between 2000 and 2009.

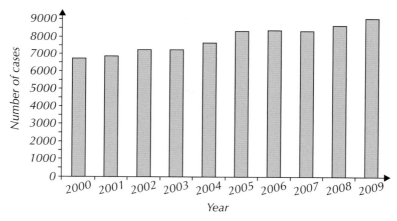

Fig. 1.1

  (i)   Describe the trend in the number of reported TB cases in the UK between 2000 and 2009.

(1 mark)

  (ii)   Calculate the approximate percentage increase in the number of cases of reported TB in the UK between 2003 and 2009. Show your working.

(2 marks)

  (iii) A newspaper headline states that "The number of TB cases in England is predicted to rise by 33% by the year 2018". Discuss this claim using the information in the graph.

(3 marks)

3 In 1918 there was a worldwide outbreak of influenza called 'Spanish flu'. The virus responsible was the **H1N1** strain — it had type 1 haemagglutinin (H1) and type 1 neuraminidase (N1) antigens on its surface.

(a) When someone is infected with Spanish flu their immune system responds. The first stage of this response involves the phagocytosis of virus particles.

(i)* Describe the sequence of steps in phagocytosis.

(6 marks)

(ii) What is the role of opsonins in phagocytosis?

(1 mark)

(iii) Outline the main stages of the immune response after phagocytosis.

(5 marks)

(b) Spanish flu circulated the globe for over a year. Explain why survivors of the Spanish flu did not contract it when exposed for a second time.

(2 marks)

(c) In 1957 there was another outbreak of influenza called 'Asian flu'. It was caused by the **H2N2** strain of influenza. Explain why survivors of the Spanish flu may have contracted Asian flu.

(3 marks)

(d) Every year new flu vaccines are developed. These contain antigens to multiple strains of influenza. Suggest why this is the case.

(1 mark)

4 Diphtheria is an infectious disease caused by a pathogenic species of bacteria. Cases of diphtheria are now very rare since the introduction of a vaccination in the early 1940s.

(a) (i) Explain how having a vaccination leads to the formation of memory B lymphocytes.

(3 marks)

(ii) Explain why individuals who don't have a particular vaccine will still gain some protection from the introduction of the vaccine.

(3 marks)

(b) Memory B lymphocytes differentiate into plasma cells which produce antibodies.

(i) Name the **three** main regions of an antibody and give the function of each region.

(3 marks)

(ii) Tick the boxes to show which **three** of the following are functions of antibodies.

Agglutinating pathogens		Activating memory T lymphocytes	
Killing pathogens directly		Mutating pathogen DNA	
Neutralising toxins		Stopping pathogens binding to cells	

(3 marks)

*The quality of your response will be assessed in this question.

1. Investigating Biodiversity

Biodiversity is an important indicator of a habitat's health — the higher the biodiversity of the habitat, the healthier that habitat is. You can work out a habitat's biodiversity using a bit of data and a nifty little equation...

Biodiversity

The term 'biodiversity' refers to the variety of living organisms in an area. It can be considered at three different levels:

1. Habitat diversity

A habitat is the area inhabited by a species. It includes the physical factors, like the soil and temperature range, and the living (biotic) factors, like availability of food or the presence of predators. Habitat diversity is the number of different habitats in an area.

> **Examples**
> - A coastal area could contain many different habitats — beaches, sand dunes, mudflats, salt marshes, etc.
> - A river valley could contain meadows, agricultural fields, streams, woodland, etc.

2. Species diversity

A species is a group of similar organisms able to reproduce to give fertile offspring. Species diversity is the number of different species (species richness) and the abundance of each species (species evenness) in an area.

> **Example**
> A woodland could contain many different species of plants, insects, birds and mammals.

3. Genetic diversity

Genetic diversity is the variation of alleles (versions of a gene) within a species or a population of a species.

> **Examples**
> - Human blood type is determined by a gene with three different alleles.
> - The variation in alleles within the dog species gives rise to different breeds, such as a Labrador or poodle.

Collecting data on biodiversity

Collecting data on biodiversity usually means finding out the number of different species in a habitat or the number of individuals in each species. In most cases though, it'd be too time-consuming to count every individual organism in a habitat. Instead, a **sample** of the population is taken. Estimates about the whole habitat are based on the sample.

Learning Objectives:

- Understand how biodiversity may be considered at different levels, including habitat biodiversity (e.g. sand dunes, woodland, meadows, streams), species biodiversity (species richness and species evenness) and genetic biodiversity (e.g. different breeds within a species).

- Know how sampling is used in measuring the biodiversity of a habitat and the importance of sampling the range of organisms in a habitat.

- Be able to carry out practical investigations collecting random and non-random samples in the field (PAG3).

- Know how sampling can be carried out, including random and non-random sampling (e.g. opportunistic, stratified and systematic).

- Know how to measure species richness and species evenness in a habitat.

- Be able to use and interpret Simpson's Index of Diversity (D) to calculate the biodiversity of a habitat, using the formula:
  $$D = 1 - (\Sigma(n/N)^2)$$
  and know the significance of both high and low values of D.

  Specification Reference 4.2.1

Random sampling

PRACTICAL ACTIVITY GROUP **3**

To make sure the sample isn't biased, it should be random.
For example, if you were looking at plant species in a field you could pick random sample sites by dividing the field into a grid using measuring tapes and use a random number generator to select coordinates — see Figure 1. Doing this makes sure that each sample site has the same **probability** of being chosen.

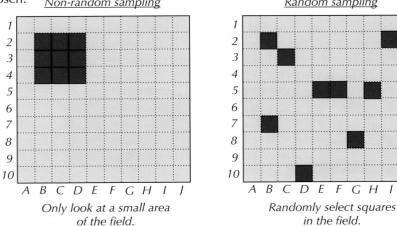

Non-random sampling

Only look at a small area of the field.

Random sampling

Randomly select squares in the field.

Figure 1: *Diagram to show non-random sampling by picking a small area (left) and random sampling using a random number generator (right).*

To ensure any variation observed in the sample isn't just due to chance, it's important to analyse the results statistically. This allows you to be more confident that the results are true and therefore will reflect what's going on in the whole population.

Non-random sampling

PRACTICAL ACTIVITY GROUP **3**

Sometimes it's necessary to take a non-random sample. For example, when there's a lot of variety in the distribution of species in the habitat and you want to make sure that all the different areas are sampled or that all the different species are sampled. There are three types of non-random sampling:

1. Systematic sampling

This is when samples are taken at fixed intervals, often along a line.

> **Example**
>
> If you were looking at plant species in a field, quadrats (square frames that you place on the ground) could be placed along a line (called a **transect**) from an area of shade in the corner to the middle of the field — see Figure 2. Each quadrat would then be a sample site.

2. Opportunistic sampling

This is when samples are chosen by the investigator. It's used because it is simple to carry out, but the data will be biased.

3. Stratified sampling

This is when different areas in a habitat are identified and sampled separately in proportion to their part of the habitat as a whole.

> **Example**
>
> A heathland may have patches of gorse in it — the heath and gorse areas would be sampled separately according to how much of each there was in the habitat.

Tip: A sample is biased if it doesn't represent the population as a whole. For example, if you were looking at the average height of students in a school but only measured the heights of people from one particular class, the sample would be biased.

Tip: The chance of something happening is the possibility it will occur. Probability is a measure of how likely events are to happen.

Tip: A random number generator will give you coordinates at random, e.g. C3, E5, etc. Then you just take your samples from these coordinates.

Tip: You can also make sure your samples are random by taking samples at different times of the day and in different weather conditions.

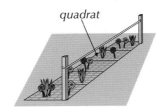

quadrat

Figure 2: *Quadrats placed along a transect line. This type of transect is called a belt transect.*

Estimating biodiversity using samples:

PRACTICAL ACTIVITY GROUP **3**

1. Choose a site to sample, e.g. a small area within the habitat being studied. You could choose this site randomly or non-randomly (see previous page).

2. Record the number of different species or count the number of individuals of each species. How you do this depends on what you're counting.

Examples

For plants you'd use a quadrat. You can then count the number of plant species and the number of individuals of each species in the quadrat.

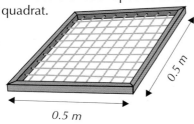

0.5 m

0.5 m

For ground insects you'd use a pitfall trap (a small pit that insects can't get out of).

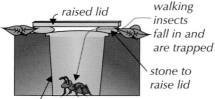

raised lid

walking insects fall in and are trapped

stone to raise lid

flowerpot or similar container

For flying insects you'd use a sweepnet (a net on a pole).

For aquatic animals you'd use a net.

Make sure you use the appropriate equipment for the organisms you're studying. E.g. a sweepnet won't help you catch millipedes because millipedes can't fly. If you're sampling mobile organisms you should make sure they can't escape before you count them and that you don't count individuals more than once.

3. Repeat the process — take as many samples as possible. This gives a better indication of the whole habitat. All your samples should be chosen in the same way as your first sample — so if you started with a random sample, all your other samples should be random too.

4. The number individuals for the whole habitat can then be estimated by calculating the mean for the data collected in each sample and multiplying it by the size of the whole habitat.

5. When sampling different habitats and comparing them, always use the same sampling technique. E.g. if you're using a series of pitfall traps you should make sure they're set up in the same way and left for the same length of time.

There are lots of different practical investigations you could do using this method.

Example

You could investigate the impact of mowing on the biodiversity of your school playing field by sampling a mowed and an un-mowed field. Calculate the biodiversity for each field using Simpson's Index (see next page).

Tip: You'll need to do a risk assessment before you carry out an investigation into biodiversity. The risks of working outdoors are quite different to ones you'd face in the lab and they'll vary depending on the environment you're working in.

Figure 3: *Pitfall traps like this one can be used to catch ground-dwelling insects.*

Tip: When you collect data on biodiversity you can damage the environment (e.g. by trampling plants) and disturb animals. It's a good idea to find ways of minimising this when you plan your investigation. It's also worth having a think about any ethical issues your investigation might raise, e.g. whether catching animals will cause them distress.

Tip: Carrying out repeats and calculating a mean will make your estimate more precise. See page 6 for more.

Species richness and species evenness

Species richness is the number of different species in an area. The higher the number of species, the greater the species richness. It's measured by taking random samples of a habitat and counting the number of different species (see previous two pages).

Species evenness is a measure of the relative abundance of each species in an area. The more similar the population size of each species, the greater the species evenness. It's measured by taking random samples of a habitat, and counting the number of individuals of each different species.

The greater the species richness and evenness in an area, the higher the biodiversity. The lower the species richness and evenness, the lower the biodiversity.

Exam Tip
If you're asked to define species richness in the exam, you need to say it's the <u>number</u> of species in an area — if you talk about variety or amount you won't get the mark.

Example

Habitat X and habitat Y both contain two different species and 30 individual organisms.

	Habitat X	Habitat Y
No. organisms in species 1	28	15
No. organisms in species 2	2	15
Total	30	30

There are two species in each habitat so the species richness in the two habitats is the same — 2. However, in habitat Y the individual organisms are more evenly distributed between the different species — there are 15 organisms of each species, compared to 28 organisms in species 1 and just 2 organisms in species 2 in habitat X. Habitat Y has greater species evenness. This suggests that habitat Y has a higher biodiversity.

Tip: A low species evenness means that one or two species dominate a habitat — other species are only present in low numbers or are not present at all.

Tip: Abundance is the number of individuals. Distribution means where the individuals are found.

Simpson's Index of Diversity

Species richness and species evenness are simple ways of measuring diversity. But species that are present in a habitat in very small numbers shouldn't be treated the same as those with bigger populations. This is where Simpson's Index of Diversity comes in.

Simpson's Index of Diversity (*D*) is a useful way of measuring species diversity. It's calculated using an equation that takes into account both species richness and species evenness. You calculate Simpson's Index of Diversity using the following formula:

$$D = 1 - \left(\sum \left(\frac{n}{N} \right)^2 \right)$$

Where...
n = Total number of organisms in one species
N = Total number of all organisms
Σ = 'Sum of' (i.e. added together)

Simpson's Index of Diversity is always a value between 0 and 1. The closer the index is to one, the more diverse the habitat and the greater its ability to cope with change (e.g. the appearance of a new predator). Low index values suggest the habitat is more easily damaged by change, making it less stable.

Tip: Change has a big effect on habitats with a low index of diversity because there aren't many species present. If one of only a few species gets wiped out, e.g. by a new predator, it makes a much bigger difference to a habitat than if one of many species gets wiped out.

The greater the species richness and evenness, the higher the value of Simpson's Index.

Example — Maths Skills

There are 3 different species of flower in this field — a red species, a white and a blue. There are 3 of the red species, 5 of the white and 3 of the blue.

There are 11 organisms altogether, so $N = 11$.

So the index of diversity for this field is:

$$D = 1 - \left(\left(\frac{3}{11} \right)^2 + \left(\frac{5}{11} \right)^2 + \left(\frac{3}{11} \right)^2 \right)$$

$$= 1 - (0.07 + 0.21 + 0.07)$$

$$= 1 - 0.35 = \textbf{0.65}$$

The field has an index of diversity of 0.65, which is fairly high.

Calculating the Index of Diversity can get quite tricky. If you've got a lot of data you might find it easier to plug the numbers into a table — that way you can make sure you don't miss out any steps.

Example — Maths Skills

A student investigates the diversity of fish species in her local pond. She finds 46 fish of 6 different species. To help her calculate Simpson's Index of Diversity for the pond she draws the following table.

Species	n (total number of organisms in species)	$\frac{n}{N}$	$\left(\frac{n}{N} \right)^2$
A	1	1 / 46	0.000473
B	6	6 / 46	0.0170
C	2	2 / 46	0.00189
D	15	15 / 46	0.106
E	3	3 / 46	0.00425
F	19	19 / 46	0.171
N (total number of all organisms) = 46			$\sum \left(\frac{n}{N} \right)^2 = 0.301$

She then uses the numbers from the table to calculate the Index:

$$D = 1 - 0.301 = \textbf{0.699}$$

Practice Questions — Application

Q1 An environmental officer is investigating the population of fish in a lake using a net. She sweeps the net through the water to catch fish.

Suggest two ways in which the environmental officer could standardise the method she uses to collect her data to ensure her results are repeatable.

Q2 The table below shows the number of individuals of each species of insect found in two ponds.

Species	Number of individuals found in Pond A	Number of individuals found in Pond B
Damselfly	3	13
Dragonfly	5	5
Stonefly	2	7
Water boatman	3	2
Crane fly	1	18
Pond skater	4	9

a) Which pond has the greatest species evenness?
   Explain your answer.

b) Use the data provided in the table and the formula given below to calculate the Index of Diversity to 3 significant figures for:

   i) Pond A,
   ii) Pond B.

$$D = 1 - (\Sigma(n/N)^2)$$
where N = total number of all organisms
and n = total number of organisms in one species.

c) Would the two ponds be likely to cope with the introduction of a new species of predator? Explain your answer.

Practice Questions — Fact Recall

Q1 Define the following terms:
   a) biodiversity,
   b) habitat,
   c) species.

Q2 Name and describe three levels at which biodiversity can be considered.

Q3 Sampling can be random or non-random.
   a) Explain why it is important to take random samples when collecting data on biodiversity.
   b) Give an example of when you might choose to take a non-random sample instead of a random sample.
   c) Give three examples of non-random sampling methods.

Q4 Define the following terms:
   a) species richness,
   b) species evenness.

Q5 Name two things needed to calculate Simpson's Index of Diversity.

Q6 What does a high Simpson's Index of Diversity value indicate?

Learning Objectives:

- Understand how genetic biodiversity may be assessed, including calculations of genetic diversity within isolated populations, such as zoos (captive breeding), rare breeds and pedigree animals.

- Be able to calculate the percentage of gene variants (alleles) in a genome, using the formula: proportion of polymorphic gene loci = number of polymorphic gene loci ÷ total number of loci.

Specification Reference 4.2.1

Tip: A <u>pedigree animal</u> is one that has been bred purely from animals of the same breed. A <u>rare breed</u> is usually a breed of farm animal that's not used in large-scale farming.

Tip: The individuals in an isolated population can only breed with each other. This increases the risk of inbreeding, which is why genetic diversity tends to be low in isolated populations.

Tip: Loci is the plural of locus. Polymorphic gene loci are those points on a chromosome that can have more than one allele.

2. Genetic Diversity

Genetic diversity is a measure of the biodiversity within a species. Measuring genetic diversity is important in helping us to understand the survivability of different species. Greater genetic diversity is linked to a greater ability to adapt and survive.

Importance of genetic diversity

You know from page 240 that genetic diversity is the variation of alleles within a species (or within a population of a species). You can do calculations to work out the genetic diversity of a population. This is important because if a population has low genetic diversity, they might not be able to adapt to a change in the environment and the whole population could be wiped out by a single event (e.g. a disease).

Populations in which genetic diversity may be low include isolated populations, such as those bred in captivity (e.g. in zoos), populations of pedigree animals and rare breeds. Calculations can be used to monitor the genetic diversity of these populations over time and efforts can be made to increase the genetic diversity of the population if needed.

> **Example**
>
> Breeding programmes in zoos are very closely managed to maximise genetic diversity. Databases are kept up to date with the details of each animal on the breeding programme. It is then decided which animals should be paired for breeding and these animals are transferred between the zoos that hold them. This helps to reduce inbreeding (breeding between closely related individuals) which reduces genetic diversity.

What is polymorphism?

You know that alleles are different versions of a gene. Alleles of the same gene are always found at the same point (called a **locus**) on a chromosome. Polymorphism describes a locus that has two or more alleles (see Figure 1).

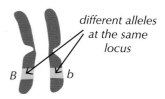

different alleles at the same locus

B   b

Figure 1: *Diagram to show polymorphism at a gene locus.*

Assessing genetic diversity

Genetic polymorphism is used to measure genetic diversity. Working out the proportion of **polymorphic gene loci** in a population gives you a measure of genetic diversity. There's a nifty formula you can use:

$$\text{proportion of polymorphic gene loci} = \frac{\text{number of polymorphic gene loci}}{\text{total number of loci}}$$

Exam Tip
Read the question carefully to check whether you're being asked for the <u>proportion</u> or the <u>percentage</u>. If you're asked for the percentage, first work out the proportion and then multiply your answer by 100.

Practice Questions — Application

Q1 The genetic diversity of a population of gorillas in a zoo is monitored. Of the 80 genes sampled, 12 were found to be polymorphic.

a) Calculate the proportion of polymorphic gene loci.

b) Suggest one way the zoo could increase the genetic diversity of its gorilla population.

c) Explain why the zoo might want to increase the genetic diversity of the population.

Q2 Two species of frog are studied to determine their genetic diversity. In species A, 66 of the genes sampled are polymorphic out of 90 genes sampled in total. In species B, 42 of the genes sampled are polymorphic out of the 90 genes sampled in total.

a) Calculate the percentage of genes that have alleles in species A.

b) Calculate the percentage of genes that have alleles in species B.

c) Suggest which of these species is more likely to be able to adapt to a change in the environment. Explain your answer.

Figure 2: *Gorilla thinking about how to increase his species' genetic diversity.*

Practice Questions — Fact Recall

Q1 What is a polymorphic gene locus?

Q2 Describe how you can assess the genetic diversity of a population.

Q3 Give the formula you can use to work out the proportion of polymorphic gene loci.

Figure 1: *View of deforested land in the Ecuadorian rainforest.*

Tip: The factors described on this page and the next two can all affect biodiversity at a local or a global level.

3. Factors Affecting Biodiversity

Remember, biodiversity can be considered at the level of habitat diversity, species diversity or genetic diversity (see page 240). Many of the things humans do affect biodiversity...

Human population growth

The human population of the planet has grown hugely in the last couple of centuries and is continuing to rise. This is decreasing biodiversity because of the following factors:

1. Habitat loss

As the human population grows, we need to develop more land for housing and to produce food. This development is destroying habitats.

> **Example**
>
> There is deforestation in the Amazon to make way for grazing and agriculture. This decreases habitat diversity. With fewer habitats for organisms to live in, species diversity also decreases.

2. Over-exploitation

A greater demand for resources (such as food, water and energy) means a lot of resources are being used up faster than they can be replenished. This can destroy habitats or it can affect species directly.

> **Example**
>
> Industrial fishing can deplete the populations of certain fish species and may even cause extinction (a species to die out). This decreases genetic diversity within populations, as well as decreasing species diversity (as a result of extinction).

3. Urbanisation

Sprawling cities and major road developments can isolate species, meaning populations are unable to interbreed and genetic diversity is decreased.

> **Example**
>
> Populations of some animals, for example snakes, living in areas isolated by roads show a lower genetic diversity than populations living in areas of continuous habitat. This is thought to be because the isolated animals are unable to migrate and breed as they usually would.

4. Pollution

As the human population grows, we're producing more waste and more pollution. High levels of pollutants can kill species or destroy habitats.

> **Examples**
>
> - High levels of fertiliser flowing into a river from nearby fields can lead to a decrease in fish species in that river. This decreases biodiversity.
> - Some of the gases that are released from factories and cars cause acid rain, which can lower the pH of rivers, lakes and soil. Many aquatic organisms can't survive below a certain pH.

Monoculture

In order to feed an ever growing number of people, large areas of land are devoted to monoculture — the growing of a single variety of a single crop.

> **Example**
>
> In Africa, large areas of land are used for palm oil plantations.

This leads to a decline in biodiversity because of the following factors:

1. Habitat loss

Habitats are lost as land is cleared to make way for the large fields, reducing habitat diversity. This is not just the case on land. Marine fish farms are often built in locations that are ideal for wild fish and other marine life.

> **Example**
>
> Mangrove forests are areas of trees that grow in tropical and sub-tropical coastal regions. They are rich in biodiversity and provide a habitat for a wide variety of plant and animal species. One of the biggest threats to mangrove forests comes from clearance to make space for shrimp farms.

2. Loss of local plants and animals

Local and naturally occurring plants and animals are seen as weeds and pests, and so are destroyed with pesticides and herbicides, reducing species diversity.

> **Example**
>
> Use of herbicides on corn farms in the USA kills the local milkweed plant, which is the main source of food for the monarch butterfly. Monarch butterfly numbers are decreasing, which may partly be as a result of this.

3. Loss of heritage varieties

Heritage (traditional) varieties of crops are lost because they don't make enough money and so are not planted any more, which reduces species diversity.

Figure 2: *Mangrove forest in Asia.*

Climate change and global biodiversity

Climate change is a significant long-term change in an area's climate, e.g. its average temperature or rainfall patterns. It occurs naturally, but the scientific consensus is that the climate change we're experiencing at the moment is caused by humans increasing emissions of greenhouse gases (such as carbon dioxide). Greenhouse gases cause global warming (increasing global average temperature), which causes other types of climate change, e.g. changing rainfall patterns. Climate change can affect biodiversity by:

Changing environmental conditions

Climate change will affect the environmental conditions in different areas of the world in different ways — some places will get warmer, some colder, some wetter and others drier. All of these changes are likely to affect global biodiversity.

One reason for this is that most species need a particular climate to survive, so a change in climate may mean that an area that was previously inhabitable becomes uninhabitable (and vice versa). This may cause an increase or decrease in the range of some species (the area in which they live). This could increase or decrease biodiversity.

Tip: The Earth is heated by the Sun. Greenhouses gases in the atmosphere absorb most of the energy that would otherwise be radiated out into space, and re-radiate it back to Earth. This keeps us warm. But too much greenhouse gas means too much heat is absorbed and re-radiated back to Earth, so we're getting warmer.

---- Example ----

The southern range limit of the Sooty Copper Butterfly has moved 60 miles north in recent decades.

Changing environmental conditions may force some species to migrate to a more suitable area, causing a change in species distribution. Migrations usually decrease biodiversity in the areas the species migrate from, and increase biodiversity in the areas they migrate to. If there isn't a suitable habitat to migrate to, the species is a plant and can't migrate, or if the change is too fast, the species may become extinct. This will decrease biodiversity.

---- Example ----

Corals die if water temperature changes by just one or two degrees. In 1998 a coral reef near Panama was badly damaged because the water temperature had increased — at least one species of coral became extinct as a result.

Exam Tip
Make sure you use the correct scientific terms in the exam — for example, talk about species not being <u>adapted</u> to a new climate rather than not liking the new climate.

Practice Question — Application

Q1 A study was carried out to investigate the effect of temperature on the changing distribution of subtropical plankton species in the north Atlantic. Data collected on global sea surface temperature and plankton distribution are shown in the figures below.

Tip: Plankton are small organisms, such as algae, which are found drifting in water.

Figure A: Graph to show changing global sea-surface temperature.

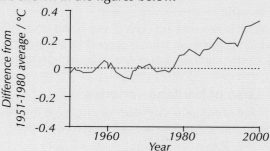

Figure B: Diagram to show subtropical plankton distribution.

■ subtropical plankton

1958-1981

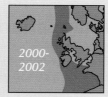
2000-2002

Tip: Don't be put off by the question having two different types of data source — just look at each one carefully and compare the trends they show.

a) Describe the data shown in Figure A and Figure B.

b) What conclusion can be drawn from this information?

c) Explain why the study can't conclude that the change in sea-surface temperature caused the change in plankton distribution.

d) Plankton are an important food source for many other marine organisms. Suggest how the change in plankton distribution may have affected biodiversity in the north Atlantic.

Practice Questions — Fact Recall

Q1 Describe one way in which human population growth affects biodiversity.

Q2 Describe how monoculture affects biodiversity.

4. Biodiversity and Conservation

As you saw on the previous few pages, several factors cause the loss of biodiversity — but luckily we have ways of conserving species. Maintaining biodiversity is important for many reasons, but the main ones are ecological, economic and aesthetic.

Ecological reasons to maintain biodiversity

The ecological reasons for maintaining biodiversity are all down to the complex relationships between organisms and their environments.

Protecting species

An ecosystem is all the organisms living in an area and all the non-living conditions, e.g. temperature. Organisms in an ecosystem are **interdependent** — they depend on each other to survive. This means that the loss of just one species can have pretty drastic effects on an ecosystem, such as:

- Disruption of food chains.

┌─ Example ─────────────────────────────────

Some species of bear feed on salmon, which feed on herring. If the number of herring decline it can affect both the salmon and the bear populations.

- Disruption of nutrient cycles.

┌─ Example ─────────────────────────────────

Decomposers like worms improve the quality of soil by recycling nutrients. If worm numbers decline, soil quality will be affected. This will affect the growth of plants and the amount of food available to animals.

There are some species on which many of the other species in an ecosystem depend and without which the ecosystem would change dramatically — these are called **keystone species**. Keystone species tend to have a relatively low population size but a huge effect on the environment. Keystone species are often predators, keeping the population of prey in check.

┌─ Example ─────────────────────────────────

The wolf is a keystone species in America. Wolf populations were eliminated in most American states during the 20th century. Without the wolves to hunt them, elk populations increased, leading to overgrazing. This led to the loss of plant species, as well as the loss of species that depend on those plants such as beavers and songbirds. The situation has since been reversed in some national parks.

Keystone species can also be modifiers — maintaining the environment needed for the ecosystem (e.g. beavers building dams), or hosts — plants that provide a particular environment, such as palm trees.

Maintaining genetic resources

Genetic resources refer to any material from plants, animals or microorganisms, containing genes, that we find valuable. Genetic resources could be crops, plants used for medicines, microorganisms used in industrial processes, or animal breeds. We need to maintain genetic resources for several reasons (see next page).

- Genetic resources provide us with a variety of everyday products, such as:

┌─ **Examples** ─────────────────────────────

- Food and drink — plants and animals are the source of almost all food and some drinks.

- Clothing — a lot of fibres and fabrics are made from plants and animals (e.g. cotton from plants and leather from animals).

- Drugs — many are made from compounds from plants (e.g. the painkiller morphine is made from poppies).

- Fuels — we use a number of organisms to produce renewable fuels, including ethanol and biogas. Fossil fuels are non-renewable (they'll run out), so other sources are of major economic importance.

- Other industrial materials — a huge variety of other materials are produced from plant and animal species, including wood, paper, dyes, adhesives, oils, rubber and chemicals such as pesticides.

- Genetic resources also allow us to adapt to changes in the environment.

┌─ **Example** ─────────────────────────────

Climate change (see page 249) may mean that some crops won't be able to grow in the same areas as they do now, e.g. there might be droughts in those areas. However, we may be able to use genes from a plant that's resistant to drought to genetically engineer a drought-resistant crop — that's if we have such genetic resources to choose from.

Tip: It's important to conserve all the organisms we currently use to make products, as well as those we don't currently use — they may provide us with new products in the future, e.g. new medicine.

Economic reasons to maintain biodiversity

Many of the genetic resources described above are important to the global economy. Products derived from plant and animal species are traded on a local and global scale. There are also other economic reasons for maintaining biodiversity, such as:

Reducing soil depletion

Monoculture is growing a single variety of a single crop (see p. 249). Continuous monoculture involves planting the same crop in the same field without interruption. So, for example, a corn crop will be planted in a field and when that crop is harvested, another corn crop will be planted pretty much straight away. Continuous monoculture causes soil depletion because the nutrients required by the crop are gradually used up. (In more traditional farming methods crops are rotated with other types of crops, so that the nutrients and organic matter are replaced.) The economic costs of soil depletion include increased spending on fertilisers (to artificially replace nutrients) and decreased yields (in the long run and if fertilisers are not used).

Tip: 'Yield' is the amount of a crop produced.

Aesthetic reasons to maintain biodiversity

Biodiversity brings joy to millions of people. Areas rich in biodiversity provide pleasant, attractive landscapes that people can enjoy. By maintaining biodiversity we protect these beautiful landscapes. The more biodiversity in an area, the more visitors the area is likely to attract — this also has economic advantages.

Figure 1: *Wastwater in the Lake District is owned and cared for by the National Trust.*

Practice Question — Application

A prairie is a large area of grassland, common in North America. Prairie dogs are small rodents that live in networks of underground burrows on prairies. They are a food source for several larger animals and birds of prey. The burrows they dig provide nests for other species, such as the burrowing owl, and their digging helps to circulate air through the soil, maintaining soil quality for plant growth. Prairie dogs are considered to be a keystone species.

Q1 Explain why prairie dogs are considered to be a keystone species and suggest what effects their removal would have on the prairie ecosystem.

Figure 2: *A prairie dog.*

Maintaining biodiversity through conservation

Biodiversity can be maintained through conservation — the protection and management of species and habitats. Conservation is important to ensure the survival of **endangered species** — species which are at risk of extinction because of a low population, or a threatened habitat. A species that is critically endangered is likely to become extinct because its population size is too small.

Exam Tip
If you're asked to define 'critically endangered' in the exam, make sure you emphasise that the species is <u>likely</u> to die out.

Types of conservation

There are two main types of conservation:

1. *In situ* conservation

In situ conservation means conservation on site — it involves protecting species in their natural habitat. Methods of *in situ* conservation include:

- Establishing protected areas such as national parks and wildlife reserves (also known as nature reserves) — habitats and species are protected in these areas by restricting urban development, industrial development and farming. A similar idea has been introduced to sea ecosystems with Marine Conservation Zones, where human activities (like fishing) are controlled.

- Controlling or preventing the introduction of species that threaten local biodiversity. For example, grey squirrels are not native to Britain. They compete with the native red squirrel and have caused a population decline. So they're controlled in some areas.

- Protecting habitats — e.g. controlling water levels to conserve wetlands and coppicing (trimming trees) to conserve woodlands. This allows organisms to continue living in their natural habitat.

- Restoring damaged areas — such as a coastline polluted by an oil spill.

- Promoting particular species — this could be by protecting food sources or nesting sites.
- Giving legal protection to endangered species, e.g. making it illegal to kill them.

Advantages and disadvantages

The advantage of *in situ* conservation is that often both the species and their habitat are conserved. This means that larger populations can be protected and it's less disruptive than removing organisms from their habitats. The chances of the population recovering are also greater than with *ex situ* methods (see below). But it can be difficult to control some factors that are threatening a species (such as poaching, predators, disease or climate change).

2. *Ex situ* conservation

Ex situ conservation means conservation off site — it involves protecting a species by removing part of the population from a threatened habitat and placing it in a new location. *Ex situ* conservation is often a last resort. Methods of *ex situ* conservation include:

- Relocating an organism to a safer area, e.g. some white rhinos have been relocated from the Congo to Kenya because they were in danger from poachers who kill them for their ivory.
- Breeding organisms in captivity then reintroducing them to the wild when they are strong enough, e.g. sea eagles have been reintroduced to Britain through a captive breeding programme. Breeding is carried out in animal sanctuaries and zoos.
- Botanic gardens are controlled environments used to grow a variety of rare plants for the purposes of conservation, research, display and education. Endangered plant species as well as species that are extinct in the wild can be grown and reintroduced into suitable habitats.
- Seed banks — seeds can be frozen and stored in seed banks for over a century without losing their fertility. Seed banks provide a useful source of seeds if natural reserves are destroyed, for example by disease or other natural disasters.

Figure 3: *Sea eagles have been reintroduced to Britain.*

Figure 4: *Lots of threatened plant species are preserved at the Royal Botanic Gardens.*

Advantages and disadvantages

The advantages of *ex situ* conservation are that it can be used to protect individual animals in a controlled environment — things like predation and hunting can be managed more easily. Competition for resources can be reduced, and it's possible to check on the health of individuals and treat them for diseases. Breeding can also be manipulated, e.g. through the use of reproductive hormones and IVF. Finally, it can be used to reintroduce species that have left an area.

But, there are disadvantages — usually only a small number of individuals can be cared for. It can be difficult and expensive to create and sustain the right environment. In fact, animals that are habituated (used to) human contact may be less likely to exhibit natural behaviour and may be more likely to catch a disease from humans. *Ex situ* conservation is usually less successful than *in situ* methods — many species can't breed successfully in captivity, or don't adapt to their new environment when moved to a new location.

Conservation and international cooperation

Conservation is much more likely to be successful when countries work together. For example, some endangered species are found in lots of countries, so it'd be pointless making hunting a species illegal in one country if poachers could just go and hunt them in another. Information about threats to biodiversity needs to be shared and countries need to decide on conservation methods and implement them together. Here are a couple of examples of successful international cooperation:

Rio Convention on Biological Diversity (CBD)

The Rio Convention on Biological Diversity is an international agreement that aims to develop international strategies on the conservation of biodiversity and how to use animal and plant resources in a sustainable way. The convention made it part of international law that conserving biodiversity is everyone's responsibility. It also provides guidance to governments on how to conserve biodiversity.

Tip: Using resources in a sustainable way means they'll still be around for future generations to use.

CITES Agreement

CITES (Convention on International Trade in Endangered Species) is an agreement designed to increase international cooperation in regulating trade in wild animal and plant specimens. The member countries all agreed to make it illegal to kill endangered species. The agreement helps to conserve species by limiting trade through licensing, and by making it illegal to trade in products made from endangered animals (such as rhino ivory and leopard skins). It's also designed to raise awareness of threats to biodiversity through education.

> **Example**
>
> Between 1979 and 1989 the number of African elephants dropped from around 1.3 million to around 600 000 because they were being hunted for their ivory tusks. In 1989, the CITES banned ivory trade to end the demand for elephant tusks so that fewer elephants would be killed for their tusks. The population of elephants in Kenya has doubled since 1989 and elephant populations in some countries, like Botswana, have been downgraded to a less endangered status.

Figure 5: *A decline in elephant populations due to hunting for their ivory tusks has led to a ban on the sale of ivory.*

Local conservation agreements

Whilst international cooperation is important, schemes at the local level are vital too. Here is an example from the UK:

The Countryside Stewardship Scheme (CSS)

The Countryside Stewardship Scheme was introduced in 1991. Some of its aims were to conserve wildlife and biodiversity, and to improve and extend wildlife habitats by promoting specific management techniques to landowners. The Government offered 10-year agreements to pay landowners who followed the management techniques they were suggesting. For example, to regenerate hedgerows, to leave grassy margins around the edges of fields where wildflowers could grow, and to graze upland areas to keep down bracken. In the year 2000, there were 10 000 agreements in England. Since the introduction of the scheme, various species have begun to rebuild in numbers, including birds such as the stone curlew, black grouse and bittern.

Figure 6: *An Australian Northern Quoll.*

Tip: Take a look back at the start of the topic if you need a reminder about economic reasons for conservation.

Practice Questions — Application

Q1 The Northern Quoll is an endangered species in Australia. The population has declined due to the cane toad which was introduced to control a pest in sugarcane fields. Some conservationists are exploring preserving the Northern Quoll *in situ* by eradicating cane toads, whereas others are considering conserving them in a nature reserve. Sugarcane is an important crop in Australia.

a) i) Suggest an advantage of *in situ* over *ex situ* conservation of the Northern Quoll.

   ii) Suggest an advantage of *ex situ* over *in situ* conservation of the Northern Quoll.

b) Suggest the potential economic impact of the *in situ* conservation of the Northern Quoll.

Practice Questions — Fact Recall

Q1 Describe the ecological reasons why it is important to maintain biodiversity.

Q2 Give one:

   a) economic reason for maintaining biodiversity.

   b) aesthetic reason for maintaining biodiversity.

Q3 What is conservation?

Q4 a) Define *in situ* conservation.

   b) Give two examples of methods used in *in situ* conservation.

Q5 a) Define *ex situ* conservation.

   b) Give two examples of methods used in *ex situ* conservation.

   c) Give one disadvantage of *ex situ* conservation over *in situ* conservation.

Q6 What is the Rio Convention on Biological Diversity (CBD)?

Q7 What is the CITES agreement?

Q8 Give two examples of management techniques suggested in the Countryside Stewardship Scheme (CSS).

Section Summary

Make sure you know:

- That biodiversity can be explored at the levels of habitat biodiversity (the number of different habitats in an area), species diversity (the number of different species and the abundance of each species in an area) and genetic diversity (the variation of alleles within a species or a population of a species).

- How to use sampling as a way of collecting data on biodiversity without having to count each individual organism in a habitat.

- That sampling can be random or non-random and that practical investigations can be carried out in the field by collecting random and non-random samples.

- How to carry out random sampling by using a grid and a random number generator, so that each random sample site has the same probability of being chosen.

- How to carry out non-random sampling to ensure all different areas in a habitat are sampled, including how to use systematic, opportunistic and stratified sampling.
- That species richness refers to the number of different species in an area and is measured by taking random samples of a habitat and counting the number of different species.
- That species evenness is a measure of the relative abundance of each species in an area and is measured by taking random samples of a habitat and counting the number of individuals of each different species.
- How to calculate Simpson's Index of Diversity using the formula: $D = 1 - (\sum(n/N)^2)$
- That habitats with a high Index of Diversity (a value close to 1) have a high biodiversity.
- That habitats with a low Index of Diversity (a value close to 0) are less stable and have a lower ability to cope with change, e.g. the introduction of a new predator, than areas of high biodiversity.
- That it is important to measure genetic diversity within isolated populations, e.g. zoos, rare breed populations and populations of pedigree animals.
- How to calculate genetic biodiversity using the formula: proportion of polymorphic gene loci = number of polymorphic gene loci ÷ total number of loci, and how to convert this into a percentage.
- That human population growth has affected biodiversity through habitat loss, over-exploitation, urbanisation and pollution.
- That monoculture has affected biodiversity through habitat loss, loss of local plants and animals and loss of heritage varieties.
- That climate change has affected biodiversity through changing environmental conditions.
- That maintaining biodiversity is important for ecological reasons (including protecting keystone species and maintaining genetic resources), economic reasons (including reducing soil depletion caused by continuous monoculture) and aesthetic reasons (including protecting landscapes).
- That *in situ* conservation involves protecting species in their natural habitat, whereas *ex situ* conservation involves protecting a species by moving part of a population from a threatened habitat and placing it in a new location.
- That *in situ* conservation includes establishing protected areas, such as wildlife reserves and marine conservation zones.
- That *ex situ* conservation includes breeding organisms in captivity (e.g. in zoos), then reintroducing them to the wild, and conserving organisms in botanic gardens and seed banks.
- That the Rio Convention on Biological Diversity (CBD) is an international agreement that aims to develop international strategies in the conservation of biodiversity and how to use animal and plant resources in a sustainable way.
- That the CITES (Convention on International Trade in Endangered Species) is an agreement designed to increase international cooperation in regulating trade in wild animal and plant specimens.
- That the Countryside Stewardship Scheme (CSS) is a local agreement to conserve wildlife and biodiversity by promoting specific management techniques to landowners.

Exam-style Questions

1   Domestic sheep are all members of the species *Ovis aries*. There are over 200 breeds of domestic sheep. The existence of these different breeds is an example of which type of diversity?

   A   habitat diversity

   B   genetic diversity

   C   species diversity

   D   breeding diversity

(1 mark)

2   A student is investigating the species diversity of insects in a 500 m² area of woodland.

   The student sampled the insect population by arranging a series of covered pitfall traps in the ground. The traps are designed so that insects fall into them while walking along the ground and are unable to escape.

   The student arranged the traps in a straight line along the edge of the woodland and left them overnight before coming back to count the insects she had caught.

   (a)   Explain what is meant by the term 'species diversity'.

(2 marks)

   (b)   Give **two** reasons why the student did not obtain a representative sample of insects living in the woodland.

(2 marks)

   (c)   The student found that the woodland had a low species evenness.
             What does a low species evenness tell you about a habitat?

(1 mark)

   (d)   The student wants to compare the species diversity of insects in the woodland with the species diversity of insects on her local common.

             Suggest **one** thing the student must do when sampling insects on the common to ensure that her findings from both habitats are comparable.

(1 mark)

3*   Polar bears are a keystone species that play an important role in the maintenance of the Arctic ecosystem. They use the ice sheets that surround the Arctic shoreline to hunt for their main prey, seals. This helps to keep the populations of seals in check and also provides leftover food for scavengers such as the Arctic fox and Arctic birds.

             Suggest and explain the effect climate change might have on the population of polar bears and the effect this might have on the Arctic ecosystem.

(6 marks)

*The quality of your response will be assessed in this question.

4   A company wishes to clear part of a wood next to a town and build a new housing estate on the land. A study was conducted on the trees found in the town centre and in the wood. The results are shown in **Fig. 4.1**.

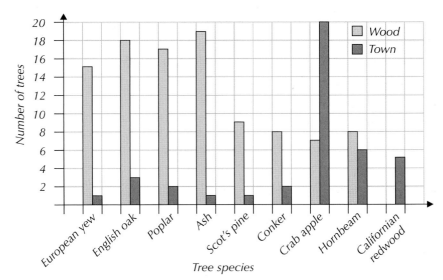

Fig. 4.1

(a)   Simpson's Index of Diversity can be calculated using the following equation:

$$D = 1 - (\Sigma(n/N)^2)$$

where **n** = Total number of organisms in one species
      N = Total number of all organisms

Use the data in **Fig. 4.1** and the formula provided above to calculate Simpson's Index of Diversity for trees in the wood and in the town.

(4 marks)

(b)   Explain what your answers to part **(a)** tell you about the town habitat and the woodland habitat.

(2 marks)

(c)   The company discovers that the wood supports a small population of red squirrels, which are an endangered species.

Suggest **two** conservation measures that could be undertaken to protect the wood's red squirrel population if the development project goes ahead.

(2 marks)

Tip: There's more on domains on page 265.

Exam Tip
You need to learn the names and order of the taxonomic groups. If you're struggling to remember the order, try this mnemonic...

<u>D</u>aft <u>K</u>ids <u>P</u>refer <u>C</u>hips <u>O</u>ver <u>F</u>loppy <u>G</u>reen <u>S</u>pinach.

1. Classification Basics

Scientists group organisms together to make them easier to study.

What is classification?

Classification is the act of arranging organisms into groups based on their similarities and differences. This makes it easier for scientists to identify them and to study them. **Taxonomy** is the study of classification. There are a few different classification systems in use, but they all involve placing organisms into groups in a **taxonomic hierarchy**.

In the hierarchy you need to know about, there are eight levels of groups (called taxonomic groups). Similar organisms are first sorted into one of three very large groups called domains, e.g. animals, plants and fungi are in the Eukarya domain. Similar organisms are then sorted into slightly smaller groups called kingdoms, e.g. all animals are in the animal kingdom (Animalia). Similar organisms from that kingdom are then grouped into a phylum. Similar organisms from each phylum are then grouped into a class, and so on down the eight levels of the taxonomic hierarchy. This is illustrated in Figure 1.

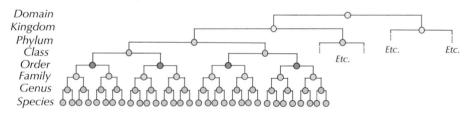

Domain
Kingdom
Phylum
Class
Order
Family
Genus
Species

Etc. *Etc.* *Etc.*

Figure 1: *A diagram illustrating the eight taxonomic groups used in classification.*

> **Example — the classification of humans**
> Domain = *Eukarya*, Kingdom = *Animalia*, Phylum = *Chordata*, Class = *Mammalia*, Order = *Primates*, Family = *Hominidae*, Genus = *Homo*, Species = *sapiens*.

As you move down the hierarchy, there are more groups at each level but fewer organisms in each group. The hierarchy ends with species — the groups that contain only one type of organism (e.g. humans, dogs, *E. coli* and about 50 million other living species).

Naming species

The nomenclature (naming system) used for classification is called the **binomial system** — all organisms are given one internationally accepted scientific name in Latin that has two parts.

The first part of the name is the genus name and has a capital letter. The second part is the species name and begins with a lower case letter. Names are always written in *italics* (or they're <u>underlined</u> if they're handwritten).

The binomial system helps to avoid the confusion of using common names.

Example

Americans call a type of bird cockatoos and Australians call them flaming galahs, but it's the same bird. If the correct scientific name is used — *Eolophus roseicapillus* — there's no confusion.

The five kingdoms

The five kingdom classification system is a bit old now (see page 265), but you still need to learn these five kingdoms and the general characteristics of the organisms in each of them:

Prokaryotae

Example: bacteria

Features: prokaryotic, unicellular (single-celled), no nucleus, less than 5 μm

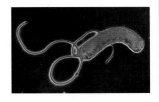

Tip: Remember, prokaryotes don't have a nucleus, eukaryotes do. There's more on the differences between prokaryotes and eukaryotes on page 38.

Protoctista

Examples: algae, protozoa

Features: eukaryotic cells, usually live in water, single-celled or simple multicellular organisms

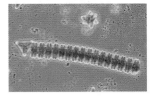

Exam Tip
Make sure you can spell the names of the different kingdoms — Latin words are tricky, but if you get them wrong, the examiners might not know what you mean and you could miss out on marks. Watch out for Prot<u>oct</u>ista in particular.

Fungi

Examples: moulds, yeasts, mushrooms

Features: eukaryotic, chitin cell wall, saprotrophic (absorb substances from dead or decaying organisms), single-celled or multicellular organisms

Plantae

Examples: mosses, ferns, flowering plants

Features: eukaryotic, multicellular, cell walls made of cellulose, can photosynthesise, contain chlorophyll, autotrophic (produce their own food)

Tip: Plants are also known as <u>photoautotrophs</u> — they produce their own food using <u>light</u>.

Animalia

Examples: nematodes (roundworms), molluscs, insects, fish, reptiles, birds, mammals

Features: eukaryotic, multicellular, no cell walls, heterotrophic (consume plants and animals)

Exam Tip
Always use the proper scientific terms where you can — e.g. write 'autotrophic' not 'produces own food' in the exam.

Phylogeny

Evolution is the gradual change in organisms over time — see page 279. It has led to a huge variety of different organisms on Earth, all of which share a common ancestry. **Phylogeny** is the study of the evolutionary history of groups of organisms. Phylogeny tells us who's related to whom and how closely related they are. This can be shown on a phylogenetic tree, like the one in Figure 2.

see page 279.

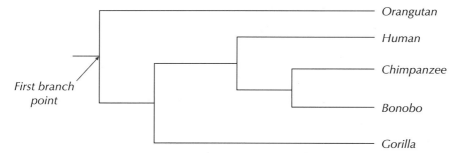

First branch point

Figure 2: Phylogenetic tree of the Hominidae family.

This tree shows the relationship between members of the Hominidae family (great apes and humans). The first branch point represents a common ancestor of all the family members. This ancestor is now extinct. Orangutans were the first group to diverge (evolve to become a different species) from this common ancestor. Each of the following branch points represents another common ancestor from which a different group diverged. Gorillas diverged next, then humans, closely followed by bonobos and chimpanzees.

According to phylogenetics, a **species** is the smallest group that shares a common ancestor — in other words, the end of a branch on a phylogenetic tree. Closely related species diverged away from each other most recently. E.g. humans and chimpanzees are closely related, as they diverged very recently. You can see this because their branches are close together. Humans and orangutans are more distantly related, as they diverged longer ago, so their branches are further apart.

Classification systems now take into account phylogeny when arranging organisms into groups. Classifying organisms in this way is known as **cladistics**.

> **Tip:** Sharing a common ancestry means that you have some of the same ancestors (relatives from previous generations). Some organisms share more recent common ancestors than others.

Figure 3: Orangutans, chimps and gorillas are all closely related.

> **Tip:** The groups at the ends of the branches on this phylogenetic tree aren't actually individual species (e.g. sharks are a group of several different species). That's because the tree has been simplified — if it continued to species level, it would be huge.

Practice Questions — Application

Q1 The diagram below shows a simplified phylogenetic tree for the phylum Chordata:

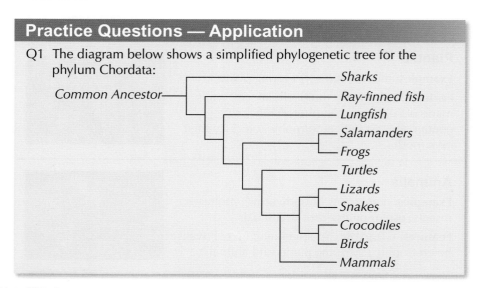

a) Which group was first to diverge from the common ancestor?

b) Are frogs more closely related to salamanders or turtles?

c) To which other group are:

  (i) birds most closely related?

  (ii) snakes most closely related?

Q2 Donkeys are part of the phylum Chordata.
The binomial name for donkeys is *Equus asinus*.

Complete the table below for the classification of the donkey.

Taxonomic Group	
	Eukarya
Kingdom	Animalia
Class	Mammalia
Order	Perrisodactyla
Family	Equidae

Tip: It might surprise you that some organisms are closely related — but just because you can't see a similarity in their features doesn't mean the phylogenetic tree is wrong.

Practice Questions — Fact Recall

Q1 What is classification?

Q2 Describe how organisms are named using the binomial system.

Q3 Give three characteristics of the kingdom Plantae.

Q4 According to phylogenetics, what is a species?

Classification systems aren't set in stone. Like living organisms, they evolve...

Evidence for classification

Early classification systems only used observable features (things you can see) to place organisms into groups. Observable features can be anatomical (structural), e.g. how many legs an organism has, or behavioural, e.g. whether an organism lives in groups. But this method has problems. Scientists don't always agree on the relative importance of different features and groups based solely on physical features may not show how related organisms are.

Example

Sharks and whales look quite similar and they both live in the sea. But they're not actually closely related — sharks are cartilaginous fish (meaning they have skeletons made of cartilage instead of bone), whereas whales are vertebrate mammals (they have a backbone) — they're from two completely different classes.

Classification systems are now based on observable features along with other evidence. This evidence tells us how similar, and therefore how closely related, organisms are. The types of evidence taxonomists look at include embryological evidence (the similarities in the early stages of an organism's development), fossil evidence and molecular evidence.

Tip: Molecular evidence is sometimes referred to as biochemical evidence.

Tip: There's more on DNA bases on page 80.

Molecular evidence

Gathering molecular evidence involves analysing the similarities in proteins and DNA. More closely related organisms will have more similar molecules. You can compare things like how DNA is stored and the sequence of DNA bases.

Example

The diagram below shows part of the DNA base sequence for gene X in three different species...

Species A: ATTGTCTGATTGGTGCTAGTCGTCGATGCTAGGTCG

Species B: ATTGT**A**TGATTGGTGCTAGTCG**G**CGATGCTAGGTCG

Species C: ATTG**ATT**GA**AA**GG**A**GCTA**C**TCGT**A**GAT**ATA**AGG**GGT**

There are 13 differences between the base sequences in species A and C, but only 2 differences between the base sequences in species A and B. This suggests that species A and B are more closely related than A and C.

You can also compare the sequence of amino acids in proteins from different organisms.

Example

Cytochrome C is a short protein found in many species. The more similar the amino acid sequence of cytochrome C in two different species, the more closely related the species are likely to be.

Changing the classification of organisms

New technologies (e.g. new DNA analysis techniques, better microscopes) can result in new discoveries being made. Scientists can share their new discoveries in meetings and scientific journals. How organisms are classified is continually revised to take account of any new findings that scientists discover.

Tip: There's more on how and why scientists share their findings on page 2.

Example

Skunks were classified in the family Mustelidae until molecular evidence revealed their DNA sequence was significantly different to other members of that family. So they were reclassified into the family Mephitidae.

Five kingdoms vs three domains

The five kingdom classification system shown on page 261 has now been replaced with the three domain system. In the older system, the largest groups were the five kingdoms — all organisms were placed into one of these groups (see Figure 1).

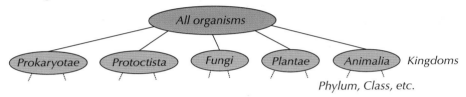

Figure 1: A diagram illustrating the top tier of the five kingdom system.

In 1990, the three domain system was proposed. This new system has three domains — large superkingdoms that are above the kingdoms in the taxonomic hierarchy (see Figure 2).

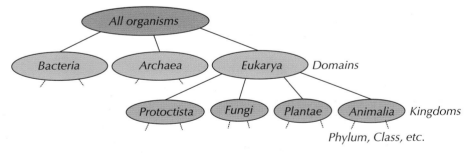

Figure 2: A diagram illustrating the top two tiers of the three domain system.

In the three domain system, organisms that were in the kingdom Prokaryotae (which contains unicellular organisms without a nucleus) are separated into two domains — the Archaea and Bacteria. Organisms with cells that contain a nucleus are placed in the domain Eukarya (this includes four of the five kingdoms). The lower hierarchy stays the same — Kingdom, Phylum, Class, Order, Family, Genus, Species. The three domain system was proposed because of new evidence, mainly molecular.

Examples

The Prokaryotae were reclassified into two domains because new evidence showed large differences between the Archaea and Bacteria.

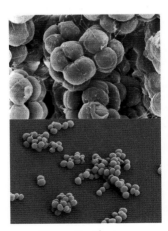

Figure 3: Electron micrographs of an Archaea species (top) and a Bacteria species (bottom). Archaea and Bacteria often look very similar, but are biochemically different.

The new evidence included:

Molecular evidence:

The enzyme RNA polymerase (needed to make RNA) is different in Bacteria and Archaea. Archaea, but not Bacteria, have similar histones (proteins that bind to DNA) to Eukarya.

Cellular evidence:

The bonds of the lipids (see page 58) in the cell membranes of Bacteria and Archaea are different. The development and composition of flagellae (see page 34) are also different.

Most scientists now agree that Archaea and Bacteria evolved separately and that Archaea are more closely related to Eukarya than Bacteria. The three domain system reflects how different the Archaea and Bacteria are.

The development of the three domain system is an example of how scientific knowledge is always changing and improving (see page 2).

Practice Questions — Application

The graph below illustrates the sequence of a small stretch of DNA in 3 different species:

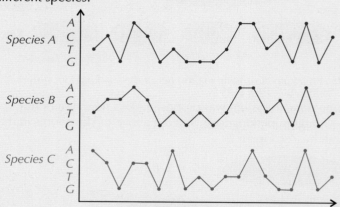

Distance along gene sequence (bp)

Tip: The distance along the gene sequence on the diagram is given as 'bp' — base pairs.

Q1 Using the graph, write down the base sequence for this stretch of DNA in each of the three species.

Q2 In how many places do the base sequences of species A and B differ?

Q3 In how many places do the base sequences of species A and C differ?

Q4 Is species A more closely related to species B or species C? Explain your answer.

Q5 To which of the two species is species C most closely related? Explain your answer.

Practice Questions — Fact Recall

Q1 Explain how proteins can be used to help classify organisms.

Q2 Describe the three domain system of classification.

Q3 Describe one piece of evidence that led to Prokaryotes being reclassified.

3. Variation

All organisms vary — it's what makes each and every one of us unique.

What is variation?

Variation is the differences that exist between individuals. Every individual organism is unique — even clones (such as identical twins) show some variation. It can occur:

Within species

Variation within a species is called **intraspecific** variation.

> **Example**
> Individual European robins weigh between 16 g and 22 g and show some variation in many other characteristics including length, wingspan, colour and beak size.

Between species

The variation between different species is called **interspecific** variation.

> **Example**
> The lightest species of bird is the bee hummingbird, which weighs around 1.6 g on average. The heaviest species of bird is the ostrich, which can weigh up to 160 kg (100 000 times as much).

Continuous variation

Continuous variation is when the individuals in a population vary within a range — there are no distinct categories.

> **Examples**
>
> **Animals**
> - Height — humans can be any height within a range (e.g. 139 cm, 175 cm, 185.9 cm, etc.), not just tall or short — see Figure 1.
> - Mass — humans can be any mass within a range.
> - Milk yield — cows can produce any volume of milk within a range.
>
>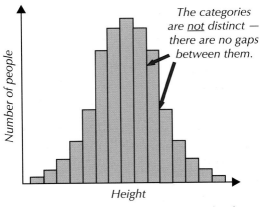
>
> *The categories are not distinct — there are no gaps between them.*
>
> **Figure 1:** *Graph to show an example of continuous variation in humans.*
>
> **Plants**
> - Surface area of leaves — the surface area of each of a tree's leaves can be any value within a range.
> - Mass — the mass of the seeds from a flower head varies within a range.
>
> **Microorganisms**
> - Width — the width of *E. coli* bacteria varies within a range.
> - Length — the length of the flagellum (see p. 34) can vary within a range.

Learning Objectives:

- Understand the different types of variation, including intraspecific and interspecific variation.
- Know the differences between continuous and discontinuous variation, including examples of a range of characteristics found in plants, animals and microorganisms.
- Understand both genetic and environmental causes of variation.

Specification Reference 4.2.2

Tip: Don't get inter- and intra-specific variation mixed up. If you're struggling, just remember — int**er** means diff**er**ent species and intr**a** means the s**a**me species.

Tip: Continuous variation can be shown by continuous data. The continuous data for height in humans is <u>quantitative</u> — this means it has values that can be measured with a number.

Figure 2: *Pea seeds can be wrinkled or smooth.*

Exam Tip
It's worth learning the examples on this page and on page 267, as well as the meanings of continuous and discontinuous variation.

Discontinuous variation

Discontinuous variation is when there are two or more distinct categories — each individual falls into only one of these categories, and there are no intermediates.

┌ **Examples** ─────────────────────

Animals

- Blood group — humans can be group A, B, AB or O (see Figure 3).

Plants

- Colour — courgettes are either yellow, dark green or light green.
- Seed shape — some pea plants have smooth seeds and some have wrinkled seeds.

Microorganisms

- Antibiotic resistance — bacteria are either resistant or not.
- Pigment production — some types of bacteria can produce a coloured pigment, some can't.

Figure 3: *Graph to show an example of discontinuous variation in humans.*

Causes of variation

Variation can be caused by genetic factors, environmental factors or a combination of both.

Genetic factors

Different species have different genes. Individuals of the same species have the same genes, but different versions of them (called **alleles**). The alleles an organism has make up its **genotype**. The differences in genotype result in variation in **phenotype** — the characteristics displayed by an organism.

┌ **Examples** ─────────────────────

Variation caused by genetic factors includes:

- Eye colour in humans (which can be blue, green, grey, brown),
- Blood type in humans (O, A, B or AB),
- Antibiotic resistance in bacteria.

You inherit your genes from your parents. This means variation caused by genetic factors is inherited.

Environmental factors

Variation can also be caused by differences in the environment, e.g. climate, food, lifestyle. Characteristics controlled by environmental factors can change over an organism's life.

┌ **Examples** ─────────────────────

Variation caused only by environmental factors includes accents and whether people have pierced ears.

Tip: Most characteristics of an organism are determined by both genes and the environment.

Both genetic and environmental factors

Genetic factors determine the characteristics an organism's born with, but environmental factors can influence how some characteristics develop.

- Height — genes determine how tall an organism can grow (e.g. tall parents tend to have tall children). But diet or nutrient availability affect how tall an organism actually grows.

- Flagellum — genes determine if a microorganism can grow a flagellum, but some will only start to grow them in certain environments, e.g. if metal ions are present.

Practice Question — Application

Q1 A twin study was performed to determine whether head circumference is influenced mainly by environmental factors or by genetic factors. 25 pairs of identical twins were selected for the study and the mean difference in the head circumference of each pair was calculated. The same was done for 25 pairs of non-identical twins and 25 pairs of unrelated individuals of the same age. The results are shown on the right.

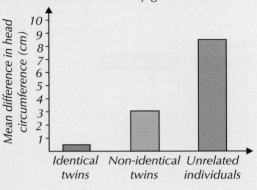

a) Is head circumference an example of continuous or discontinuous variation?

b) Describe the data.

c) Do you think that genetic or environmental factors have a larger effect on head circumference? Explain your answer.

A similar study was performed on adults to determine the effects of genetic and environmental factors on activity levels. Pairs of identical twins, pairs of non-identical twins and pairs of unrelated individuals of the same age were asked to wear a pedometer and the mean difference in steps taken per day was recorded. The results are shown on the right.

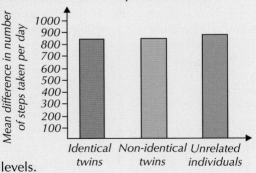

d) Explain what the results show about the role of genetics in determining activity levels.

Practice Questions — Fact Recall

Q1 What is: a) intraspecific variation? b) interspecific variation?

Q2 Describe the difference between continuous variation and discontinuous variation. Give an example of each.

Q3 Give one example of a characteristic that is influenced by both genetic factors and environmental factors.

4. Investigating Variation

To investigate variation, you usually take samples of a population.
There's more on taking samples on page 241.

Mean and standard deviation

You can use the mean and standard deviation to measure how much variation there is in a sample.

Mean

The mean is an average of the values collected in a sample.
Find it using this formula:

$$\text{mean} = \frac{\text{total of all the values in your data}}{\text{the number of values in your data}}$$

Example — **Maths Skills**

The heights of different seedlings in a group are: 6 cm, 4 cm, 7 cm, 6 cm, 5 cm, 8 cm, 7 cm, 5 cm, 7 cm and 9 cm.

To calculate the mean, add all of the heights together and divide by the number of seedlings:

Mean height = (6 + 4 + 7 + 6 + 5 + 8 + 7 + 5 + 7 + 9) ÷ 10 = 64 ÷ 10
= **6.4 cm**

Tip: When you calculate the mean, check that it's within the range of values that you used in the calculation. If the mean isn't within the range, you know you've calculated it wrong. E.g. the mean here should be between 4 and 9 cm.

The mean can be used to tell if there is variation between samples.

Examples

- The mean height of a species of tree in woodland A = 26 m, woodland B = 32 m and woodland C = 35 m. So the mean height varies.
- The mean number of leaves on a clover plant in field X = 3, field Y = 3 and field Z = 3. So the mean number of leaves does not vary.

Most samples will include values either side of the mean, so you end up with a bell-shaped graph — this is called a **normal distribution** (see Figure 1). A normal distribution is symmetrical about the mean.

Tip:
Normal distribution (symmetrical):

Not a normal distribution (skewed):

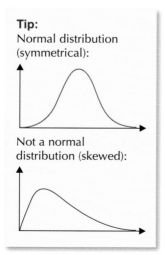

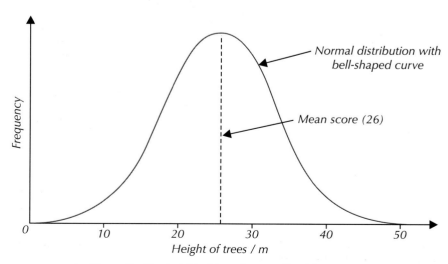

Figure 1: *The height of trees in woodland A.*

Standard deviation

The standard deviation tells you how much the values in a single sample vary. It's a measure of the spread of values about the mean. Sometimes you'll see the mean written as, for example, 9 ± 3. This means that the mean is 9 and the standard deviation is 3, so most of the values are spread between 6 and 12.

Both of the graphs in Figure 2 show a normal distribution. However, the values in a sample can vary a little or a lot:

Exam Tip
You won't get marks for describing the standard deviation as the spread of results — it's the spread of values <u>about the mean</u>.

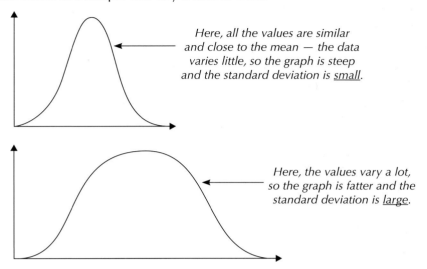

Here, all the values are similar and close to the mean — the data varies little, so the graph is steep and the standard deviation is <u>small</u>.

Here, the values vary a lot, so the graph is fatter and the standard deviation is <u>large</u>.

Figure 2: *A normal distribution curve with a small standard deviation (top) and with a large standard deviation (bottom).*

Example

Height of trees in woodland A:
mean = 26,
standard deviation = 3

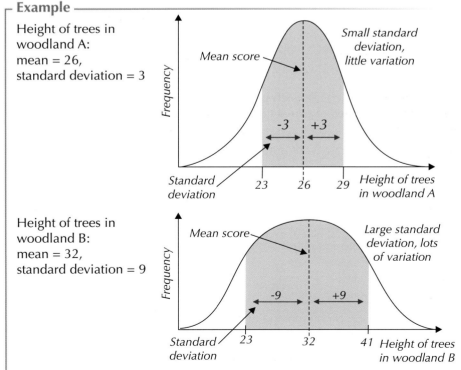

Exam Tip
You need to know how to interpret data that includes standard deviations for your exam.

Height of trees in woodland B:
mean = 32,
standard deviation = 9

Tip: Values with a larger standard deviation show greater variation.

So the trees are generally taller in woodland B, but there's a greater variation in height compared to woodland A.

Calculating standard deviation

Figure 3 shows the formula for finding the standard deviation of a group of values:

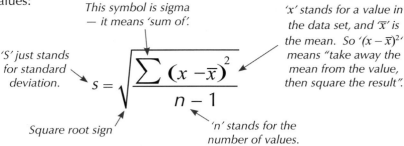

This symbol is sigma — it means 'sum of'.

'x' stands for a value in the data set, and 'x̄' is the mean. So '$(x - \bar{x})^2$' means "take away the mean from the value, then square the result".

'S' just stands for standard deviation.

$$S = \sqrt{\frac{\sum (x - \bar{x})^2}{n - 1}}$$

Square root sign

'n' stands for the number of values.

Figure 3: *Explanation of the formula for standard deviation.*

Example — Maths Skills

The table below shows the height of four different trees in a forest.

Tree	Height (m)
A	22
B	27
C	26
D	29

To find the standard deviation:

▪ Write out the equation:

$$S = \sqrt{\frac{\sum (x - \bar{x})^2}{n - 1}}$$

▪ Work out the mean height of the trees, $\bar{x}$:

$$(22 + 27 + 26 + 29) \div 4 = \mathbf{26}$$

▪ Work out $(x - \bar{x})^2$ for each value of x. For each tree height in the table, you need to take away the mean, then square the answer:

A: $(22 - 26)^2 = (-4)^2 = \mathbf{16}$ B: $(27 - 26)^2 = 1^2 = \mathbf{1}$
C: $(26 - 26)^2 = 0^2 = \mathbf{0}$ D: $(29 - 26)^2 = 3^2 = \mathbf{9}$

▪ Add up all these numbers to find $\sum (x - \bar{x})^2$:

$$16 + 1 + 0 + 9 = \mathbf{26}$$

▪ Divide this number by the number of values, n, minus 1. Then take the square root to get the answer:

$$26 \div 3 = 8.66...$$
$$\sqrt{8.66...} = \mathbf{2.94 \text{ to 2 s.f.}}$$

Standard deviation is one method of calculating the dispersion of data. Another method of calculating dispersion is by looking at the range — see page 11. This is simply the difference between the highest and lowest figures in the data. Standard deviation is more useful than the range because it takes into account all the values in the data set, whereas the range only uses two. This makes the range more likely to be affected by an anomalous result (an unusually high or low value in the data set) than standard deviation.

Q1 The graph below shows the wing spans of two different species of bird, both of which live in the same area of woodland.

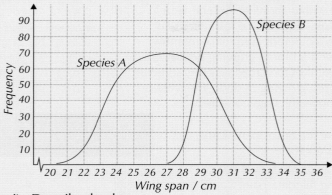

a) i) Describe the data.

ii) Which species shows a greater variation in wingspan? Explain your answer.

iii) Suggest a reason for the difference in wingspan between species A and B. Give a reason for your answer.

b) How much longer is species B's mean wing span than species A's? Give your answer as a percentage.

Q2 The table on the right shows the length of five rainbow boa snakes measured by conservationists investigating the effect of habitat loss on the well-being of the species. Using the formula below, calculate the standard deviation of this data.

$$s = \sqrt{\frac{\sum (x - \bar{x})^2}{n - 1}}$$

Snake	length (cm)
A	177
B	182
C	190
D	187
E	191

Exam Tip
Always show your working in calculation questions — don't just guess an answer. You could pick up marks for using the correct method, even if your final answer is wrong.

Correlations in variation

If you need to work out whether there's a correlation (relationship) between a genetic or environmental factor and variation in a particular characteristic, you can calculate the **Spearman's rank correlation coefficient** (r_s). As well as telling you whether or not the two variables are related, r_s will tell you how strongly they're related. It uses the formula:

$$r_s = 1 - \frac{6\sum d^2}{n(n^2 - 1)}$$ where 'd' is the 'difference in rank between data pairs' and 'n' is the total number of data pairs

Tip: Spearman's rank is a type of statistical test — see page 16 for more. See page 23 for more on correlations.

The result of the test is a number between -1 and +1. If the figure is -1, then there is a perfect negative correlation between the two variables. If the figure is +1, then there's a perfect positive correlation. The closer the figure is to 0, the weaker the correlation is. It'll all become clear with an example...

Example — Maths Skills

A team of biologists investigated how different amounts of rainfall affect the height of a particular crop.

Tip: The amount of rainfall received by a crop is an environmental factor. The height of the crop shows continuous variation.

In a laboratory facility, they prepared 7 test fields of the crop, where all conditions needed for plant growth could be controlled. All conditions except the amount of rainfall (simulated with a sprinkler system) were kept constant. Each of the test fields was exposed to a different amount of monthly rainfall over a 6 month growing period. The average height of the crops was measured at the end of the growing period. The table on the right shows the data collected.

Monthly Rainfall (mm)	Average height of crop (cm)
20	20.1
30	22.3
40	19.9
50	25.7
60	36.3
70	45.2
80	58.1

To calculate the Spearman's rank correlation coefficient:

1. First, rank both sets of data, keeping the data pairs together. The highest value for each variable is given the rank of 1, the second highest value is ranked 2, etc.

Monthly Rainfall (mm)	Rank	Average height of crop (cm)	Rank
20	7	20.1	6
30	6	22.3	5
40	5	19.9	7
50	4	25.7	4
60	3	36.3	3
70	2	45.2	2
80	1	58.1	1

2. Then work out the difference in rank between the two values in each data pair (d) and square it to calculate d^2.

Monthly Rainfall (mm)	Rank	Average height of crop (cm)	Rank	Difference between ranks (d)	d^2
20	7	20.1	6	1	1
30	6	22.3	5	1	1
40	5	19.9	7	2	4
50	4	25.7	4	0	0
60	3	36.3	3	0	0
70	2	45.2	2	0	0
80	1	58.1	1	0	0

3. Now count the number of data pairs (n). There are 7 data pairs here, so $n = 7$.

4. Now you can put all this information into the Spearman's rank formula:

$$r_s = 1 - \frac{6\sum d^2}{n(n^2 - 1)} = 1 - \frac{6(1 + 1 + 4 + 0 + 0 + 0 + 0)}{7(7^2 - 1)}$$

$$= 1 - \frac{6 \times 6}{7 \times 48} = 1 - \frac{36}{336}$$

$$= \mathbf{0.893} \text{ (3 s.f.)}$$

Because the figure is positive and close to 1, this suggests that there is a positive correlation between monthly rainfall and the average height of this crop.

Once you've got your result, you need to find out if it's statistically significant or not. First, you need to come up with a **null hypothesis**. When you're investigating correlations, the null hypothesis should always be that there is no correlation between the factors you're investigating — even if you expect that there will be. So the null hypothesis for the example above could be "there is no correlation between monthly rainfall and the average height of this crop".

Tip: A data pair consists of the two corresponding figures for each variable. E.g. 20 mm monthly rainfall and an average crop height of 20.1 cm make up one data pair.

Tip: A positive correlation means that as one variable increases, so does the other. A negative correlation means that as one variable increases, the other decreases. See page 23 for more.

Tip: You usually come up with the null hypothesis before you start your investigation — but we've explained how to calculate the correlation coefficient first here for clarity.

The result of the Spearman's rank test allows you to decide whether the null hypothesis can be rejected. To determine whether the null hypothesis can be rejected, you consult a table of **critical values** (see Figure 4).

The result is compared to the critical value at p = 0.05, which corresponds to *n* for the data you're looking at (in this case, 7). This value represents the point at which the correlation you're investigating would occur 95 out of 100 times, so there's only a 5% chance that the correlation is down to chance. You can reject the null hypothesis if the result of your test is higher than this value. If your result is a negative number, you ignore the minus sign when comparing it to the critical value. In this example, the Spearman's rank correlation coefficient (0.893) is higher than the relevant critical value, so the null hypothesis can be rejected. The result is statistically significant and the positive correlation is unlikely to be due to chance.

n	p = 0.05
7	0.786
8	0.738
9	0.700
10	0.648
11	0.618
12	0.587

Figure 4: *A table of critical values for the Spearman's rank test.*

Tip: When you're checking your result against the critical value, always make sure that you use the right critical value for the number of data pairs that you've investigated.

Tip: If your result is not statistically significant, it means the correlation could just be down to chance.

Practice Question — Application

Q1 A group of scientists were investigating whether the average milk yield of a herd of cows is affected by the amount of space each cow in the herd has in a field. Herds of 30 cows were kept in different sized fields for a month, where they had different amounts of space per cow. Each day, each cow was milked and the volume of milk it produced was recorded. An average daily milk yield was then calculated for each herd of cows from each of the different sized fields. The results are shown in the table on the right.

Space per cow (km²)	Average Daily Milk Yield (dm³)
0.004	32.1
0.005	36.2
0.006	37.4
0.007	34.3
0.008	36.7
0.009	38.9
0.010	37.6
0.011	33.4

a) Using the formula on the right, calculate the Spearman's rank correlation coefficient for this data.

$$r_s = 1 - \frac{6\sum d^2}{n(n^2 - 1)}$$

b) Using the table of critical values in Figure 4 above, determine whether the null hypothesis "there is no correlation between the average daily milk yield of a herd of cows and the amount of space per cow in a field" should be accepted or rejected.

Exam Tip
Don't let the context put you off. In your exam, the background information you get given could be about anything. Just pick out the information that you need and carry out the test like in the example.

Practice Questions — Fact Recall

Q1 How do you calculate a mean?

Q2 What shape is the graph of a data set with a normal distribution?

Q3 What does standard deviation measure?

- Know the different types of adaptations of organisms to their environment, including anatomical, physiological and behavioural adaptations.
- Understand why organisms from different taxonomic groups may show similar anatomical features, including the marsupial mole and placental mole.

Specification Reference 4.2.2

Tip: Organisms that are well adapted to their environment have a <u>selective advantage</u> over less well adapted organisms.

Figure 1: *When American possums feel threatened, they 'play dead' to escape attack.*

Figure 2: *An otter's streamlined body helps it to move easily through water.*

5. Adaptations

Variation gives some organisms an advantage over others...

What are adaptations?

All the variation between and within species means that some organisms are better adapted to their environment than others. Being adapted to an environment means an organism has features that increase its chances of survival and reproduction, and also the chances of its offspring reproducing successfully. These features are called **adaptations** and can be behavioural, physiological and anatomical (see below).

Adaptations develop because of evolution by natural selection (see page 279). In each generation, the best-adapted individuals are more likely to survive and reproduce — passing on the alleles for their adaptations to their offspring. Individuals that are less well adapted are more likely to die before reproducing.

Types of adaptations

There are three main types of adaptations that you need to know about.

1. Behavioural adaptations

These are ways an organism acts that increase its chance of survival.

Examples

- Possums sometimes 'play dead' — if they're being threatened by a predator they play dead to escape attack. This increases their chance of survival.
- Scorpions dance before mating — this makes sure they attract a mate of the same species, increasing the likelihood of successful mating.

2. Physiological adaptations

These are processes inside an organism's body that increase its chance of survival.

Examples

- Brown bears hibernate — they lower their rate of metabolism (all the chemical reactions taking place in their body) over winter. This conserves energy, so they don't need to look for food in the months when it's scarce — increasing their chance of survival.
- Some bacteria produce antibiotics — these kill other species of bacteria in the area. This means there's less competition, so they're more likely to survive.

3. Anatomical (structural) adaptations

These are structural features of an organism's body that increase its chance of survival.

Examples

- Otters have a streamlined shape — making it easier to glide through the water. This makes it easier for them to catch prey and escape predators, increasing their chance of survival.
- Whales have a thick layer of blubber (fat) — this helps to keep them warm in the cold sea. This increases their chance of survival in places where their food is found.

Q1 The common pipistrelle bat lives throughout Britain on farmland, or in open woodland, hedgerows and urban areas. It feeds by flying and catching insects in the air.

a) Some adaptations of the common pipistrelle bat are shown in the table below. Put a tick to show whether each adaptation is behavioural, physiological or anatomical.

Adaptation		Behavioural	Physiological	Anatomical
	Light, flexible wings			
	Male bats make mating calls to attract females			
	Bats lower their metabolism to hibernate over winter			

b) For each of the adaptations in the table above, suggest how it helps the common pipistrelle bat to survive.

Exam Tip
Read any information you're given in the exam carefully — it's there to help you answer the question.

Convergent Evolution

Organisms from different taxonomic groups may have similar features even though they're not closely related — for example, whales and sharks (see page 264). This is usually because the organisms have evolved in similar environments and to fill similar ecological niches. When two species evolve similar characteristics independently of one another (because they've adapted to live in similar environments) it's called **convergent evolution**.

There are examples of convergent evolution between the distantly-related marsupial and placental mammals.

Tip: For a reminder about what a taxonomic group is, take a look at page 260.

Marsupial and placental mammals

There are three different groups of mammals. Most mammals are placental mammals, while some are marsupials (and a very few are egg-laying monotremes).

Marsupials are found mainly in Australia and the Americas. They diverged from placental mammals many millions of years ago and have been evolving separately ever since. There are a few distinct differences between marsupial mammals (e.g. kangaroos) and placental mammals (e.g. humans):

Marsupial Mammals	Placental Mammals
Have a short gestation period (pregnancy).	Have a longer gestation period.
Don't develop a full placenta.	Develop a placenta during pregnancy, which allows the exchange of nutrients and waste products between the fetus and the mother.
Are born early in their development and climb into their mother's pouch. Here they become attached to a teat and receive milk while they continue to develop.	Are born more fully developed.

Figure 3: *The offspring of marsupials like this kangaroo are born earlier on in development than placental mammals. They climb into their mother's pouch, where they continue to develop.*

Figure 4: *A marsupial mole (eating a gecko, top) and a placental mole (bottom). These moles have independently evolved to have similar features.*

Although marsupial and placental mammals have been evolving separately for many millions of years, the evolution of some species has converged.

Example

There are many different species of mole. Most are placental moles, but there are also two species of marsupial mole.

Marsupial moles and placental moles aren't closely related — they evolved independently on different continents. They do share similar anatomical features though, e.g. they look alike (see Figure 4). That's because they've both evolved to live in similar environments. Both types of mole live in tunnels in the ground and they burrow to reach their food supply (e.g. earthworms, insects and other invertebrates). Their adaptations to this lifestyle include:

- Small or nonexistent eyes because they don't need to be able to see underground.
- No external ears, to keep a streamlined head for burrowing.
- Scoop-shaped and powerful front paws, which are good for digging.
- Claws that are specialised for digging.
- A tube shaped body and cone shaped head, which makes it easier to push through sand or soil.

Exam Tip
Make sure that you learn the example of marsupial and placental moles as animals that have similar adaptations but aren't closely related. It might come up in the exam.

Practice Question — Application

Q1 Brushtail possums and ring-tailed lemurs are both animals that spend a significant amount of time in trees. Despite not being closely related both have evolved opposable thumbs, which can move independently of other digits. This improves the possums' and lemurs' grips. Most animals do not have opposable thumbs.

    a) What type of adaptation are opposable thumbs?

    b) Suggest why brushtail possums and ring-tailed lemurs have independently evolved opposable thumbs.

Practice Questions — Fact Recall

Q1 Why is it helpful for an organism to be adapted to its environment?

Q2 What is a physiological adaptation?

Q3 List five adaptations shared by both marsupial and placental moles and explain how each one is linked to the moles' lifestyle.

6. The Theory of Evolution

Evolution is the slow and continual change of organisms from one generation to the next. Darwin and Wallace came up with a neat little theory to explain it...

Darwin's contribution

Scientists use theories to attempt to explain their observations — Charles Darwin was no exception. Darwin made four key observations about the world around him.

Darwin's observations:

1. Organisms produce more offspring than survive.
2. There's variation in the characteristics of members of the same species.
3. Some of these characteristics can be passed on from one generation to the next.
4. Individuals that are best adapted to their environment are more likely to survive.

Natural selection

Darwin wrote the **theory of evolution by natural selection** to explain his observations. His theory was that:

- Individuals within a population show variation in their phenotypes (their characteristics).

- Selection pressures (environmental factors such as predation, disease and competition) create a struggle for survival.

- Individuals with better adaptations (characteristics that give a selective advantage, e.g. being able to run away from predators faster) are more likely to survive and have reproductive success — in other words, they reproduce and pass on their advantageous adaptations to their offspring.

- Over time, the proportion of the population possessing the advantageous adaptations increases.

- Over generations this leads to evolution as the favourable adaptations become more common in the population.

We now know that genes determine many of an organism's characteristics and that individuals show variations in their phenotypes partly as a result of genetic variation, i.e. the different alleles they have. When an organism with advantageous characteristics reproduces, the alleles that determine those characteristics may be passed on to its offspring.

Example — peppered moths

- Peppered moths show variation in colour — there are light ones (with alleles for light colour) and dark ones (with alleles for dark colour).
- Before the 1800s there were more light moths than dark moths.
- During the 1800s, pollution had blackened many of the trees that the moths lived on.
- Dark coloured moths were now better adapted to this environment — they were better camouflaged from predators, so would be more likely to survive, reproduce and pass on the alleles for their dark colouring to their offspring.
- During this time the number of dark moths increased and the alleles for dark colour became more common in the population.

Learning Objectives:

- Know the contribution of Darwin and Wallace in formulating the theory of evolution by natural selection.

- Understand the mechanism by which natural selection can affect the characteristics of a population over time and appreciate that genetic variation, selection pressure and reproductive success (or failure) results in an increased proportion of the population possessing the advantageous characteristic(s).

- Know the evidence for the theory of evolution by natural selection, including fossil, DNA and molecular evidence.

Specification Reference 4.2.2

Tip: The opposite is also true — organisms without advantageous adaptations are less likely to survive and reproduce.

Tip: When Darwin published his theory in 1859, he didn't know about genes and alleles.

Figure 1: *Two colours of peppered moth on tree bark.*

Wallace's contribution

Tip: Natural selection is one process by which evolution occurs.

Alfred Russel Wallace, a scientist working at the same time as Darwin, played an important part in developing the theory of evolution by natural selection. He independently came up with the idea of natural selection and wrote to Darwin about it. He and Darwin published their papers on evolution together and acknowledged each other's work — although they didn't always agree about the mechanisms involved in natural selection.

Wallace's observations provided lots of evidence to support the theory of evolution by natural selection. For example, he realised that warning colours are used by some species (e.g. butterflies) to deter predators from eating them and that this was an example of an advantageous adaptation that had evolved by natural selection.

Unfortunately for Wallace, it wasn't until Darwin published his famous book 'On the Origin of Species' that other scientists began to pay attention to the theory. In this book Darwin gave lots of evidence to support the theory and expanded on it. For example, he wrote about all the species that he had observed during his voyage to South America and the Galápagos Islands in the 1830s. The book is partly why Darwin is usually better remembered than Wallace — even though Wallace helped to come up with the theory.

Evidence to support evolution

There's plenty of evidence to support evolution, such as...

Fossil record evidence

Fossils are the remains of organisms preserved in rocks. By arranging fossils in chronological (date) order, gradual changes in organisms can be observed that provide evidence of evolution.

Tip: The evidence supporting evolution isn't always perfect, e.g. there are sometimes gaps in the fossil record. This is because fossils don't always form and when they do, they can be easily damaged or destroyed.

Example

The fossil record of the horse shows a gradual change in characteristics, including increasing size, lengthening of the limbs and hoof development.

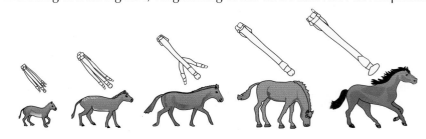

Figure 2: Suggested evolution of the horse.

Molecular evidence — DNA

The theory of evolution suggests that all organisms have evolved from shared common ancestors. Closely related species diverged (evolved to become different species) more recently.

Tip: There's more on DNA base sequences on pages 89-90.

Evolution is caused by gradual changes in the base sequence of organisms' DNA. So, organisms that diverged away from each other more recently should have more similar DNA, as less time has passed for changes in the DNA sequence to occur. This is exactly what scientists have found.

Humans, chimps and mice all evolved
from a common ancestor. Humans and
mice diverged a long time ago, but humans
and chimps diverged quite recently.
The DNA base sequence of humans and
chimps is 94% the same, but human and
mouse DNA is only 85% the same.

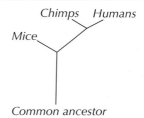

In eukaryotes, most DNA is found in the cell nucleus. But scientists don't just
analyse nuclear DNA to find out about evolutionary relationships. Eukaryotic
organisms also have DNA in their mitochondria, so scientists can also look at
differences in mitochondrial DNA to see how closely related organisms are.

Molecular evidence — proteins and other molecules

In addition to DNA, the similarities in other molecules provide evidence.
Scientists compare the sequence of amino acids in proteins, and compare
antibodies. Organisms that diverged away from each other more recently
have more similar molecules, as less time has passed for changes in proteins
and other molecules to occur.

Practice Questions — Application

Q1 The cytochrome C protein is found in almost all living organisms.
Suggest how scientists might use cytochrome C to provide evidence
for evolution.

Q2 There are many different species of rat snake, all found in different
habitats and with slightly different colourings. The black rat snake
lives in wooded habitats and has a dark, brown-black colouring
(see Figure 3). Describe how natural selection could explain the
evolution of a rat snake with black colouring in a wooded habitat.

Figure 3: *A black rat snake
climbing up a tree.*

Practice Questions — Fact Recall

Q1 State two observations made by Darwin that led him to develop his
theory of evolution.

Q2 What are selection pressures?

Q3 Name the scientist who published a paper on the theory of evolution
by natural selection at the same time as Darwin.

Q4 Explain how the following can provide evidence for evolution:
a) the fossil record, b) DNA.

7. More on Evolution

When pests and pathogens evolve to become resistant to the substances we use to control them, it can have serious implications for humans.

The evolution of pesticide resistance

Pesticides are chemicals that kill pests (e.g. insects that damage crops). Scientists have observed the evolution of pesticide resistance in many species of insect.

Examples

- Some populations of mosquito have evolved resistance to the pesticide DDT.
- Some populations of pollen beetles (which damage the crop oilseed rape) are resistant to pyrethroid pesticides.

The evolution of pesticide resistance can be explained by natural selection:

- There is variation in a population of insects. Genetic mutations make some insects naturally resistant to a pesticide.
- If the population of insects is exposed to that pesticide, only the individuals with resistance will survive to reproduce.
- The alleles which cause the pesticide resistance will be passed on to the next generation. Over many generations, the population will evolve to become more resistant to the chemical.

Example — DDT resistance in mosquitoes

DDT was first used to kill malaria-carrying mosquitoes around the time of WWII. In the 1950s, DDT-resistant mosquitoes began to appear in areas of widespread DDT use. Here's what happened:

- Genetic mutations gave some mosquitoes an allele that made them naturally resistant to DDT.
- When a mosquito population was exposed to DDT, mosquitoes without the allele for DDT resistance were killed, but individuals with the allele survived, reproduced and passed on the allele to the next generation.
- Over many generations, DDT resistance became widespread in mosquito populations that had been exposed to DDT.

The implications of pesticide resistance for humans

Crop infestations with pesticide-resistant insects are harder to control — some insects are resistant to lots of different pesticides. It takes farmers a while to figure out which pesticide will kill the insect and in that time all the crop could be destroyed.

If the insects are resistant to specific pesticides (ones that only kill that insect), farmers might have to use broader pesticides (those that kill a range of insects), which could kill beneficial insects. And if disease-carrying insects (e.g. mosquitoes) become pesticide-resistant, the spread of disease could increase.

A population of insects could also evolve resistance to all pesticides in use. To prevent this, new pesticides need to be produced. This takes time and costs money.

Learning Objective:

- Understand how evolution in some species has implications for human populations, including the evolution of pesticide resistance in insects and drug resistance in microorganisms.
  Specification Reference 4.2.2

Tip: The pesticide is acting as a <u>selection pressure</u>. Its presence determines which alleles become more common in the population, i.e. the alleles for pesticide resistance.

Tip: Mutations are changes to the DNA base code (see p. 87). They can produce new alleles, e.g. alleles for pesticide resistance.

Tip: Beneficial insects include natural pest predators (e.g. ladybirds), as these feed on pest species, removing them from the crop.

The evolution of drug resistance

You might remember from page 234 that scientists have observed the evolution of antibiotic resistance in many species of bacteria, e.g. MRSA. Other pathogens have evolved resistance to specific drugs too.

Tip: Antibiotic resistance is becoming a huge problem. See page 235 for more.

Example

Some of the protoctists that cause malaria are resistant to several drugs used to treat malaria.

The implications of drug resistance for humans

Infections caused by drug-resistant microorganisms are harder to treat — especially if the microorganism is resistant to lots of different drugs. It can take doctors a while to figure out which drugs will get rid of the infection, and in that time the patient could become very ill or die.

There could come a point where a pathogen has become resistant to all the drugs we currently use against it. To prevent this, new drugs need to be developed. This takes time and costs a lot of money.

Practice Question — Application

Q1 *P. falciparum* is a species of protoctist that causes malaria. Between the 1950s and 1990s, malaria caused by *P. falciparum* was most commonly treated with the drug chloroquine. During this period, *P. falciparum* developed widespread resistance to chloroquine.

a) Suggest how *P. falciparum* evolved to become resistant to chloroquine.

b) Some populations of *P. falciparum* are now resistant to multiple anti-malarial drugs. Explain the implications this may have for:

   i) people infected with malaria,

   ii) the drug companies that make anti-malarial drugs.

Section Summary

Make sure you know...

- That organisms can be classified into a taxonomic hierarchy consisting of the following eight groups: domain, kingdom, phylum, class, order, family, genus, species.
- That the binomial system is used to give each organism a two part scientific (Latin) name — the first part is the name of the organism's genus and the second part is the name of its species — and that this helps to avoid the confusion of using common names.
- The defining features of the Prokaryotae, Protoctista, Fungi, Plantae and Animalia kingdoms.
- That phylogeny is the study of the evolutionary history of groups of organisms (i.e. how closely related they are) and that it can be used to help classify organisms.
- That classification systems were originally based only on observable features, but that scientists now use a range of different evidence to classify organisms (including similarities in DNA base sequences and similarities in biological molecules, such as proteins).
- The similarities and differences between the 'three domain' and 'five kingdom' classification systems.

- That the three domain classification system was introduced because of new molecular evidence.
- That variation is the differences that exist between individuals and that it can occur within a species (intraspecific variation) or between species (interspecific variation).
- That continuous variation is where the individuals in a population vary within a range — there are no distinct categories.
- That discontinuous variation is where there are two or more distinct categories and each individual falls into only one of these categories.
- How to describe the differences between continuous and discontinuous variation using examples from plants, animals and microorganisms.
- That variation can be caused by genetic factors, environmental factors or a combination of both.
- How to use standard deviation to measure the amount of variation in a sample (how spread out the data is either side of the mean).
- How to use the Spearman's rank correlation coefficient to determine whether there is significant correlation between two variables.
- That an adaptation is a feature that increases an organism's chances of survival and reproduction, and also the chances of its offspring reproducing successfully.
- That adaptations can be behavioural, physiological or anatomical (structural).
- The reasons why organisms from different taxonomic groups may show similar anatomical features even though they're not closely related, including the example of marsupial moles and placental moles.
- The contributions of Charles Darwin and Alfred Russel Wallace to the theory of evolution by natural selection.
- How natural selection affects the characteristics of a population over time — including the roles of genetic variation, selection pressure and reproductive success.
- That fossil evidence, along with DNA and other molecular evidence, provides support for evolution.
- How insects evolving resistance to pesticides and microorganisms evolving resistance to drugs has implications for humans.

Exam-style Questions

1   The organism *Halobacterium salinarum* is classified as Archaea under the three domain system.

(a)   Fill in the blanks in the table below to show how *H. salinarum* is classified.

Domain	Archaea
Kingdom	Euryarchaeota
Phylum	Euryarchaeota
	Halobacteria
Order	Halobacteriales
	Halobacteriaceae
Species	

(2 marks)

(b)   Under the five kingdom classification system, *H. salinarum* would have been classified as Prokaryotae.

(i)   Give **two** characteristics of the Prokaryotae kingdom.

(2 marks)

(ii)   Explain why the three domain system does **not** contain the Prokaryotae kingdom.

(2 marks)

(iii)   Give **one** similarity between the three domain classification system and the five kingdom classification system.

(1 mark)

2   The **RuBisCO gene** is found in all plants.

When a new species of plant is being classified, this gene is often compared with the gene in other species to determine evolutionary relatedness.

(a)   Describe how a scientist could compare the RuBisCO gene in two different species of plant to determine how closely related they are.

(2 marks)

(b)   Why is the RuBisCO gene useful for determining relationships between plant species?

(1 mark)

(c)   The RuBisCO gene codes for an enzyme. Describe how a scientist could compare the RuBisCO enzyme in two different species of plant to determine how closely related they are.

(2 marks)

(d)   Classification of plants was originally based only on observable features. Explain why taxonomists now consider other evidence when classifying plant species.

(2 marks)

3   **Fig. 3.1** shows the use of an anti-aphid pesticide on a farm and the number of aphids found on the farm over a period of time.

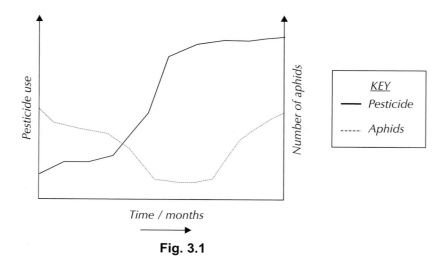

Fig. 3.1

  (a) (i) Describe the changes shown in the data in **Fig. 3.1**.

(3 marks)

    (ii) Explain how the changes you described in **part i)** may have occurred.

(4 marks)

  (b)   Suggest **one** implication these changes may have for the farmer.

(2 marks)

4   The bat *Anoura fistulata* has a very long tongue (up to one and a half times the length of its body).

      The tongue enables the bat to feed on the nectar inside a deep tubular flower found in the forests of Ecuador.

  (a)   The bat's tongue is an **anatomical** adaptation to feeding on deep flowers.

    (i) What is an adaptation?

(2 marks)

    (ii) Give **two** other types of adaptation an organism can have to its environment.

(2 marks)

  (b)   Describe how natural selection can explain the evolution of *Anoura fistulata's* long tongue.

(4 marks)

  (c)   A team of biologists were trying to determine how recently *Anoura fistulata* diverged from another species of bat. Explain how molecular evidence could be used to determine how recently the species diverged from each other.

(4 marks)

Exam Help

1. The Exams

You'll take two exams as part of OCR A AS biology. Everything you need to know about them is summarised below.

It seems obvious, but if you know exactly what will be covered in each of the exams, how much time you'll have to do them and how they'll be structured, you can be better prepared. So let's take a look at the ins and outs of the exams you'll be facing for AS Biology...

How are the exams structured?

OCR A AS Biology is examined in two papers that are each worth 50% of the total marks.

Paper	Total marks	Time	Modules assessed
Breadth in biology	70	1 hour 30 minutes	1, 2, 3 & 4
Depth in biology	70	1 hour 30 minutes	1, 2, 3 & 4

- 'Breadth in biology' has a section of multiple choice questions worth 20 marks and then a section of short answer questions worth 50 marks.
- 'Depth in biology' includes both short answer questions and extended response questions.

Solving problems in a practical context

In the exams, you'll get plenty of questions set in a 'practical context'. As well as answering questions about the methods used or the conclusions drawn (see pages 26-27), you'll need to be able to apply your scientific knowledge to solve problems set in these contexts.

Example

1   A scientist is investigating how the rate of an enzyme-controlled reaction is affected by substrate concentration. The results are shown in **Fig. 1.1**.

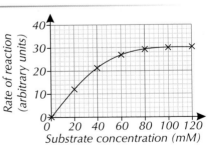

Fig. 1.1

(a)   Suggest why the graph levels off at substrate concentrations higher than 80 mM.

(2 marks)

You should remember from page 103 that once all the enzymes' active sites are full (the saturation point has been reached) adding more substrate won't increase the rate of reaction any further — which is why the rate levels off.

Exam Tip
If you're sitting the A-level in Biology rather than the AS, you'll be sitting a different set of exams to the ones described here.

Exam Tip
Both AS exam papers cover Modules 1 to 4 — this means you could be asked a question on anything in this book, so make sure you know it all inside out.

Exam Tip
The extended response questions are marked with an asterisk (*) and require you to write a longer answer with a logical structure. You will be assessed on your line of reasoning as well as how relevant your points are.

Exam Tip
Both papers will test synoptic skills — your ability to draw together concepts from all of the different modules.

Exam Tip
Questions like this can look bit scary, but you just have to apply what you already know about Biology to a real-life example. There are plenty of questions like this for you to have a go at in this book.

2. Command Words

Command words are just the bits of a question that tell you what to do.

You'll find answering exam questions much easier if you understand exactly what they mean, so here's a brief summary table of the most common command words:

Command word:	What to do:
Give / Name / State	Give a brief one or two word answer, or a short sentence.
Identify	Pick out information or say what something is.
Describe	Write about what something's like, e.g. describe the structure of fish gills.
Outline	Write about the main points in a topic.
Explain	Give reasons for something.
Suggest	Use your scientific knowledge to work out what the answer might be.
Justify	Show or prove something is right.
Calculate	Work out the solution to a mathematical problem.
Evaluate	Give the arguments both for and against an issue, or the advantages and disadvantages of something. You also need to give an overall judgement.

Exam Tip
When you're reading exam questions, underline the command words. That way you'll know exactly what type of answer to give.

Exam Tip
If you're answering a longer 'evaluate' question make a mental list of the pros and cons first, so you know what you want your answer to include before you start writing.

Exam Tip
Make sure you take a calculator and ruler into both your exams to help you with the calculation questions. A pencil and a spare pen may come in handy as well.

Some questions will also ask you to answer 'using the information/data provided' (e.g. a graph, table or passage of text) or 'with reference to figure X' — if so, you must refer to the information, data or figure you've been given or you won't get the marks. Some questions may also ask you to answer 'using your calculation' — it's the same here, you need to use your answer to a particular calculation, otherwise you won't get the marks.

Not all of the questions will have command words — instead they may just ask a which / what / how type of question.

3. Time Management

Time management is really important in your exams — it's no good writing a perfect answer to a 3 mark question if it takes you an hour.

For AS Biology, you get just over a minute per mark in each paper. So if you get stuck on a short question sometimes it's worth moving onto another one and then coming back to it if you have time. Bear in mind that you might want to spend a bit longer than a minute per mark on the extended response questions in the 'Depth in biology' paper.

If you've got any time left once you've finished the paper, hold off on celebrating and have a look back through the questions. You can use the time to go back to any questions you've skipped, check your answers to calculation questions and make sure you haven't accidentally missed any questions out.

Answers

Module 1

Development of Practical Skills

1. Planning an Experiment
Page 8 — Application Questions
Q1 a) the light intensity / distance of light source from the shoot
    b) E.g. temperature, shoot used
    c) E.g. repeat the experiment three times at each distance and calculate a mean.
Q2 a) E.g. a gas syringe / an upturned measuring cylinder filled with water.
    b) Hydrogen peroxide with no enzyme added.
    In reality, water should be added instead of the enzyme so that the overall volume of the reaction mixture is kept the same.

Page 8 — Fact Recall Questions
Q1 That if you repeat the experiment (using the same equipment and method), you will get the same results.
Q2 Results that answer the original question.
Q3 The variable that's measured in an experiment.
Q4 It shows that only the independent variable (the variable being changed) is affecting the dependent variable.
Q5 It shows what a positive result should look like and that a positive result is possible for the experiment.
Q6 The dangers of the experiment. Who is at risk from any dangers. How the risk can be reduced.

2. Carrying Out an Experiment
Page 10 — Fact Recall Questions
Q1 5.3 cm^3
Q2 To allow time for the water bath/solutions to heat up.
Q3 A table that shows you how many of each value there are.
Q4 A result that doesn't fit in with the rest of the results.

3. Processing Data
Page 12 — Application Questions
Q1 a) $4.2 - 3.1 = \textbf{1.1 dm}^3$
    b) In numerical order, the results are:
       3.1, 3.2, 3.4, 3.5, 3.5, 3.7, 3.9, 3.9, 3.9, 4.2
       So the median is $(3.5 + 3.7) \div 2 = \textbf{3.6 dm}^3$
       and the mode is $\textbf{3.9 dm}^3$.
Q2 Solution A: $(0.81 + 0.84 + 0.82) \div 3 = \textbf{0.82}$
   Solution B: $(0.54 + 0.55) \div 2 = \textbf{0.55}$
   Solution C: $(0.12 + 0.12 + 0.15) \div 3 = \textbf{0.13}$
   The third repeat for solution B is an anomalous result, so you should not include it when calculating the mean.
Q3 Decrease in number of individuals: $292 - 105 = 187$
   Difference in number of years: $2015 - 1995 = 20$
   So the mean decrease per year was $187 \div 20 = \textbf{9.35.}$

Page 14 — Application Questions
Q1 $36 \div 65 = 0.55$
   $0.55 \times 100 = \textbf{55\%}$
Q2 a) Hospital A:
      percentage change $= \dfrac{(29 - 22)}{22} = \dfrac{7}{22} \times 100 = 32\%$
      Hospital B:
      percentage change $= \dfrac{(19 - 14)}{14} = \dfrac{5}{14} \times 100 = 36\%$
      Hospital C:
      percentage change $= \dfrac{(31 - 25)}{25} = \dfrac{6}{25} \times 100 = 24\%$
      So the hospital with the largest percentage change is **B**.
    b) $24 : 16$
       $24 \div 8 = 3, 16 \div 8 = 2$
       3 : 2

Page 16 — Application Questions
Q1 4.5×10^{-3}
Q2 a) $4.53 \times 3.142 = 14.23326 = \textbf{14.2}$ (3.s.f.)
    b) $0.315 \div 0.025 = 12.6 = \textbf{13}$ (2.s.f.)
Q3 There is a significant difference between the mean heights of the two groups of seedlings — the difference is not due to chance (at the 95% confidence limit).

4. Presenting Data
Page 22 — Application Questions
Q1 A histogram, because it is frequency data and the independent variable is continuous.
Q2 a) E.g. $3.8 \text{ cm}^3 \div 30 \text{ min} = \textbf{0.13 cm}^3\textbf{min}^{-1}$
    b) For this answer you need to work out the equation of the graph in the form $y = mx + c$:
       First, find the gradient, e.g. $2.2 \text{ cm}^3 \div 30 \text{ min} = 0.073$ $\text{cm}^3 \text{min}^{-1}$ so $m = 0.073$
       Then c is where the line crosses the y-axis $= 0$.
       So the equation of the line can be written as $y = 0.073x + 0$, or just $y = 0.073x$.
       When $x = 50 \text{ min}, y = 0.073 \times 50 = \textbf{3.7 cm}^3$
Q3

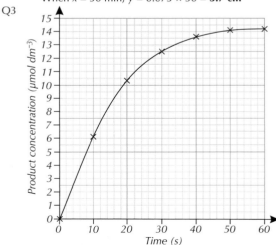

5. Drawing Conclusions and Evaluating

Page 27 — Application Questions
Q1 a) ± 0.25 cm³
    b) (0.25 ÷ 6.0) × 100 = 4.2%
Q2 a) No — e.g. the highest rate of reaction shown on the
        graph is at 40 °C, but the investigation only measured
        the rate at 10 °C increases. The rate of reaction at in-
        between temperatures wasn't measured — it is possible
        that the enzyme could work best at a temperature
        between 30 °C and 40 °C or between 40 °C and 50 °C.
    b) E.g. the rate could be measured three times at each
        temperature and a mean rate of reaction could be
        calculated.
    c) No, because the results of the experiment are specific to
        enzyme X. It is not possible to tell if the results will be
        the same for any other enzyme.

Exam-style Questions — page 29
1   D *(1 mark)*.
    Here are the answers for each option —
    A: (0.5 ÷ 50) × 100 = 1%, B: (0.05 ÷ 5) × 100 = 1%,
    C: (0.1 ÷ 10) × 100 = 1%, D: (0.25 ÷ 15) × 100 = 1.7%.
2   a) i) E.g. anomalous results (such as Repeat 1 at 10 °C)
            are easier to spot *(1 mark)*. A mean value can be
            calculated, which will reduce the effect of random
            error on the results/make the results more precise
            (1 mark).
        ii)
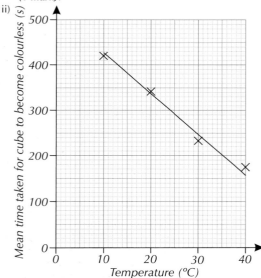
        *(3 marks — 1 mark for correctly labelled axes using
        appropriate scales, 1 mark for correctly plotted points,
        1 mark for appropriate line of best fit.)*
    b) The graph shows negative correlation. *(1 mark)*
        *Negative correlation is when one variable increases as the
        other decreases. Here, as the temperature increases, the
        mean time taken decreases.*
    c) For temperatures between 10 °C and 40 °C, the time
        taken for the cube to turn colourless decreases as the
        temperature increases *(1 mark)*.
    d) E.g. by wearing gloves/lab coats/safety goggles for the
        duration of the experiment to protect the skin/eyes
        (1 mark). By heating the acid in a water bath (rather
        than over a Bunsen burner) to prevent accidental boiling
        (1 mark).

    e) Any two from: the method of preparing the agar / the
        size/surface area of the agar cubes / the concentration
        of hydrochloric acid / the volume of hydrochloric acid.
        (1 mark for each)
        *You can read all about the method for this diffusion
        investigation on page 125.*

Module 2

Section 1 — Cell Structure

1. Cells and Organelles

Pages 34-35 — Application Questions
Q1 a) Mitochondria — these are the site of aerobic respiration
        in the cell / where ATP is produced.
        *You should be able to tell that both organelles are
        mitochondria by the cristae (folded structures) inside them.
        Don't be thrown by their slightly odd shapes.*
    b) Golgi apparatus — this processes and packages new
        lipids and proteins. It also makes lysosomes.
    c) Chloroplast — photosynthesis takes place here.
        *You can clearly see the granum and lamellae in this organelle,
        which should tell you that it's a chloroplast.*
    d) Cilia — used to move substances along the cell surface.
Q2 a) nucleolus
    b) cell wall
    c) Image B because there is a large vacuole and a cell
        wall present. Animal cells don't have either of these
        structures.

Page 35 — Fact Recall Questions
Q1 A — cell wall, B — cytoplasm, C — mitochondrion,
    D — nucleus, E — chloroplast, F — vacuole, G — cell
    membrane, H — ribosome.
Q2 Any three from, e.g. cell wall / plasmodesmata / vacuole /
    chloroplasts.
Q3 The nucleus controls the cell's activities (by controlling the
    transcription of DNA). The nuclear pores allow substances
    to move between the nucleus and the cytoplasm. The
    nucleolus makes ribosomes.
Q4 Any one from: To digest invading cells. / To break down
    worn out components of the cell.
Q5 The rough endoplasmic reticulum is covered in ribosomes,
    whereas the smooth endoplasmic reticulum is not.
Q6 It synthesises and processes lipids.
Q7 Golgi apparatus
Q8 centriole
Q9
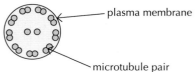

2. Organelles Working Together

Page 37 — Application Questions
Q1 Normal Golgi apparatus would look like a group of
    flattened linear sacs, lined up next to each other, rather than
    appearing small, round and disconnected.
    *Although normally you might expect to see some round
    vesicles adjacent to the Golgi apparatus.*

Q2 E.g. proteins often undergo further processing (e.g. sugar chains are trimmed or more are added) in the Golgi apparatus. If the apparatus is deformed in some way, these modifications might not take place, and so the proteins produced may not function correctly or at all.

Q3 E.g. the cytoskeleton is involved in the transport of vesicles around the cell. Vesicles are used to transport proteins in protein synthesis. If the cytoskeleton is disrupted, proteins may not be transported between the RER and the Golgi apparatus, preventing them from being modified, or between the Golgi and the cell surface, preventing them from being secreted from the cell.

Page 37 — Fact Recall Questions

Q1 The ribosomes on RER make proteins that are excreted or attached to the cell membrane. Proteins produced at the RER are folded and processed there.

Q2 The cytoskeleton supports the cell's organelles, keeping them in position. It also helps to strengthen the cell and maintain its shape. It transports organelles and materials within the cell. It can also cause the cell to move.

3. Prokaryotic Cells

Page 38 — Fact Recall Questions

Q1 Any three from, e.g: prokaryotes are smaller than eukaryotes. / Prokaryotic DNA is circular, eukaryotic DNA is linear. / Prokaryotes don't have a nucleus, eukaryotes do. / In eukaryotes, if a cell wall is present, it is made of cellulose or chitin. The cell wall in prokaryotes is made of a polysaccharide that isn't cellulose or chitin. / Prokaryotes have fewer organelles than eukaryotes and no membrane-bound organelles, e.g. mitochondria. / Prokaryote flagella are made of the protein flagellin arranged in a helix, whereas in eukaryotes flagella are made of microtubules arranged in a '9 + 2' formation. / Prokaryotes have smaller ribosomes than eukaryotes.

Q2 Any one from, e.g: they both contain ribosomes/DNA/ cytoplasm/a plasma (cell surface) membrane. / They may both contain flagella/a cell wall.

4. How Microscopes Work

Page 40 — Application Questions

Q1 a) image size ÷ magnification = object size
   8 mm ÷ 3150 = **0.0025 mm**

   b) image size ÷ magnification = object size
   18 mm ÷ 3150 = **0.0057 mm**

   Always make sure you show your working in questions like these — you could pick up some marks for using the correct calculation, even if you end up with the wrong final answer.

Q2 object size × magnification = image size
   0.00002 mm × 40 = **0.0008 mm**

Q3 First you need to convert 0.023 µm to millimetres by dividing by 1000.
   0.023 µm ÷ 1000 = 0.000023 mm
   magnification = image size ÷ object size
   0.035 mm ÷ 0.000023 mm = **× 1522**

Q4 image size ÷ magnification = object size
   13 mm ÷ 7000 = 0.0019 mm
   Then times by 1000 to convert to µm
   0.0019 mm × 1000 = **1.9 µm**

Q5 a) image size ÷ object size = magnification
   16 mm ÷ 2 mm = **× 8**

   b) object size × magnification = image size
   3 mm × 50 = **150 mm**

Q6 First you need to convert 10 µm to millimetres by dividing by 1000.
   10 µm ÷ 1000 = 0.01 mm
   image size ÷ object size = magnification
   10 mm ÷ 0.01 mm = **× 1000**

Page 43 — Application Questions

Q1 *E. coli* bacterium — light microscope, TEM, SEM
   nuclear pore — TEM, SEM
   human egg cell — light microscope, TEM, SEM
   DNA helix — TEM, SEM
   mitochondrion — light microscope, TEM, SEM
   influenza virus — TEM, SEM

   Answering this question is a lot easier if you know the maximum resolution for each type of microscope — it could come up in the exam, so make sure you learn it.

Q2 E.g. Team One might use an SEM. HIV is 0.12 µm in diameter, so it needs to be viewed under an electron microscope as these have a higher maximum resolution than light microscopes. Also, the team is looking at surface proteins and SEM images can show the surface of a specimen and can be 3D. The second team might use a TEM as they want to view the virus's internal structures. A TEM would allow them to do this because it uses thin slices of the specimen material and has a higher maximum resolution than either light microscopes or SEMs.

Q3 The team could use a laser scanning confocal microscope. This type of microscope uses a laser beam which would cause the fluorescent dyes to give off fluorescent light and show where the different types of protein are located. This type of microscopy is also suitable for thick samples so can generate images at different depths within the tissue sample.

Page 43 — Fact Recall Questions

Q1 magnification = image size ÷ object size

Q2 Magnification is how much bigger the image is than the specimen, whereas resolution is how detailed the image is and how well a microscope distinguishes between two points that are close together.

Q3 Fluorescent dyes

Q4 TEMs use electromagnets to focus a beam of electrons, which is then transmitted through the specimen. Denser parts of the specimen absorb more electrons, which makes them look darker on the image you end up with.

Q5 SEMs scan a beam of electrons across the specimen. This knocks off electrons from the specimen, which are gathered in a cathode ray tube to form an image.

Q6 SEM

Q7 a) 0.2 µm
   b) 0.0002 µm
   c) 0.002 µm

Q8 TEM

Q9 TEM

   The maximum resolution of a light microscope is 0.2 µm and the maximum resolution of a SEM is 0.002 µm, so you wouldn't be able to see something that was 0.001 µm with either of these.

5. Using Microscopes

Page 47 — Application Question

Q1 a) Total length of 5 divisions on stage micrometer
= 2 μm × 5 = 10 μm
Length of each graticule division
= 10 μm ÷ 8 = **1.25 μm**

For this question you first need to work out the total length of the 5 stage micrometer divisions. When you've got this you just need to divide this length by the number of eyepiece graticule divisions it's equal to, to give you the length represented by one eyepiece graticule division.

b) 12 × 1.25 = **15 μm**
The cell is the same width as 12 divisions on the eyepiece graticule scale, so you need to multiply the width of one division by 12.

Page 48 — Fact Recall Questions

Q1 To prevent the object being viewed from appearing white if it is completely transparent.

Q2 Particular stains can be used to make particular parts of cells show up.

Q3 Any two from: e.g. methylene blue, Giemsa stain, haematoxylin, eosin.

Q4 E.g. dry mounting and wet mounting.

Q5 cover slip

Q6 The eyepiece.

Q7 It is a microscope slide with an accurate scale that is used to work out the value of the divisions on the eyepiece graticule at a particular magnification.

Exam-style Questions — pages 49-50

1 a) i) Production of ATP *(1 mark)*.
      ii) Abnormal mitochondria might not produce as much ATP as normal mitochondria *(1 mark)*. This means the heart tissue may not have sufficient energy to work properly/for muscle contraction *(1 mark)*.
   b) i) Any two from: abnormal mice have more mitochondria *(1 mark)* / smaller mitochondria *(1 mark)* / mitochondria with a smaller/lighter/less dense matrix *(1 mark)* / mitochondria with fewer cristae *(1 mark)*.
      ii) object size is 1.5 μm = 1.5 μm ÷ 1000 = 0.0015 mm
         magnification = image size ÷ object size
         = ~23 mm ÷ 0.0015 mm = **× 15333** (allow values between × 14667 to × 15333)
         (2 marks for correct answer, 1 mark if only working is correct.)

2 a) i) No *(1 mark)*. The microscope has a resolution of 0.2 μm/200 nm so it can't be used to distinguish between objects that are smaller than 0.2 μm/200 nm — such as the ribosomes *(1 mark)*.
      If you convert the diameter of the ribosomes and the resolution of the microscope into the same units, (e.g. both nm or both μm) it's easier to see that the ribosomes are too small for the microscope to pick up.
      ii) The ribosomes in the bacterial cells would be smaller than those in the stomach cells *(1 mark)*. This is because bacteria are prokaryotic cells which have smaller ribosomes than the eukaryotic stomach cells *(1 mark)*.

      iii) Any two from, e.g. the stomach cell would not have chloroplasts / a vacuole / a cell wall / plasmodesmata *(2 marks)*.
      iv) Using more than one stain would allow the scientist to see specific parts of the cell *(1 mark)*.
   b) object size = image size ÷ magnification
      = 4 ÷ 100 = **0.04 mm**
      (2 marks for correct answer, 1 mark if only working is correct)
   c) **5-6 marks:**
      The answer describes the full process of production and secretion of proteins (the digestive enzymes) that are to be released from the cell. There is a full explanation of the role of the ribosome(s), rough endoplasmic reticulum (RER), vesicle(s), Golgi apparatus and plasma membrane. The answer has a clear and logical structure. The information given is relevant and detailed.
      3-4 marks:
      The answer describes most of the process of production and secretion of proteins (the digestive enzymes) that are to be released from the cell. There is some explanation of the roles of the different organelles in the process. The answer has some structure. Most of the information given is relevant and there is some detail involved.
      1-2 marks:
      One or two steps involved in the process of production and secretion of proteins (the digestive enzymes) are referenced.
      The answer has no clear structure. The information given is basic and lacking in detail. It may not all be relevant.
      0 marks:
      No relevant information is given.
      Here are some points your answer may include:
      New proteins are made at the ribosomes on the rough endoplasmic reticulum. They're then folded and processed (e.g. sugar chains added) in the rough endoplasmic reticulum before being transported to the Golgi apparatus in vesicles. Here the proteins may undergo further processing (e.g. sugar chains trimmed). The proteins then enter vesicles to be transported to the plasma membrane where the proteins are secreted.

3 a) Bacteria are prokaryotic cells, so the penicillin inhibits the synthesis of their cell walls, eventually leading to cell lysis and death *(1 mark)*. Human cells are eukaryotic animal cells, and so have no cell wall, so penicillin antibiotics leave these cells unaffected *(1 mark)*.
   b) i) E.g. because electron microscopes have a higher resolution *(1 mark)* so they can be used to look at smaller objects (like bacteria) in more detail *(1 mark)*.
      ii) A transmission electron microscope/TEM *(1 mark)*. Transmission electron micrographs show a 2D cross section through a sample as seen in Fig 3.1 *(1 mark)*.
   c) Any two from, e.g. a prokaryotic cell is smaller than a eukaryotic cell *(1 mark)*. / There is no nucleus present in a prokaryotic cell *(1 mark)*. / There are fewer organelles present in a prokaryotic cell *(1 mark)*. / There are no mitochondria present in a prokaryotic cell *(1 mark)*. / Ribosomes are smaller in a prokaryotic cell than in a eukaryotic cell *(1 mark)*. / The DNA in a prokaryotic cell is circular, not linear *(1 mark)* / A prokaryotic cell may contain plasmids *(1 mark)*.

Section 2 — Biological Molecules

1. Water
Page 53 — Fact Recall Questions
Q1 Any three from: e.g. it is a reactant in lots of chemical reactions. / It transports substances. / It helps with temperature control./It is a coolant. / It is a habitat. / It is a solvent.

Q2 Because it has a slight negative charge on one side and a slight positive charge on the other.

Q3

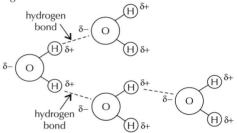

Q4 A weak bond between a slightly positively charged hydrogen atom in one molecule and a slightly negatively charged atom in another molecule.

Q5 E.g.

When drawing a hydrogen bond between two water molecules, make sure you draw it between one hydrogen atom and one oxygen atom.

Q6 Because when water is heated, a lot of the heat energy is absorbed by the hydrogen bonds between water molecules. So it takes a lot of energy to increase the temperature of the water.

Q7 Because it has a high latent heat of evaporation, which means it uses up a lot of (heat) energy when it evaporates from a surface. This cools the surface and helps to lower the temperature.

Q8 It makes water very cohesive and a good solvent.

Q9 a) B, e.g. because the water molecules are being held further apart in diagram B / the water molecules have formed a lattice shape.

b) In cold temperatures ice forms an insulating layer on top of water. This means the organisms that live in the water below do not freeze and can still move around.

Q10 The slightly negatively charged ends of the water molecules will be attracted to the positive ion, meaning the positive ion will get surrounded by water molecules.

2. Macromolecules and Polymers
Page 54 — Fact Recall Questions
Q1 A polymer is a large, complex molecule, composed of many monomers joined together.

Q2 A monomer is a small, basic molecular unit that makes up a polymer.

Q3 Any two from, e.g. monosaccharides / amino acids / nucleotides.

Q4 A chemical bond is formed between the monomers and a molecule of water is released.

Q5 A hydrolysis reaction.

3. Carbohydrates
Page 57 — Application Question
Q1 a)

This diagram looks a bit different from other disaccharide diagrams. It's because the OH group needed to form the glycosidic bond is at the top of the galactose molecule rather than the bottom.

b)

Page 57 — Fact Recall Questions
Q1 Carbon, hydrogen and oxygen / C, H and O.

Q2 A hexose monosaccharide has six carbon atoms and a pentose monosaccharide has five carbon atoms.

Q3 a)

Be careful when drawing alpha glucose or beta glucose — it's only the groups on the right-hand side of the molecule that are different between the two types of glucose.

b)

Q4 glycosidic

There are lots of words similar to 'glycosidic' in biology so make sure you spell it right — you might not get the mark in the exam if you don't.

Q5 α-glucose and fructose

Q6 Glycogen is made from long, branched chains of α-glucose. It has lots of side branches which means that stored glucose can be released quickly. It's a very compact molecule which makes it good for storage.

Q7 one cellulose molecule

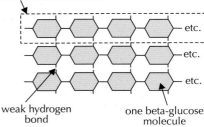

weak hydrogen bond   one beta-glucose molecule

4. Lipids
Page 60 — Fact Recall Questions
Q1 Carbon, hydrogen and oxygen / C, H and O.

Q2 A molecule of glycerol and three fatty acids.

Q3 ester bond

Q4 A saturated fatty acid doesn't have any double bonds between its carbon atoms, an unsaturated fatty acid does.

Q5 Because they contain lots of chemical energy and they're insoluble.

Q6 Phospholipid heads are hydrophilic and their tails are hydrophobic, so they form a double layer (the bilayer of cell membranes) with their heads facing out towards the water on either side. The centre of the bilayer is hydrophobic, so water-soluble substances can't easily pass through it.

Q7 They help to strengthen the cell membrane by making it less fluid and more rigid.

5. Proteins
Page 62 — Application Questions
Q1 a) E.g.

$$H_2N - \overset{\overset{\displaystyle H}{|}}{\underset{\underset{\displaystyle H}{|}}{C}} - \overset{\overset{\displaystyle O}{\|}}{C} - \overset{\overset{\displaystyle H}{|}}{N} - \overset{\overset{\displaystyle \overset{\displaystyle H_3C \quad CH_3}{\diagdown\diagup}}{CH}}{\underset{\underset{\displaystyle H}{|}}{C}} - COOH$$

b) E.g.

$$H_2N - \overset{\overset{\displaystyle CH_3}{|}}{\underset{\underset{\displaystyle H}{|}}{C}} - \overset{\overset{\displaystyle O}{\|}}{C} - \overset{\overset{\displaystyle H}{|}}{N} - \overset{\overset{\displaystyle H}{|}}{\underset{\underset{\displaystyle H}{|}}{C}} - COOH$$

c) E.g.

$$H_2N - \overset{\overset{\displaystyle H}{|}}{\underset{\underset{\displaystyle H}{|}}{C}} - \overset{\overset{\displaystyle O}{\|}}{C} - \overset{\overset{\displaystyle H}{|}}{N} - \overset{\overset{\displaystyle CH_3}{|}}{\underset{\underset{\displaystyle H}{|}}{C}} - \overset{\overset{\displaystyle O}{\|}}{C} - \overset{\overset{\displaystyle H}{|}}{N} - \overset{\overset{\displaystyle \overset{\displaystyle H_3C \quad CH_3}{\diagdown\diagup}}{CH}}{\underset{\underset{\displaystyle H}{|}}{C}} - COOH$$

Q2

$$H_2N - \overset{\overset{\displaystyle H}{|}}{\underset{\underset{\displaystyle H}{|}}{C}} - COOH \quad \text{and} \quad H_2N - \overset{\overset{\displaystyle CH_2OH}{|}}{\underset{\underset{\displaystyle H}{|}}{C}} - COOH$$

Page 65 — Fact Recall Questions
Q1 amino acids

Q2 A chain of more than two amino acids joined together.

Q3

$$H_2N - \overset{\overset{\displaystyle R}{|}}{\underset{\underset{\displaystyle H}{|}}{C}} - COOH$$

You could have drawn your amino group like this; $\overset{\displaystyle H}{\underset{\displaystyle H}{\diagdown}} N-$

or your carboxyl group like this; $-C\overset{\diagup O}{\diagdown OH}$

Both ways are fine and would get you marks in the exam.

Q4 Carbon, oxygen, hydrogen, nitrogen and sulfur.

Q5 peptide

Q6 a) condensation
   b) hydrolysis

Q7 Hydrogen bonds form between the –NH and –CO groups of the amino acids in the chain. This makes it automatically coil into an alpha helix or beta pleated sheet.

Don't get the secondary structure of a protein confused with the tertiary structure or quaternary structure. In the tertiary structure, hydrogen bonds form between some of the R groups on the polypeptide chain. In the quaternary structure, hydrogen bonds may form between different polypeptide chains.

Q8 a) tertiary
   b) A — hydrogen bond, B — ionic bond, C — disulfide bond
   c) When two molecules of the amino acid cysteine come close together, the sulfur atom in one cysteine bonds to the sulfur in the other cysteine.

Q9 It is the way two or more polypeptide chains of a protein are assembled together.

Q10 The globular structure of haemoglobin means that the hydrophilic side chains are on the outside of the molecule and the hydrophobic side chains face inwards. This makes haemoglobin soluble in water, which makes it good for transporting oxygen in the blood.

Q11 A protein with a non-protein group attached.

Q12 E.g. they are soluble and reactive

Q13 a) It forms connective tissue in animals.
   b) E.g. it's very strong so it can form rigid structures (such as bone).

6. Inorganic ions
Page 67 — Application Question
Q1 $C - Cl^-$

Page 67 — Fact Recall Questions
Q1 a) H^+
   b) NH_4^+
   c) PO_4^{3-}
   d) OH^-

Q2 E.g. calcium (Ca^+) ion / phosphate (PO_4^{3-}) ion

Q3 E.g. sodium (Na^+) and potassium (K^+) ions

Q4 E.g. ammonium (NH_4^+) and nitrate (NO_3^-) ions

Q5 E.g. hydrogencarbonate (HCO^{3-}) ion

Q6 The pH would increase / the solution would become more alkaline.

294   Answers

7. Biochemical Tests for Molecules
Page 68 — Application Questions
Q1 Orange juice and goat's milk.
Q2 As a (negative) control.

Page 70 — Application Question
Q1 Solution A — no reducing sugars present, but non-reducing sugars might be present.
Solution B — reducing sugars are present.
Here, think carefully about what sugars have been tested for and what the different colours of the results indicate. Remember that a negative result for a reducing sugar test doesn't rule out non-reducing sugars.

Page 73 — Application Question
Q1 8 mg cm^{-3}

Page 73 — Fact Recall Questions
Q1 a) sodium hydroxide solution
b) copper(II) sulfate solution
c) It would be purple.
Q2 iodine test
Q3 Shake the sample with ethanol for about a minute then pour the solution into water. Any lipid will show up as a milky emulsion.
Q4 Add Benedict's reagent to a test sample and heat it in a water bath that's been brought to the boil. Look at the colour of the sample for the result. A positive result would be coloured green, yellow, orange or brick red and a negative result would be blue.
Q5 a) A device that measures the strength of a coloured solution by seeing how much light passes through it.
b) Carry out the Benedict's test on the unknown solution. Remove the precipitate from the solution and use a colorimeter with a red filter to measure the absorbance of the Benedict's solution remaining in the tube. Finally using the calibration curve, read off an estimate for the glucose concentration of the sample.
Make sure you're clear about what goes into the colorimeter — it's what's left in the tube after the precipitate has been removed, not the precipitate itself.
Q6 A biosensor is a device that uses a biological molecule to detect a chemical. When it comes into contact with the chemical it detects, the biological molecule produces a signal which is then converted to an electrical signal by a transducer. The electrical signal is then processed.

8. Separating Molecules
Page 76 — Application Question
Q1 a) R_f value $= \dfrac{\text{distance moved by the solute}}{\text{distance moved by the solvent}}$

Solute A: R_f value $= 2.8 \div 7.2 = \mathbf{0.39}$
Solute B: R_f value $= 3.3 \div 7.2 = \mathbf{0.46}$
Solute C: R_f value $= 5.3 \div 7.2 = \mathbf{0.74}$
b) Solute A is alanine, solute B is tyrosine and solute C is leucine.

Page 76 — Fact Recall Questions
Q1 Chromatography is used to separate out the components of a mixture.
Q2 A liquid solvent.
Q3 A thin layer of solid (e.g. silica gel) on a glass or plastic plate.
Q4 R_f value $= \dfrac{\text{distance moved by the solute}}{\text{distance moved by the solvent}}$

Exam-style Questions — pages 78-79
1 a)

	Observation	Starch present
Plant A	**dark, blue-black colour**	*Yes*
Plant B	**browny-orange colour**	*No*

(1 mark for each correct answer)
Make sure you emphasise that a positive result would be a dark colour — you won't get a mark in the exam if you just say it turns blue.
b) i) amylopectin *(1 mark)*
ii) Amylose is a long, unbranched chain of α-glucose *(1 mark)*. It has a coiled structure/cylindrical shape *(1 mark)*. These features make it compact meaning it's good for storage *(1 mark)*.
c) i) Any three from: e.g. starch is used to store energy whereas cellulose is used to strengthen cell walls. / Starch is made from α-glucose whereas cellulose is made from β-glucose. / Starch has a compact shape whereas cellulose is a long, straight molecule. / The bonds between the glucose molecules in starch (amylose) are angled whereas the bonds between glucose molecules in cellulose are straight *(3 marks for 3 correct answers)*.
ii) *(1 mark)*

You have to flip the glucose molecule on the right-hand side, so that the –OH groups of both glucose molecules are close together — this is where the glycosidic bond forms and a molecule of water is lost.
iii) During hydrolysis reactions *(1 mark)* molecules of water *(1 mark)* break apart the glycosidic bonds *(1 mark)*.
2 a) It is the sequence of amino acids in the polypeptide chain *(1 mark)* joined together with peptide bonds *(1 mark)*.
b) ionic *(1 mark)*, disulfide *(1 mark)*, hydrogen *(1 mark)*, positively *(1 mark)*, negatively *(1 mark)*
c) Add a few drops of sodium hydroxide solution to the test sample *(1 mark)*. Then add some copper(II) sulfate solution *(1 mark)*. If protein is present, the solution will turn purple *(1 mark)*. If there's no protein present, the solution will stay blue *(1 mark)*.
3 a) Different pigments will be spend different amounts of time in the mobile phase *(1 mark)*. The pigments that spend longer in the mobile phase will travel further, so the pigments separate out *(1 mark)*.
b) R_f value $= 3.7 \text{ cm} \div 9.0 \text{ cm} = \mathbf{0.41}$ *(1 mark)*
c) Any two from: e.g. a different solvent was used / a different stationary phase was used / the experiment was carried out at a different temperature *(1 mark for each correct answer. Maximum of 2 marks available.)*.

Section 3 — Nucleotides and Nucleic Acids

1. Nucleotides
Page 82 — Fact Recall Questions
Q1   nucleotides
Q2   A = phosphate group, B = deoxyribose (sugar),
      C = (nitrogenous) base
Q3   Part B/the sugar would be ribose rather than deoxyribose.
Q4   adenine, guanine
Q5   cytosine, uracil
      *Remember, uracil replaces thymine as a pyrimidine base
      in RNA.*
Q6   A purine base contains two carbon-nitrogen rings joined
      together, where as a pyrimidine base only has one
      carbon-nitrogen ring. (So a pyrimidine base is smaller
      than a purine base.)
Q7   One or more phosphate groups/inorganic phosphates (P_i).
Q8   A molecule of ADP is made from adenine, a ribose sugar
      and two phosphate groups.
      *If you're asked to describe the structure of ADP in the exam,
      make sure you're specific and put that it's ribose. If you just
      put 'sugar' you won't get the mark.*

2. Polynucleotides and DNA
Page 85 — Application Questions
Q1   a) TGACAGCATCAGCTACGAT
      b) ACGTGGTACACCATTTAGC
Q2   A white precipitate of DNA might not form, as the
      temperature in the water bath may not be high enough to
      stop the enzymes in the cells from working. This means the
      enzymes may break the DNA down and less DNA will be
      available to form a precipitate.
Q3   a) 22
      b) 12
      c) 12
      *If there are 34 base pairs in total and 22 of them contain
      adenine, then the other 12 must contain both cytosine and
      guanine — it's all to do with complementary base pairing.*

Page 85 — Fact Recall Questions
Q1   a) phosphodiester bonds
      b) The phosphate group of one nucleotide and the pentose
          sugar of another.
Q2   Two DNA polynucleotide strands join together by hydrogen
      bonding between complementary base pairs — A with T
      and G with C. The antiparallel strands then twist round
      each other to form the DNA double-helix.
Q3   E.g. break up the cells in your sample and mix with a
      solution of detergent, salt and distilled water. Incubate the
      mixture in a water bath at 60 °C for 15 minutes and then
      put it in an ice bath to cool down. When it's cooled, filter
      the mixture and transfer a sample of the mixture to a boiling
      tube. Add protease (and RNase) enzymes to the filtered
      mixture. Slowly dribble some cold ethanol down the side
      of the tube, so that it forms a layer on top of the DNA-
      detergent mixture. Leave the tube for a few minutes, and
      then remove any white precipitate of DNA that forms using
      a glass rod.

3. DNA Replication
Page 87 — Application Question
Q1   a) In the bacteria that were grown in heavy nitrogen broth
          then light nitrogen broth, each DNA molecule contained
          50% heavy nitrogen and 50% light nitrogen.
          This suggests that half of the new strands are from the
          original heavy nitrogen DNA, and therefore that the
          DNA has replicated semi-conservatively.
      b) It means that the original DNA strand can act as a
          template for the new strand — free-floating DNA
          nucleotides can join up with exposed bases on the
          original strand by complementary base pairing.
      c) E.g they could have controlled all the variables, e.g. the
          other nutrients in the broth. / They could have used a
          negative control, e.g. bacteria grown in broth without
          any nitrogen.
          *If you get a question like this in the exam, try to give
          specific suggestions about how the results you're being
          asked about could be made valid — don't just talk about
          ways of improving validity in general.*

Page 87 — Fact Recall Questions
Q1   hydrogen bonds
Q2   It joins nucleotides on the new DNA strand together.
Q3   To make sure genetic information is conserved (stays the
      same) each time the DNA in a cell is replicated.
Q4   A mutation is any change to the DNA base sequence.

4. Genes and Protein Synthesis
Page 90 — Application Questions
Q1   a) 4
      b) 6
      c) 9
      *To work out how many amino acids are coded for by a sequence
      you need to count the number of complete triplets that are
      in the sequence. Remember that the genetic code is non-
      overlapping.*
Q2   a) His-Tyr-Tyr-Arg-Gly-Cys-His-Arg-Gly
      b) Arg-Tyr-Asp-Asp-Cys-His-Gly-Tyr-His
      *For questions like this, it's a good idea to split up the mRNA
      base sequence into groups of three letters (CAU/UAC/UAC,
      etc.). Then you'll be able to see what's going on more easily.*
Q3   E.g. GACUACUGCAGAAGAGGCUGCGGCUACCAU
      GGCGAC
      *There are lots of possible combinations you could have given
      here, because each of the amino acids in the table is coded for
      by more than one codon*

Page 90 — Fact Recall Questions
Q1   It's the sequence of bases that codes for amino acids.
Q2   a) mRNA/messenger RNA
      b) tRNA/transfer RNA
      *If you get a question like this in the exam you need to be
      specific. Always write down the type of RNA you mean
      (e.g. mRNA) rather than just 'RNA'.*
Q3   rRNA helps to catalyse the formation of peptide bonds
      between amino acids.

Q4 a) A sequence of three mRNA bases in a gene.
   b) Each mRNA codon codes for an amino acid or tells the cell when to start or stop production of a protein.
   c) triplet
Q5 a) Base triplets don't share their bases.
   b) The same specific base triplets code for the same amino acids in all living things.

5. Transcription and Translation
Page 92 — Application Question
Q1 It will inhibit protein synthesis. By inhibiting RNA polymerase, α–amanitin will prevent the transcription of mRNA from DNA, preventing protein synthesis from taking place.

Page 93 — Application Questions
Q1 E.g. it may affect the function of the ribosomes, preventing them from translating mRNA into amino acids. This could prevent/impair protein synthesis.
You don't need to have learnt about Diamond-Blackfan anaemia to answer this question — so long as you know the process of translation, you can work out the answer.
Q2 It could be shorter and so could be a different protein. Translation of the mRNA sequence only continues until a stop codon is reached. Any codons after the stop codon would not be translated into amino acids.

Pages 93-94 — Fact Recall Questions
Q1 An mRNA copy of a gene.
Q2 An enzyme. RNA polymerase attaches to the DNA double-helix, and it lines up free RNA nucleotides alongside the template strand. It then moves along the DNA strand, assembling a complementary mRNA sequence from free RNA nucleotides.
Q3 The hydrogen bonds between the strands re-form and the strands coil back into a double-helix.
Q4 a) A tRNA molecule with an anticodon that's complementary to the start codon on the mRNA attaches itself to the mRNA by complementary base pairing. A second tRNA molecule attaches itself to the next codon on the mRNA in the same way, and so on.
   b) translation
Don't get transcription and translation mixed up in the exam — it's easy to do and it means you'd miss out on a mark.
   c) A stop codon on the mRNA molecule.

Exam-style Questions — pages 95-96
1 D *(1 mark)*
2 A *(1 mark)*
3 a) AGCGGUUGUUGUGAG *(1 mark)*
      5 amino acids *(1 mark)*
   b) i) ribosome *(1 mark)*

ii) **5-6 marks:**
The answer describes the full process of translation with full and correct references to the roles that tRNA and rRNA play in the process.
The answer has a clear and logical structure.
The information given is relevant and detailed.
3-4 marks:
The answer describes most of the process of translation with some references to tRNA and rRNA. The answer has some structure. Most of the information given is relevant and there is some detail involved.
1-2 marks:
One or two steps involved in the process of translation are given, but with lack of reference to both tRNA and rRNA.
The answer has no clear structure. The information given is basic and lacking in detail. It may not all be relevant.
0 marks:
No relevant information is given.
Here are some points your answer may include:
tRNA molecules carry amino acids to the ribosome. A tRNA molecule with an anticodon that's complementary to the start codon on the mRNA attaches itself to the mRNA by complementary base pairing. A second tRNA molecule attaches itself to the next codon on the mRNA in the same way and rRNA in the ribosome catalyses the formation of a peptide bond between the two amino acids. The first tRNA molecule moves away, leaving its amino acid behind. A third tRNA molecule binds to the next codon on the mRNA, its amino acid binds to the first two and the second tRNA molecule moves away. This process continues until there's a stop codon.

4 a) Deoxyribose sugar *(1 mark)*, a phosphate group *(1 mark)* and a nitrogenous base *(1 mark)*.
   b) i) The DNA will lose its double-helix structure/the two DNA strands will unravel *(1 mark)*. This is because the double helix/two DNA strands are held together by hydrogen bonding between the base pairs *(1 mark)*.
      ii) adenine *(1 mark)*, guanine *(1 mark)*
If you get a question in the exam that says, 'Name two...' don't hedge your bets and write down three or four possible answers — any wrong answers will cancel out the correct answers and you won't pick up any marks at all.
   c) i) unzips *(1 mark)*, template *(1 mark)*, complementary *(1 mark)*, adenine *(1 mark)*, DNA polymerase *(1 mark)*
      ii) semi-conservative replication *(1 mark)*

5 a) The sugar in mRNA is ribose not deoxyribose *(1 mark)*. Uracil replaces thymine as a base in mRNA *(1 mark)*. mRNA is a single polynucleotide strand — a DNA molecule is made up of two polynucleotide strands *(1 mark)*.
   b) mRNA carries a complementary copy of a gene/section of DNA *(1 mark)* out of the nucleus to the ribosomes (in the cytoplasm) *(1 mark)*.

c) i) A sequence of DNA nucleotides that codes for a
protein/polypeptide *(1 mark)*.
   ii) E.g if there is a mutation in the sequence of DNA
nucleotides, it could affect the amino acid sequence
(1 mark). This can cause an abnormal protein to
be produced *(1 mark)*. The abnormal protein might
function better than the normal protein — or it might
not work at all *(1 mark)*.
d) The genetic code is described as degenerate because
some amino acids are coded for by more than one base
triplet *(1 mark)*.

Section 4 — Enzymes

1. Action of Enzymes
Page 100 — Application Question
Q1 No glucose was produced because, unlike with maltase, the
shape of the active site of sucrase is not complementary to
the shape of maltose. This means that maltose can't bind
to sucrase to form an enzyme-substrate complex, so no
reaction is catalysed.

Page 100 — Fact Recall Questions
Q1 A substance that speeds up a chemical reaction without
being used up in the reaction itself.
Q2 a) intracellular
   b) extracellular
   Remember, intracellular enzymes are found inside cells,
   so extracellular enzymes are found outside cells.
Q3 a) Because it breaks down the harmful hydrogen peroxide
(H_2O_2) produced by some cellular reactions into oxygen
(O_2) and water (H_2O), which are harmless.
   b) Intracellular
Q4 The hydrolysis of starch to maltose.
Q5 a) It catalyses the hydrolysis of peptide bonds —
turning big polypeptides into smaller ones.
   b) Extracellular
Q6 The enzyme's tertiary structure.
Q7 An enzyme-substrate complex.
Q8 a) B
   b) The activation energy needed for the reaction with the
presence of an enzyme.
Q9 Activation energy is needed to start a chemical reaction.
The activation energy is often provided as heat. With the
presence of an enzyme, the activation energy required
to start a reaction is lowered. Therefore not as much
heat is needed, so the reaction can take place at lower
temperatures than it could do without an enzyme.
Q10 The substrate has a complementary shape to the active site.
This means they fit together the same way that a key fits
into a lock. They form an enzyme-substrate complex and
catalyse the reaction.
Q11 In the 'lock and key' model the active site has a fixed shape
that is complementary to the substrate, but in the 'induced
fit' model the substrate has to make the active site change
shape slightly to allow the substrate to bind tightly.

2. Factors Affecting Enzyme Activity
Page 103 — Application Question
Q1 a) i) C — the enzyme is still active at 80 °C.
This means the bacteria can live at very high
temperatures and therefore is hyperthermophilic.

   ii) A — the enzyme is active at temperatures between
0 and 17 °C. This means the bacteria can live at very
cold temperatures, so is psychrotrophic.
b) A — There would be no enzyme activity at all as the
enzyme would be denatured at temperatures over 17 °C.
B — There would be some enzyme activity but the rate
of reaction would gradually decrease until temperatures
of around 70 °C were reached. At this point the enzyme
would be denatured and there would be no further
enzyme activity at higher temperatures.
C — There would be an increasing amount of enzyme
activity. The rate of reaction would gradually increase as
the temperature increased.

Page 103 — Fact Recall Questions
Q1 At higher temperatures there is more kinetic energy, so
molecules move faster. This makes the substrate molecules
more likely to collide with the enzymes' active sites.
The energy of these collisions also increases, which means
each collision is more likely to result in a reaction.
Q2 A very high temperature makes the enzyme's molecules
vibrate more. This vibration breaks some of the bonds/
hydrogen bonds and ionic bonds that hold the enzyme in
shape. The active site changes shape and the enzyme and
substrate no longer fit together. The enzyme is denatured.
Q3 That the rate of reaction quadruples when the temperature is
raised by 10 °C.
Q4 e.g. pH
Q5 At first, increasing the enzyme concentration increases
the rate of the reaction. This is because the more enzyme
molecules there are in a solution, the more likely a
substrate molecule is to collide with an active site and
form an enzyme-substrate complex. The rate of reaction
continues to increase until the substrate concentration
becomes a limiting factor. At this point the rate of the
reaction levels off.
Q6 The rate of reaction stays constant. All active sites are
occupied so increasing the substrate concentration has
no effect.
Don't ever say that the enzymes are used up — say that all
the active sites are occupied.

3. Enzyme-Controlled Reactions
Page 107 — Application Questions
Q1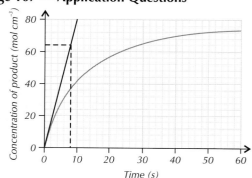
change in y ÷ change in x = 64 mol cm^{-3} ÷ 8 s
= **8 mol cm^{-3} s^{-1}**
(accept answers between 6.5 mol cm^{-3} s^{-1} and 10 mol cm^{-3} s^{-1})
Tangents are tricky things to draw — there'll usually be a small
range of acceptable answers that will get the mark.
Q2 a) Any two from: e.g. temperature, pH, enzyme
concentration.

b)

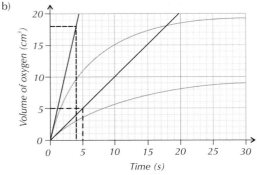

$2\ mol\,dm^{-3}$ — change in $y \div$ change in $x = 18\ cm^3 \div 4\ s$
$$= 4.5\ cm^3 s^{-1}$$
(accept answers between $3.3\ cm^3 s^{-1}$ and $5\ cm^3 s^{-1}$)
$1\ mol\,dm^{-3}$ — change in $y \div$ change in $x = 5\ cm^3 \div 5\ s$
$$= 1\ cm^3 s^{-1}$$
(accept answers between $0.8\ cm^3 s^{-1}$ and $1.3\ cm^3 s^{-1}$)
So $2\ mol\,dm^{-3} : 1\ mol\,dm^{-3} = $ **4.5 : 1**
Your answer depends on the values calculated for the tangents — it should fall between 6.25 : 1 and 2.5 : 1. See pages 13-14 for help on calculating ratios.

Page 107 — Fact Recall Question
Q1 E.g. set up boiling tubes containing the same volume and concentration of hydrogen peroxide. To keep the pH constant, add equal volumes of a suitable buffer solution to each boiling tube. Fill a measuring cylinder with water, turn it upside down and place it in a trough of water. Feed a delivery tube attached to a bung into the measuring cylinder. Put each boiling tube in a water bath set to a different temperature (e.g. 10 °C, 20 °C, 30 °C and 40 °C) along with another tube containing catalase. Wait 5 minutes before moving onto the next step so the enzyme gets up to temperature. Use a pipette to add the same volume and concentration of catalase to each boiling tube. Then quickly attach the bung and delivery tube. Record how much oxygen is produced in the first minute (60 s) of the reaction. Use a stopwatch to measure the time. Repeat the experiment at each temperature three times, and use the results to find a mean volume of oxygen produced. Calculate the mean rate of reaction at each temperature by dividing the volume of oxygen produced by the time taken (i.e. 60 s).

4. Cofactors and Enzyme Inhibition
Page 110 — Application Questions
Q1 a) Ethanol has a similar shape to methanol. This means it will act as a competitive inhibitor, binding to the active site of alcohol dehydrogenase and blocking methanol molecules. This means lower levels of methanol will be hydrolysed so the toxic product (formaldehyde) won't build up to fatal levels.
b)

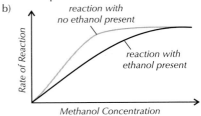

Your curve should be lower than the rate of reaction without any ethanol present. The reaction won't stop completely as some of the methanol molecules will still bind with the active sites. The plateau should be later as the reaction won't reach its maximum rate until the methanol concentration is much higher. The curve should start at zero.
Q2 a) A non-competitive inhibitor, because it binds to the enzyme away from the active site.
b) The rate of the reaction decreases because there are more inhibitor molecules present, which bind to glycogen phosphorylase molecules and alter the shape of their active sites. This means there are fewer active sites in the solution able to bind with glycogen, so the rate of the reaction slows down.
c) i) B. Increasing the concentration of the substrate won't make any difference to the rate of the reaction as enzyme activity will still be inhibited.
ii) A. Increasing the concentration of the enzyme will mean there are more active sites available for the substrate so the rate of the reaction increases.

Page 112 — Application Question
Q1 a) End-product inhibition.
b) The amount of substance two being produced would be reduced. This is because when enzyme five is inhibited, it increases the amount of substance four in pathway one, so that more substance five is made. Substance five inhibits enzyme one via end-product inhibition, so a higher concentration of substance five increases the amount of end-product inhibition on enzyme one. This reduces the amount of substance two being produced.
This will continue until the amount of substance five decreases again, lifting the inhibition on enzyme one.

Page 112 — Fact Recall Questions
Q1 A non-protein substance that binds to an enzyme and activates it.
Q2 The coenzyme is used by an enzyme and is changed during the reaction. A second enzyme then uses the changed coenzyme. During this reaction the coenzyme is changed back to its original form.
Q3 A cofactor that is tightly bound to the enzyme.
Q4 a) Away from the active site.
b) At the active site.
Q5 a) Weak, hydrogen or ionic bonds.
b) Strong, covalent bonds.
Q6 E.g. cyanide is an irreversible, non-competitive inhibitor of cytochrome c oxidase. Cyanide molecules bind to cytochrome c oxidase away from the active site. This causes the active site to change shape so the substrate molecules can no longer bind to it. / Malonate is a competitive inhibitor of succinate dehydrogenase. Malonate molecules have a similar shape to the substrate, so they compete with the substrate molecules to bind to succinate dehydrogenase's active site. They block the active site, so no substrate molecules can fit in it. / Arsenic is a non-competitive inhibitor of pyruvate dehydrogenase. Arsenic molecules bind to pyruvate dehydrogenase away from the active site. This causes the active site to change shape so the substrate molecules can no longer bind to it.
Don't fret if you've given a different example of a poison here. Just make sure when you mark it that it's spelt correctly and that you've clearly described how it works.
Q7 Some enzymes are produced as inactive precursor enzymes, which are unable to catalyse reactions until they become activated.

1 a) i) They lower it *(1 mark)*.
   ii) In synthesis reactions, attaching to the enzyme holds the substrate molecules close together, reducing any repulsion between them *(1 mark)*. In breakdown reactions, fitting into an enzyme's active site puts a strain on the bond in the substrate, causing it to break more easily *(1 mark)*.
  b) i) **5-6 marks:**
     The answer fully describes the induced fit model in reference to the context of the question.
     The answer has a clear and logical structure.
     The information given is relevant and detailed.
     3-4 marks:
     The answer describes most of the features of the induced fit model with some reference to the context of the question.
     The answer has some structure. Most of the information given is relevant and there is some detail involved.
     1-2 marks:
     Only one or two of the features of the induced fit model are referenced, and not in the context of the question.
     The answer has no clear structure. The information given is basic and lacking in detail. It may not all be relevant.
     0 marks:
     No relevant information is given.
     Here are some points your answer may include:
     Catechol and oxygen have a complementary shape to catecholase's active site. This lets them bind to the enzymes's active site. This forms an enzyme-substrate complex. Catechol and oxygen cause the active site to change shape slightly. This means that they bind more tightly to the enzyme. The enzyme-product complex is formed and then benzoquinone and water are released from catecholase**.**
   ii) The 'lock and key' model *(1 mark)*. In this model the active site does not change shape *(1 mark)*.
  c) In a fridge. At cooler temperatures the catechol, oxygen and catecholase molecules have less kinetic energy than they would at room temperature *(1 mark)*. This makes the substrate molecules/catechol and oxygen less likely to collide with the catecholase active sites *(1 mark)*. Also, the energy of the collisions is lower, meaning each collision is less likely to result in a reaction *(1 mark)*. Therefore, in a fridge the rate of the reaction would be lower/benzoquinone would be produced more slowly, so the apple would brown more slowly *(1 mark)*.
     Accept reverse theory, i.e. more kinetic energy at higher temperatures.
  d) i) Copper is an inorganic cofactor *(1 mark)* which binds to catecholase *(1 mark)* and helps it form an enzyme-substrate complex with catechol and oxygen more easily *(1 mark)*.
     Even though the question doesn't tell you what type of cofactor copper is, you can work out that it must be inorganic because copper is a metal.
   ii) E.g. inorganic cofactors don't directly participate in the reaction but organic cofactors do *(1 mark)*. Inorganic cofactors aren't used up or changed during the reaction but organic factors are changed/recycled *(1 mark)*.

  e) E.g. there would be less copper to bind to catecholase *(1 mark)* so fewer enzyme molecules would be able to form enzyme-substrate complexes *(1 mark)*. This would decrease the rate of the reaction, slowing the browning of the apple *(1 mark)*.

2 a) i) *(1 mark for a value between pH 4 and pH 5)*
   ii) pH 1 and pH 9 *(1 mark)*. There is no reaction at these pH levels *(1 mark)*.
  iii) The H^+ and OH^- ions found in acids and alkalis can break the weak ionic bonds/hydrogen bonds that hold the enzyme's tertiary structure in place *(1 mark)*. This changes the shape of the active site *(1 mark)* so it is no longer complementary in shape to the substrate/will not bind to the substrate to catalyse the reaction *(1 mark)*.
     Remember, it's the change in shape of the <u>active site</u> that means the reaction can't be catalysed.
   iv) E.g. temperature *(1 mark)* and substrate concentration *(1 mark)*.
  b) i) A. The rate at which diglycerides and fatty acids are produced/the reaction rate is higher without the presence of orlistat *(1 mark)*.
   ii) Molecules of orlistat have a similar shape to triglycerides *(1 mark)*. They bind to the active sites of gastric lipase and block the entry of triglycerides *(1 mark)*. This means the reaction that produces diglycerides and fatty acids can't take place as quickly *(1 mark)*.

Section 5 — Biological Membranes

1. Cell Membranes — The Basics

Page 118 — Application Questions

Q1 a) E.g. to keep the enzymes needed for photosynthesis all in one place / to compartmentalise photosynthesis, making photosynthetic reactions more efficient.
  b) E.g. to control what substances enter and leave the cell. / To allow cell communication. / To allow cell recognition.
Q2 E.g. using carrier proteins/channel proteins in the membrane.
Q3 E.g. energy-releasing organelles require lots of substances (e.g. nutrients, enzymes, ATP) to travel across their membranes. Some of these substances will require help from proteins to get across the membrane, so these membranes will have a higher protein content.

Page 121 — Application Questions

Q1 Freezing the raspberries will have caused ice crystals to form and pierce the cell-surface/plasma membranes, making the membranes highly permeable when they thawed. This will have caused the red pigment to leak out of the raspberry cells as they defrosted.
Q2 a) E.g. the size of the beetroot cubes. / The beetroot the cubes came from. / The volume of methanol solution the cubes were soaked in. / The temperature of the equipment and surroundings.
  b) Any two from: e.g. it should be turned on and left for five minutes to stabilise. / It should be set up so it's using the correct (blue) filter/a wavelength of about 470 nm. / It should be calibrated to zero (using a cuvette containing distilled water).

c) A. As the concentration of methanol increased, more of the lipids in the beetroot's cell membranes would dissolve. This would cause the cells to lose their structure and become more permeable. More pigment would be released from the beetroot cubes, so the absorbance of the surrounding liquid would increase.

Page 121 — Fact Recall Questions
Q1 It allows some molecules through but not others.
Q2 Any three from: e.g. they act as a barrier between an organelle and the cytoplasm. / They can form vesicles to transport substances between different areas of the cell. / They control which substances enter and leave an organelle. / Membranes within organelles act as a barrier between the membrane contents and the rest of the organelle. / They can be the site of chemical reactions.
Q3 A = glycoprotein, B = glycolipid, C = cholesterol, D = protein channel, E = phospholipid (head)
Q4 'Hydrophilic' means 'attracts water'. Hydrophobic means 'repels water'.
Q5 The centre of the phospholipid bilayer is hydrophobic, so the membrane doesn't allow water-soluble substances through it.
Q6 Some proteins in the membrane allow the passage of large or charged particles that would otherwise find it difficult to cross the membrane.
Q7 a) Helps make the membrane less fluid and more stable. Creates a barrier to polar substances.
    b) Stabilise the membrane by forming hydrogen bonds with surrounding water molecules. Act as receptors in cell signalling. Are sites where drugs, hormones and antibodies bind. Act as antigens and allow self-recognition.
Q8 The phospholipid bilayer starts to melt and the membrane becomes more permeable. Water inside the cell expands, putting pressure on the membrane. Channel proteins and carrier proteins in the membrane denature so they can't control what enters or leaves the cell, further increasing the permeability of the membrane.

2. Cell Membranes and Signalling
Page 123 — Application Questions
Q1 The drug is a complementary shape to the membrane-bound receptor — this means it will bind to the receptor, blocking the messenger molecule from doing so. This will prevent the messenger molecule from triggering a response in the cell.
Q2 The mutated receptor is not a complementary shape to the messenger molecule. This means the messenger molecule is unable to bind to it and trigger a response in the target cells.
Q3 The messenger molecule can only bind to receptors with a complementary shape. Different cells have different membrane-bound receptors. Only liver cells have the correct receptor, so only liver cells can respond to the messenger molecule.
    The key thing to remember here is that messenger molecules can only bind to membrane-bound receptors that have a complementary shape to their own.

3. Diffusion and Osmosis
Page 126 — Application Questions
Q1 The ink molecules are moving from an area of higher concentration (the original drop of ink) to an area of lower concentration (the surrounding water).
Q2 a) The distance the particles have to travel is further, so the rate of diffusion will decrease.
    b) The surface area of the cell will increase, so the rate of diffusion will increase.
    c) The concentration gradient will increase, so the rate of diffusion will increase.
Q3 a) E.g. she could cut equal-sized cubes of the agar jelly containing potassium permanganate. She could then prepare several boiling tubes containing the same concentration and volume of hydrochloric acid and place them in water baths set to different temperatures. She could then add one cube to each boiling tube and time how long it takes each cube to turn colourless.
    b) She should expect the cube in the highest temperature to go colourless fastest.

Page 130 — Application Questions
Q1 a) Water molecules will move from the cheek cells into the salt solution.
    A −300 kPa solution has a higher water potential (it's less negative) than a −325 kPa solution.
    b) Water molecules will move into the apple slices from the beaker of water.
    c) There will be no net movement of water molecules as the water potential in both solutions is the same/the solutions are isotonic.
Q2 a) The potato cells have a lower water potential than the sucrose solution, so they gain water by osmosis. This causes the vacuoles to swell and the cell contents to push against the cell wall, making the cells turgid.
    b) E.g. The cells in both solutions will become flaccid (limp). This is because they have a higher water potential than the sucrose solutions, so will lose water by osmosis. The cells may lose so much water that they become plasmolysed.

Page 130 — Fact Recall Questions
Q1 The net movement of particles from an area of higher concentration to an area of lower concentration.
Q2 It's a passive process.
Q3 Molecules that can pass freely through the membrane, e.g. small, non–polar molecules (and water).
Q4 E.g. The concentration gradient. The thickness of the exchange surface. The surface area of the exchange surface. The temperature.
Q5 osmosis
Q6 Water potential is the potential/likelihood of water molecules to diffuse out of or into a solution.
Q7 a) The cell will swell and could burst as water moves into it by osmosis.
    b) The cell will become turgid (swollen) as water moves into it by osmosis, causing the vacuole to swell and the contents of the vacuole and cytoplasm to push against the cell wall.
    c) The cell will become flaccid (limp) as water moves out of the cell by osmosis. The cell may eventually lose so much water that it becomes plasmolysed.

4. Facilitated Diffusion and Active Transport

Pages 133-134 — Application Questions

Q1 a) vesicle
   b) Exocytosis. In step A, a vesicle containing the chemical messenger moves towards the membrane of neurone 1. In steps B and C, the vesicles fuse with the membrane and release their contents outside the cell.
   c) E.g. through a channel protein using facilitated diffusion.

Q2 a) As the rate of sodium ion active transport increases, so does the rate of oxygen consumption. This is because sodium ion active transport requires energy from ATP. As the rate of active transport increases, the rate of aerobic respiration must also increase in order to produce more ATP, which means the rate of oxygen consumption must increase too.
   Remember, ATP is produced by the mitochondria during aerobic respiration — and aerobic respiration uses oxygen.
   b) None. Facilitated diffusion doesn't require energy from ATP, so there would be no need for the rate of oxygen consumption to increase.

Page 135 — Application Question

Q1

Transport system	A plant cell taking in water	Calcium ions moving into a cell against a concentration gradient	A muscle cell taking in polar glucose molecules	White blood cell taking in anthrax bacteria
Osmosis	✓	✗	✗	✗
Facilitated diffusion using channel proteins	✓	✗	✗	✗
Facilitated diffusion using carrier proteins	✗	✗	✓	✗
Active transport using carrier proteins	✗	✓	✓	✗
Endocytosis	✗	✗	✗	✓
Exocytosis	✗	✗	✗	✗

Page 135 — Fact Recall Questions

Q1 In simple diffusion, small, non-polar molecules pass freely through the plasma membrane. Facilitated diffusion uses carrier proteins and channel proteins to aid the movement of large molecules and charged particles through the plasma membrane.

Q2 Similarity: both facilitated diffusion and active transport use carrier proteins to transport molecules across plasma membranes.
   Differences: in facilitated diffusion, molecules move down a concentration gradient. In active transport, molecules are moved against a concentration gradient.
   Facilitated diffusion is a passive process, it doesn't require energy. Active transport is an active process that does require energy.

Q3 a) A molecule attaches to a carrier protein in the membrane. The protein then changes shape and releases the molecule on the opposite side of the membrane.
   b) Channel proteins form pores in the membrane for charged particles to diffuse through.

Q4 A cell surrounds a substance or object with its plasma membrane. The membrane then pinches off to form a vesicle inside the cell, which contains the ingested substance or object.

Q5 E.g. a digestive enzyme / a hormone / a lipid

Exam-style Questions — pages 137-138

1 a) i) The potential/likelihood of water molecules to diffuse out of or into a solution *(1 mark)*.
      ii) The cells in Fig. 1.2 have lost water by osmosis *(1 mark)*. This has caused the cytoplasm and plasma membranes to pull away from the cell walls *(1 mark)*. The cells are plasmolysed *(1 mark)*.
      iii) The net movement of water molecules will still be out of the cell by osmosis, causing the cell to shrink *(1 mark)*.
   b) i) Any four from: In the fluid mosaic model, phospholipid molecules form a continuous double layer/bilayer *(1 mark)*. Cholesterol molecules fit between the phospholipids, making the membrane less fluid and more rigid *(1 mark)*. Protein molecules are scattered throughout the bilayer, like tiles in a mosaic *(1 mark)*. Some protein molecules, called glycoproteins, have a polysaccharide/carbohydrate chain attached *(1 mark)*. / Some lipids, called glycolipids, also have a polysaccharide/carbohydrate chain attached *(1 mark)*.
      (Maximum of 4 marks available.)
      ii) E.g. any two from: Plasma membranes control which substances enter and leave the cell. / Plasma membranes allow recognition by other cells. / Plasma membranes allow cell communication.
      (2 marks for 2 correct answers.)

2 a) i) The centre of the phospholipid bilayer is hydrophobic *(1 mark)*. It forms a barrier to the diffusion of water-soluble substances including most polar molecules *(1 mark)*. Glucose is a polar molecule that can't diffuse directly across the membrane *(1 mark)*.
      ii) No. The glucose moves down its concentration gradient/facilitated diffusion is a passive process *(1 mark)*.
      iii) It is a carrier protein *(1 mark)* that changes shape when glucose binds to it, causing the glucose to be released on the opposite side of the membrane *(1 mark)*.
   b) The movement of molecules against their concentration gradient *(1 mark)* using energy (from ATP) *(1 mark)*.

3 a) E.g. in case the cubes did not all start out at exactly the same mass *(1 mark)*. / To enable a fair comparison between the cubes *(1 mark)*.
   b) 16% (accept 15-17%) *(1 mark)*
   Don't forget that pure water is always 0 kPa.
   c) i) The water potential in these three solutions must have been lower than the water potential of the potato cells *(1 mark)*, so water moved out of the cells by osmosis *(1 mark)*.
      ii) −425 kPa (accept any answer between −400 and −450 kPa) *(1 mark)*
   The cells won't lose or gain any mass in an isotonic solution, so all you need to do is read the water potential off the graph where the change in mass equals zero.

d) E.g. they could do repeats of the experiment for each concentration of sucrose solution and calculate a mean percentage change in mass *(1 mark)*.
There's more on precise results in Module 1 of this book.
e) Before 12 hours *(1 mark)* because the rate of osmosis will be faster due to the increase in surface area *(1 mark)*.

Section 6 — Cell Division and Cellular Organisation

1. The Cell Cycle and Mitosis
Page 142 — Application Question
Q1 a)

Stage of Mitosis	Step Number
Anaphase	3
Telophase	4
Prophase	1
Metaphase	2

b) i) B
   ii) C
To answer this you need to quickly go through each stage of mitosis in your head and think about the main thing that's happening, e.g. in metaphase all the chromosomes are in the middle of the cell. Then ask yourself if you can see that in the photo.
c) The centromeres are dividing, separating each pair of sister chromatids. The spindles are contracting, pulling chromatids to opposite ends of the cell, centromere first.

Page 142 — Fact Recall Questions
Q1 The process that all body cells in multicellular organisms use to grow and divide.
Q2 interphase
Q3 It's checked for any damage that may have occurred.
Q4 For growth of multicellular organisms and for repairing damaged tissues.
Q5 During prophase the chromosomes condense, getting shorter and fatter. The centrioles start moving to opposite ends of the cell, forming the spindle. The nuclear envelope breaks down and chromosomes lie free in the cytoplasm.
Q6 metaphase
Q7 anaphase
Q8 A cleavage furrow forms to divide the cell membrane and the cytoplasm divides.
Q9 two
Q10 False
    Mitosis produces two genetically identical daughter cells.

2. Sexual Reproduction and Meiosis
Page 146 — Application Questions
Q1 a) metaphase 1
    b) anaphase 2
    There are half the number of chromosomes in this cell (compared to the previous cell) and they're being pulled apart — that's how you know it must be in anaphase 2.
    c) prophase 1
    d) metaphase 2

Q2

Page 146 — Fact Recall Questions
Q1 a) diploid
    b) haploid
    c) diploid
Q2 a) The chromosomes condense, homologous chromosomes pair up and crossing-over occurs. The centrioles start moving to opposite ends of the cell, forming the spindle fibres, and the nuclear envelope breaks down.
    b) The homologous pairs line up across the centre of the cell and attach to the spindle fibres by their centromeres.
    c) The spindles contract, pulling the homologous pairs apart (one chromosome goes to each end of the cell).
    d) A nuclear envelope forms around each group of chromosomes and the cytoplasm divides so there are now two haploid daughter cells.
Q3 The two daughter cells from meiosis 1 undergo prophase 2, metaphase 2, anaphase 2 and telophase 2. Four haploid daughter cells are produced.
Q4 a) Crossing-over of chromatids and the independent assortment of chromosomes
    b) Crossing-over is when chromatids twist around each other and bits of chromatid swap over. The resulting chromosomes contain the same genes but now have a different combination of alleles. This means that when the chromatids separate at meiosis 2, each of the four daughter cells will contain chromatids with different alleles. The independent assortment of chromosomes is when different combinations of maternal and paternal chromosomes go into each daughter cell.

3. Stem Cells and Differentiation
Pages 150-151 — Application Questions
Q1 a) If the cells on the outside of the cornea become damaged, the limbal stem cells will be able to differentiate into new cornea cells to replace them.
    b) Because the number of different types of cell that adult stem cells can differentiate into is limited, so they may not be able to differentiate into nerve cells, which are the type of cell required to treat Alzheimer's.
Q2 E.g. epithelial cells have microvilli, which increase the cell's surface area for absorption of nutrients.
    The key thing here is to link what you know about epithelial cells to the information you're given in the question — in this case that they're found in the small intestine. Food is absorbed in the small intestine, so you should be able to work out the answer.

Page 151 — Fact Recall Questions
Q1 An unspecialised cell that can develop into different types of cell.
Q2 The process by which a cell becomes specialised for its job.
Q3 a) i) red blood cells
        ii) white blood cells
    You could remember that <u>neu</u>trophils are white blood cells by thinking of white as a <u>neu</u>tral colour.
    b) In the bone marrow.

Q4 The stem cells that form xylem and phloem are found in the meristems. Stem cells of the vascular cambium divide and differentiate to become xylem vessels and phloem sieve tubes.

Q5 In heart disease, the heart tissue can become damaged. The body is unable to sufficiently replace damaged heart cells. Stem cells could be used to make replacement heart cells to repair the damaged tissue.

Q6 Parkinson's is caused by a loss of a type of nerve cell in the brain that produces a chemical called dopamine. Stem cells could be transplanted into patients to help regenerate the dopamine-producing cells.

Q7 a) Any one from: e.g. erythrocytes have a biconcave disc shape which provides a large surface area for gas exchange. / Erythrocytes don't have a nucleus so there's more room for haemoglobin, the protein that carries oxygen.

b) Any one from: e.g. neutrophils have a flexible shape which allows them to engulf foreign particles or pathogens. / Neutrophils have a large number of lysosomes in their cytoplasm which contain digestive enzymes to break down engulfed foreign particles or pathogens.

It's dead important that you know the functions and adaptations of erythrocytes, neutrophils, squamous and ciliated epithelial cells, sperm cells, palisade mesophyll cells, root hair cells and guard cells — you could be asked about any of them in the exam and they're easy marks if you learn them properly.

Q8 a) To carry out photosynthesis.

b) To absorb water and mineral ions from the soil.

Q9 In the light, guard cells take up water (into their vacuoles) and become turgid. Their thin outer walls and thickened inner walls force them to bend outwards, opening the stomata. This allows the leaf to exchange gases for photosynthesis.

4. Tissues, Organs and Systems
Page 154 — Application Question
Q1 a) A = companion cell, B = ordinary plant cell, C = sieve cell

b) Phloem tissue

Pages 154-155 — Fact Recall Questions
Q1 A group of cells (plus any extracellular material secreted by them) that are specialised to work together to carry out a particular function.

Q2 false

Q3 a) Squamous epithelium is made up of a group of cells/a single layer of flat cells that are specialised to work together to provide a thin exchange surface for substances to diffuse across quickly.

b) Ciliated epithelium is made up of a group of cells/a layer of cells covered in cilia, which are specialised to work together to move a substance along, e.g. mucus in the lungs.

If you're asked why a particular tissue is classified as a tissue in the exam, make sure you include the function of that tissue in your answer.

Q4 Muscle tissue is made up of bundles of elongated cells called muscle fibres.

Q5 Cartilage is a type of connective tissue that is found in the joints and also provides shape and support to the ears, nose and windpipe.

Q6 E.g. xylem, phloem.

Q7 A group of different tissues that work together to perform a particular function.

Q8 An organ system is where different organs work together to carry out a particular function.

Q9 E.g. the respiratory system. It is an organ system because it is made up of the lungs, trachea, larynx, nose, mouth and diaphragm which work together to carry out gas exchange.

Exam-style Questions — pages 156-157
1 a) 12-16 hours and 36-40 hours *(1 mark)*, because the mass of DNA doubles *(1 mark)*.

b) 24 hours and 48 hours *(1 mark)*, because the mass of DNA halves / the mass of the cell halves *(1 mark)*.

c) E.g. the cell is growing *(1 mark)* and new organelles and proteins are made *(1 mark)*. The cell replicates it's DNA *(1 mark)* and checks the DNA for damage *(1 mark)*.

d) i) Two (at 24 and 48 hours) *(1 mark)* because the mass of the cell and its DNA doubles and halves twice *(1 mark)*.

ii) At 72 hours *(1 mark)*.

In graphs with two scales, make sure you match the correct line (or bar) to the correct scale before you read off a value.

e) i) At opposite poles, chromatids uncoil and become long and thin again *(1 mark)*. A nuclear envelope forms around each group of chromosomes, so there are two nuclei *(1 mark)*.

ii) Mitosis is important for growth *(1 mark)*, repair *(1 mark)*, and asexual reproduction *(1 mark)*.

Don't forget that mitosis is not just used for growth and repair in multicellular organisms — some organisms use it for asexual reproduction too.

2 a) Sperm cells use their tails to swim to the egg *(1 mark)*. If a large proportion of sperm cells can't do this successfully, there's less chance of a sperm cell successfully fertilising the egg *(1 mark)*.

b) They have lots of mitochondria to provide the energy to swim *(1 mark)* and they have an acrosome, which contains digestive enzymes to enable the sperm to penetrate the surface of the egg *(1 mark)*.

3 a) Any two from: e.g. it has a large surface area for absorbing water and mineral ions from the soil *(1 mark)*. / It has a thin, permeable cell wall for absorbing water and mineral ions from the soil *(1 mark)*. / The cytoplasm contains extra mitochondria to provide the energy needed for active transport *(1 mark)*.

b) i) In meristems / the vascular cambium *(1 mark)*.

ii) Xylem is a group of cells, including xylem vessel cells and parenchyma cells *(1 mark)*, that are specialised to work together to transport water around the plant and support the plant *(1 mark)*.

4 a) i) The DNA is being replicated to produce two copies of each chromosome *(1 mark)*.

ii) The chromosomes are condensing and are arranging themselves into homologous pairs *(1 mark)*.

iii) Meiosis 1 occurs — the homologous pairs are separated, halving the chromosome number *(1 mark)*.

iv) Meiosis 2 occurs — the pairs of sister chromatids are separated, generating haploid cells *(1 mark)*.

b) i) E.g. the daughter cells are genetically different *(1 mark)* and are haploid/contain half the number of chromosomes as the parent cell *(1 mark)*.

   ii) When homologous chromosomes come together in meiosis 1, the chromatids are able to twist around each other and bits of the chromatids can swap over *(1 mark)*. Each of the chromatids now has a different combination of alleles *(1 mark)*, which means that each of the four daughter cells resulting from meiosis contain chromatids with different alleles *(1 mark)*.

Module 3

Section 1 — Exchange and Transport

1. Specialised Exchange Systems
Page 159 — Application Question
Q1 a) i) A — surface area = $6 \times 2 \times 2 = $ **24 cm^2**
      B — surface area = $(4 \times 4 \times 2) + (2 \times 2 \times 2)$
                    $= 32 + 8 = $ **40 cm^2**
      C — surface area = $4\pi r^2$
                    $= 4 \times \pi \times 2.5^2$
                    $= $ **79 cm^2** (2 s.f.)
   ii) A — volume = $2 \times 2 \times 2 = $ **8 cm^3**
      B — volume = $2 \times 4 \times 2 = $ **16 cm^3**
      C — volume $= \frac{4}{3}\pi r^3$
                    $= \frac{4}{3} \pi \times 2.5^3$
                    $= $ **65 cm^3** (2 s.f.)
   iii) A — SA:V = $24:8$ (or $3:1$)
      B — SA:V = $40:16$ (or $5:2$ or $2.5:1$)
      C — SA:V = $79:65$ (or $1.2:1$)
   You should have got the same answers for shape C whether you used π as 3.14 or the π button on your calculator. If an exam question specifies which value to use for π, make sure you do what it says.
   b) A
   Simplify all of the ratios to 1 in order to compare them, e.g. A = 3:1, B = 2.5:1 and C = 1.2:1 — it's then obvious that A is the largest ratio.

Page 162 — Application Questions
Q1 The concentration gradient of oxygen between the alveoli and the capillaries will be lower than normal, so the rate of diffusion, and therefore gas exchange, will be slower.
Q2 Less air, and so less oxygen, would be inhaled in each breath. This means the concentration gradient of oxygen between the alveoli and the capillaries will be less steep, slowing the rate of diffusion.
Q3 a) The alveoli are enlarged/much larger in the diseased lungs than in the healthy lungs.
   b) Having enlarged alveoli means there's a smaller surface area for gas exchange, slowing the rate of diffusion of oxygen into the blood. So a patient with emphysema would have a low level of oxygen in the blood.
   These questions are all asking you to think about factors that affect the efficiency of gas exchange surfaces. The key things to think about are the size of the surface area, how good the blood supply and/or ventilation is (to maintain steep concentration gradients) and the thickness of the exchange surface (or the length of the diffusion pathway).

Page 162 — Fact Recall Questions
Q1 a) E.g. oxygen, glucose.
   b) E.g. carbon dioxide, urea.
Q2 Some cells are deep within the body, so the distance between them and the outside environment is too great for diffusion to take place quickly. Larger animals have a low surface area : volume ratio. This means they don't have a large enough area exposed to the environment to be able to exchange all the substances they need quickly enough using diffusion. Multicellular organisms have a higher metabolic rate than single-celled organisms, so they use up oxygen and glucose faster than diffusion could provide them.
Q3 a) Plant roots are covered in root hair cells, which vastly increase the surface area of the root, so the rate of absorption of water and mineral ions from the soil is increased.
   b) E.g. being thin and having a good blood supply and/or ventilation.
Q4 Fish gills contain a large network of capillaries, which keeps them well-supplied with blood. They're also well-ventilated by fresh water that constantly passes over them. These features help to maintain a concentration gradient of O_2, which increases the rate at which O_2 diffuses into the blood.

2. Gas Exchange in Mammals
Page 165 — Application Question
Q1 a) bronchus
   b) A = cartilage, B = ciliated epithelium, C = elastic fibres

Page 165 — Fact Recall Questions
Q1 a) To secrete mucus.
   b) To beat the mucus (plus trapped dust and microorganisms) away from the alveoli.
Q2 Elastic fibres help the process of breathing out. On breathing in, the lungs inflate and the elastic fibres are stretched. The fibres then recoil to help push air out of the lungs when exhaling. Elastic fibres are found in the trachea, bronchi, bronchioles and alveoli.
Q3 The trachea, bronchi and all but the smallest bronchioles.
Q4 Cartilage in the trachea is found in large C-shaped pieces/rings. Cartilage in the bronchi is found in smaller pieces and is interspersed with smooth muscle.

3. Ventilation in Mammals
Page 168 — Application Questions
Q1 Accept 0.5 dm^3 or 0.55 dm^3
Q2 11 breaths per minute
Q3 The air that's breathed out is a mixture of oxygen and carbon dioxide. The carbon dioxide is absorbed by the soda lime and the oxygen gets used up by respiration, so the total volume of gas in the spirometer decreases with time.

4. Gas Exchange in Fish and Insects
Page 171 — Application Questions
Q1 A concentration gradient would still be maintained between the water and the blood, but it would be less steep. This means the fish wouldn't be able to take in as much oxygen as it would in clean water.

Q2 a) It increases steadily.
To answer this question you need to look at the arrow head of the red line — it's pointing upwards so the oxygen concentration of the blood is increasing.
    b) It decreases steadily.
    c) 80%
    d) Because at point X the oxygen concentration of the water is higher than in the blood (about 92%) — so oxygen has diffused into the blood down its concentration gradient.

Page 171 — Fact Recall Questions
Q1 Each gill is made of lots of thin plates called gill filaments/ primary lamellae. These are covered in lots of tiny structures called gill plates. Gill plates have a thin surface layer of cells and a good blood supply.

Q2 The counter-current system works by maintaining a steep concentration gradient between the water and the blood. Blood flows through the gill plates in one direction and water flows over the gill plates in the opposite direction. This means that water with a relatively high oxygen concentration always flows next to blood with a lower oxygen concentration. Oxygen then diffuses into the blood from the water down the concentration gradient.

Q3 The fish opens its mouth, which lowers the floor of the buccal cavity, causing its volume to increase. This causes the pressure inside the cavity to decrease, which causes water to be sucked into the cavity. When the fish closes its mouth, the floor of the buccal cavity is raised again. This causes the volume inside the cavity to decrease and the pressure inside to increase, forcing water out of the cavity and across the gill filaments.

Q4 A bony flap that protects the gills of fish.

Q5 The increase in pressure (caused by the decrease in volume of the buccal cavity) causes the operculum to open, to allow the water to leave the gills.

Q6 Through the spiracles on the surface of the insect's body.

Q7 Carbon dioxide from the cells moves down its concentration gradient towards the spiracles to be released into the atmosphere.

Q8 Insects can use rhythmic movements to change the volume of their bodies and move air in and out of the spiracles. They can also use the movement of their wings whilst flying to pump their thoraxes.

5. Dissecting Gas Exchange Systems
Page 173 — Application Question
Q1 a) Because it can be easier to avoid damaging the tissue underneath where you're cutting when using scissors rather than a scalpel.
    b) A network of very thin, silvery-grey tubes.
    c) These are rings of chitin that act to support the tracheae.

Page 173 — Fact Recall Questions
Q1 To pin a specimen in place during the dissection.
Q2 To hold and manipulate smaller parts of the specimen.
Q3 Under the operculum.

Exam-style Questions — pages 175-176
1 a) intercostal *(1 mark)*, contract *(1 mark)*, ribcage *(1 mark)*, volume *(1 mark)*, pressure *(1 mark)*
    b) vital capacity *(1 mark)*
    c) i)   The person breathed out/expired *(1 mark)*.
Watch out here — the spirometer trace shows the volume of gas in the lungs, not the volume of gas in the spirometer. The volume of gas in the lungs will decrease when the person breathes out.
        ii) 14 breaths / minute *(1 mark)*
If the question doesn't tell you what units to give your answer in, just pick sensible ones.
        iii) The trace would slope downwards *(1 mark)*. This is because the volume of gas in the spirometer would decrease over time *(1 mark)*, as oxygen would be used up in respiration *(1 mark)* and carbon dioxide would be absorbed by the soda lime in the spirometer *(1 mark)*.
    d) E.g. repeat the measurement several/at least three times and find the mean of the results *(1 mark)*.
There are lots of possible answers here — just use your common sense. (See Module 1 for more on precise results.)

2 a) surface area $= 4\pi r^2$
$$= 4 \times \pi \times 0.7^2$$
$$= 6 \ \mu m^2 \ (1 \ s.f.)$$
        volume $= \dfrac{4}{3}\pi r^3$
$$= \dfrac{4}{3}\pi \times 0.7^3$$
$$= 1 \ \mu m^3 \ (1 \ s.f.)$$
    surface area : volume $= $ **6:1** *(1 mark)*
    b) Because it is a single-celled organism with a short diffusion pathway *(1 mark)* and a large surface area to volume ratio *(1 mark)*. This means it can exchange substances quickly across its outer surface *(1 mark)*.
To help you answer this question, think about why multicellular organisms do have a gaseous exchange system — it's because the diffusion pathway is too big, they have a small surface area : volume ratio and their rate of metabolism is higher, so they use up glucose and oxygen quicker. These characteristics mean that diffusion would be too slow.

3 a) width of alveolus = width of image ÷ magnification
       = 9 mm ÷ 60
       = 0.15 mm × 1000 (to convert to micrometres)
       = **150 μm**
       (1 mark for correct calculation,
       2 marks for correct answer)
The question tells you to give your answer in μm, so you need to remember to convert your answer from mm to μm. If you're a bit rusty on this, check out p. 39.
    b) E.g. the walls of the alveoli have been destroyed in the diseased alveoli *(1 mark)*. Destruction of the alveolar walls reduces the surface area of the alveoli *(1 mark)*, so the rate of gaseous exchange would decrease *(1 mark)*.
    c) There would be a steeper concentration gradient of oxygen between the alveoli and the capillaries *(1 mark)*. This would increase the rate of diffusion of oxygen into the blood *(1 mark)*.

4 a) To beat mucus (plus trapped dust and microorganisms) away from the alveoli *(1 mark)*.

b) i) Any one from, e.g. to support the trachea *(1 mark)*. / To stop the trachea from collapsing *(1 mark)*.
   ii) the bronchi *(1 mark)*
c) Any one from, e.g. goblet cells *(1 mark)* — to secrete mucus *(1 mark)*. / Smooth muscle *(1 mark)* — to control the trachea's diameter *(1 mark)*. / Elastic fibres *(1 mark)* — to recoil and push air out of the lungs whilst breathing out/expiring *(1 mark)*.

Section 2 — Transport in Animals

1. Circulatory Systems
Page 179 — Fact Recall Questions
Q1 Any two from: multicellular organisms are relatively big. / Multicellular organisms have a low surface area to volume ratio. / Many multicellular organisms have a high metabolic rate. / A lot of multicellular organisms are very active, so their cells need a constant, rapid supply of glucose and oxygen.
Q2 E.g. mammals.
Q3 a) Because blood only passes through the heart once for a complete circuit of the body.
   b) Because blood is enclosed inside blood vessels.
Q4 Because the blood isn't enclosed in blood vessels all the time. Instead it flows freely through the body cavity.

2. Blood Vessels
Page 182 — Application Question
Q1 The water potential of the capillary is higher because there is less albumin in the blood so there is a lower oncotic pressure. This means less water is absorbed by osmosis back into the capillary at the venule end of the capillary bed, which leads to an increase in tissue fluid.

Page 182 — Fact Recall Questions
Q1 a) Arteries need to carry blood away from the heart under high pressure so they have thick muscular walls with elastic tissue which stretch and recoil as the heart beats, helping to maintain the high pressure. They also have a folded endothelium which enables the artery to expand, again maintaining high pressure.
   b) Capillaries exchange substances like glucose and oxygen with body cells so the walls of capillaries are only one cell thick for efficient diffusion.
   c) Veins carry blood back to the heart under low pressure so they have a wide lumen, with little elastic or muscle tissue. They also contain valves to stop the blood flowing backwards.
Q2 Arterioles are much smaller than arteries and they have less elastic tissue.
Q3 venules
Q4 The fluid that surrounds cells in tissues.
Q5 At the arteriole end the hydrostatic pressure inside the capillaries is higher than the hydrostatic pressure in the tissue fluid. This means fluid is forced out of the capillaries and into the spaces around the cells, forming tissue fluid.
Q6 lymph vessels
Q7 a) E.g. any two from: blood contains red blood cells, tissue fluid does not. / Blood contains white blood cells, tissue fluid contains very few white blood cells. / Blood contains platelets, tissue fluid usually does not. / Blood contains proteins, tissue fluid contains very few proteins.

b) E.g. tissue fluid contains very few white blood cells, most white blood cells are in the lymph.

3. Heart Basics
Page 186 — Application Questions
Q1 The left atrium is contracting.
Q2 It is closed because the left ventricle is relaxing, so the pressure is higher in the aorta than in the ventricle, forcing the semi-lunar valve shut.
Q3 The left ventricle is relaxing.
Q4 The left atrium is filling up.
   At point D, the increase in atrial pressure can't be due to the left atrium contracting because the diagram shows that the left ventricle is relaxing — i.e. the left ventricle doesn't contract next. So you need to think about what happens in the left atrium as the left ventricle is relaxing — it's filling up with blood to prepare for the next atrial contraction.
Q5 It is open because the ventricle is relaxing, reducing the pressure in the chamber. The atrium has been filling, increasing the pressure in the chamber. So as the pressure in the atrium becomes higher than that in the ventricle, the atrioventricular valve will open.

Page 186 — Fact Recall Questions
Q1 right side
Q2 A — inferior vena cava
   B — left atrium
   C — aorta
   D — right atrium
   E — coronary artery
   F — right ventricle
   G — left ventricle
   H — vena cava
Q3 a) semi-lunar valves
   b) They stop blood flowing back into the heart after the ventricles contract.
Q4 An ongoing sequence of contraction and relaxation of the atria and ventricles that keeps blood continuously circulating round the body.
Q5 The volume of the atria decreases and the pressure increases.
Q6 cardiac output = heart rate × stroke volume

4. Electrical Activity of The Heart
Page 190 — Application Questions
Q1 a) From 1st R wave to 2nd R wave:
      1.24 − 0.42 = 0.82 s
      60 ÷ 0.82 = **73 bpm**
   To work out heart rate (in bpm) you need to divide — not multiply — 60 by the length of one heartbeat (in s).
   b) From 1st R wave to 2nd R wave:
      1.42 − 0.52 = 0.90 s
      60 ÷ 0.90 = **67 bpm**
Q2 ECG B shows a slower heart rate than that of ECG A (67 bpm compared to 73 bpm). ECG B shows a longer interval between contraction of the atria (the P wave) and contraction of the ventricles (QRS complex) than ECG A (about 0.3 s compared to 0.1 s).

Page 190 — Fact Recall Questions

Q1 a) sino-atrial node

b) It sets the rhythm of the heartbeat by sending regular waves of electrical activity over the atrial walls. This causes the right and left atria to contract at the same time.

Q2 non-conducting collagen tissue

Q3 It conducts waves of electrical activity from the atrioventricular node to the Purkyne tissue.

Q4 It carries the waves of electrical activity into the muscular walls of the right and left ventricles, causing them to contract simultaneously, from the bottom up.

Q5 a) electrocardiogram

b) E.g. tachycardia / bradycardia / ectopic heartbeat / fibrillation

5. Haemoglobin
Page 194 — Application Questions

Q1

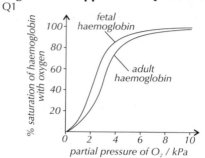

Q2 The dissociation curve for fetal haemoglobin is to the left of the dissociation curve for adult haemoglobin because it has a higher affinity for oxygen than adult haemoglobin. This means fetal haemoglobin takes up oxygen (becomes more saturated) in lower partial pressures of oxygen than adult haemoglobin.

Don't get the dissociation curve for fetal haemoglobin mixed up with a curve showing the Bohr effect, which would be to the right of the normal adult haemoglobin dissociation curve.

Page 194 — Fact Recall Questions

Q1 oxyhaemoglobin

Q2 In the alveoli / lungs. This is the site where oxygen first enters the blood so it has the highest concentration of oxygen.

Q3 How saturated haemoglobin is with oxygen at any given partial pressure.

Q4 More oxygen is available to cells during activity.

Q5 It would shift the oxygen dissociation curve right.

Q6 carbonic anhydrase

Q7 a) It splits up to give hydrogen ions/H^+ and hydrogencarbonate ions/HCO_3^-.

b) The increase in hydrogen ions/H^+ causes oxyhaemoglobin to unload its oxygen so that haemoglobin can take up the hydrogen ions/H^+.

Q8 The chloride shift is when chloride ions (Cl^-) diffuse into red blood cells to compensate for the loss of hydrogencarbonate ions (HCO_3^-) from them.

Exam-style Questions — pages 196-197

1 B *(1 mark)*

The QRS complex is caused by contraction of the ventricles. The Purkyne tissue carries the electrical activity to the walls of both ventricles to make them contract simultaneously. The P wave is caused by contraction of the atria and a higher wave indicates more electrical charge is passing through the heart, which results in a stronger contraction. The T wave is due to relaxation (repolarisation) of the ventricles.

2 a) The semi-lunar valves are open *(1 mark)* so the pressure must be higher in the ventricles than the pulmonary artery/aorta *(1 mark)*. This means the blood is moving (from the ventricles) into the pulmonary artery/aorta *(1 mark)*.

If you get a diagram of the heart in your exam that looks a bit different from this, just look to see where the valves are and whether they're open or closed — then you should be able to answer the question.

b) Atrioventricular valves / AV valves *(1 mark)*. They prevent the back-flow of blood into the atria when the ventricles contract *(1 mark)*.

c) i) A double circulatory system means that blood passes through the heart twice for each complete circuit of the body *(1 mark)*.

ii) One circuit sends deoxygenated blood from the heart to the lungs, then returns the blood to the heart after it has picked up oxygen *(1 mark)*. This oxygenated blood is then sent out from the heart round the rest of the body in the second circuit *(1 mark)*. The advantage of this system is that by returning to the heart to be pumped again, oxygenated blood travels to the rest of the body more quickly than if it was to travel directly from the lungs *(1 mark)*.

3 a) B. During the bike ride the man's respiration rate would have increased, raising the pCO_2 *(1 mark)*. This would have increased the rate of oxygen unloading, so the dissociation curve would have shifted to the right *(1 mark)*.

b) The Bohr effect *(1 mark)*.

c) The increased rate of respiration during the bike ride would have caused more carbon dioxide to be produced, most of which would have been converted in the red blood cells into carbonic acid *(1 mark)* by the enzyme carbonic anhydrase *(1 mark)*. The carbonic acid would then split to give hydrogen ions/H^+ and hydrogencarbonate ions/HCO_3^-, which would diffuse out of the red blood cells and into the plasma *(1 mark)*.

4 a) AVN — B *(1 mark)*, right ventricle — F *(1 mark)*, pulmonary vein — D *(1 mark)*

b) It prevents the waves of electrical activity from being passed directly from the atria to the ventricles *(1 mark)*.

c) There must be a delay so that the atria empty before the ventricles contract *(1 mark)*.

d) The atrioventricular valve/AVN passes the waves of electrical activity onto the bundle of His *(1 mark)*. The bundle of His conducts the waves of electrical activity to the Purkyne tissue *(1 mark)*. The Purkyne tissue carries the waves of electrical activity into the muscular walls of the right and left ventricles *(1 mark)*.

5 a) i) X because it's an artery *(1 mark)*.
As the blood travels round the circulatory system the pressure of the blood gradually decreases and it is returned to the heart at low pressure via the veins.
      ii) E.g. vessel Y contains valves, vessel X doesn't *(1 mark)*. Vessel X contains more elastic tissue than vessel Y *(1 mark)*. Vessel X contains a thicker muscle layer than vessel Y *(1 mark)*.
   b) At the start of the capillary bed the hydrostatic pressure inside the capillaries is higher than the pressure in the tissue fluid *(1 mark)*. The difference in pressure forces fluid out of the capillaries and into the spaces around the cells, forming tissue fluid *(1 mark)*.
   c) E.g. blood contains red blood cells, lymph doesn't *(1 mark)*. Blood contains platelets, lymph doesn't *(1 mark)*.

Section 3 — Transport in Plants

1. Xylem and Phloem
Page 201 — Application Questions
Q1 W, because it is situated underneath the xylem tissue.
Q2 a) sieve plate
    b) Pit — it allows water and mineral ions to move into and out of the xylem vessels.

Page 202 — Fact Recall Questions
Q1 It would be too slow to meet their metabolic needs because plants are multicellular, so have a small surface area to volume ratio.
Q2

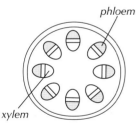

phloem

xylem

If you're drawing both the xylem and the phloem on a diagram remember to label them, so that the examiner knows which is which.
Q3 A — xylem
    B — phloem
Q4 water and mineral ions
    Remember, xylem vessels don't just transport water, they transport mineral ions too.
Q5 lignin
Q6 Sucrose/sugars.
Q7 a) living cells
    b) Any two from, e.g. they contain a very thin layer of cytoplasm. / They have no nucleus. / They have few organelles.
Q8 Companion cells carry out the living functions for sieve cells. (They provide energy for the active transport of solutes.)
Q9 E.g. use a scalpel to slice a thin cross-section of the stem (either longitudinal or transverse). Add a drop of water to a microscope slide and then place the section onto it. Add one or two drops of a stain, e.g. TBO, wait for about a minute and then carefully place the coverslip on the slide. View the specimen under a light microscope.

2. Water Transport
Page 205 — Application Questions
Q1 root hair (cell)
Q2 C
Q3 Casparian strip
Q4 Structure E is the xylem, used to transport water (and mineral ions) to all parts of the plant. If the xylem is blocked some plant cells won't receive enough water and the plant may wilt.

Page 205 — Fact Recall Questions
Q1 Water enters the root from the soil through the root hair cells. It then passes through the cortex, including the endodermis, before it reaches the xylem.
Q2 In the symplast pathway, water moves through the cytoplasm in the root cells to the xylem via osmosis. Plasmodesmata connect the cytoplasm of neighbouring cells. In the apoplast pathway water moves through the cell walls of the root. Water diffuses through the cell walls and passes through the spaces between them. However, the apoplast pathway is blocked at the endodermis cell layer by a waxy strip in the cell walls called the Casparian strip.
    The water then has to take the symplast pathway until it reaches the xylem.
    Be careful not to get the symplast and apoplast pathways mixed up — in the symplast pathway water moves through the cytoplasm.
Q3 The loss/evaporation of water from a plant's surface/leaves.
Q4 The movement of water from a plant's roots to its leaves.
Q5 Adhesion is where water molecules are attracted to the walls of the xylem vessels. It helps water rise up through the xylem vessels.

3. Transpiration
Page 209 — Application Questions
Q1 B. E.g. there is a layer of hairs on the epidermis, which traps moist air around the stomata, reducing the water potential gradient between the leaf and the air, and slowing transpiration down. / The stomata are sunken in pits, which trap moist air, reducing transpiration by lowering the water potential gradient. / The leaf is curled, which traps moist air. This reduces the water potential gradient between the leaf and the air, slowing down transpiration. This also lowers the exposed surface area for losing water and protects the stomata from wind.
Q2 a) 10 °C — $(15 + 12 + 14) \div 3 =$**13.7 mm**
        20 °C — $(19 + 16 + 19) \div 3 =$ **18.0 mm**
        30 °C — $(25 + 22 + 23) \div 3 =$ **23.3 mm**
    b) See graph below. The bubble would move approximately 21 mm in 10 minutes at 25 °C.

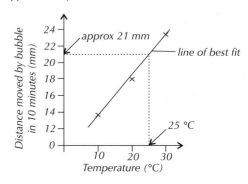

c) As the temperature increased, the distance moved by the bubble in 10 minutes increased too. This means the rate of transpiration increased with increasing temperatures. At higher temperatures water molecules have more energy so they evaporate from the cells inside the leaf faster. This increases the water potential between the inside and outside of the leaf, making water diffuse out of the leaf faster.

Q3 a) A hydrophyte because it lives in an aquatic habitat.
b) The stems may contain large air spaces to help the plant float. They may also be flexible because they are supported by the water around them, so they don't need rigid stems for support. Being flexible will also help to protect them from damage in strong water currents. The leaves may contain large air spaces to allow them to float, which increases the amount of light they receive. They may also have stomata on the upper surface of their leaves, which helps to maximise gas exchange, and be flexible (for the same reason as the stems).

Page 209 — Fact Recall Questions

Q1 gas exchange/photosynthesis
Q2 An increase in wind increases transpiration rate. Lots of air movement blows away water molecules from around the stomata. This increases the water potential gradient, which increases the rate of transpiration.
Q3 E.g. light intensity, temperature and humidity.
Q4 That water uptake by a plant is directly related to water loss by the leaves.
Q5 Cacti have a thick, waxy layer on the epidermis — this reduces water loss by evaporation because the layer is waterproof (water can't move through it). They have spines instead of leaves — this reduces the surface area for water loss. Cacti also close their stomata at the hottest times of the day when transpiration rates are the highest.
Q6 e.g. water lilies

4. Translocation
Page 212 — Application Questions

Q1 You would expect to see the sap flowing out more quickly near the leaves than at the bottom of the stem. This is because the pressure would be higher at the source (most likely the leaves), and lower towards the sink (most likely nearer the bottom of the plant).
Q2 The active loading of sucrose into the phloem requires ATP. ATP is needed to actively transport H^+ ions out of the companion cells into the surrounding tissue against their concentration gradient, which sets up a concentration gradient into the companion cells. H^+ ions then bind to a co-transport protein along with a molecule of sucrose. The movement of the H^+ ions down their concentration gradient is used to move sucrose into the companion cells against its concentration gradient. The same process occurs to move sucrose from the companion cells into the phloem tissue, where it is transported to the sink via translocation.
A metabolic inhibitor would prevent this process from occurring so the process of active loading and translocation would stop.

Page 212 — Fact Recall Questions

Q1 It's the movement of solutes/assimilates to where they're needed in a plant.
Q2 In a plant a source is where assimilates/solutes are made, whereas a sink is where assimilates/solutes are used up.

Q3 a) At the roots active transport is used to actively load solutes/assimilates into the sieve tubes. This lowers the water potential inside the sieve tubes, so water enters the tubes, from the xylem and companion cells, by osmosis. *Remember, water always flows from a higher water potential to a lower water potential.*
b) At the sink solutes/assimilates are removed from the phloem to be used up. This increases the water potential inside the sieve tubes, so water leaves the tubes by osmosis.
Q4 The process used to move substances at the source into the companion cells from surrounding tissues, and from the companion cells into the sieve tubes, against a concentration gradient.

Exam-style Questions — pages 214-215

1 C *(1 mark)*
The rate of water movement will decrease as it gets darker because the rate of transpiration will decrease (as the stomata close). Water is transported towards the xylem via osmosis, which is a passive process (so ATP is not needed). The water is moving by the apoplast pathway through the cell walls until it reaches the Casparian strip in the endodermis. Then it takes the symplast pathway through the cytoplasm. Water moves from an area of high water potential (in the roots) to an area of relatively lower water potential (in the leaves).

2 a) Y *(1 mark)*
b) The stem because, e.g. the xylem and phloem are distributed in a ring around the outside of the cross-section *(1 mark)*.
c) It helps support the walls of the xylem and stops them collapsing inwards *(1 mark)*. The spiral/ring pattern allows flexibility and prevents the stem from breaking *(1 mark)*.
d) Fig. 2.2 because there are lots of air spaces *(1 mark)*.
e) Any one from: e.g. stomata may only be present on the upper surface of floating leaves *(1 mark)*. / It may have flexible leaves/stems *(1 mark)*.

3 a) i) Reading off graph, distance moved by bubble in 5 minutes at 1.5 arbitrary units of light intensity = 15 mm
$15 \div 5 = \textbf{3 mm min}^{-1}$
(2 marks for the correct answer, otherwise 1 mark for showing a calculation of 'distance ÷ time')
ii) The lighter it gets, the wider stomata open *(1 mark)*. This increases the rate at which water evaporates from the leaves, which creates more tension *(1 mark)*. The whole column of water moves up the xylem because water molecules are cohesive *(1 mark)*. The increased tension causes the water to move faster, meaning that the bubble moves further in a shorter amount of time *(1 mark)*.
b) E.g. the experiment should be repeated with a light intensity of zero *(1 mark)*.
c) E.g. when the stomata in a plant open to let carbon dioxide in / when stomata open for gas exchange *(1 mark)* this lets water move out down its water potential gradient *(1 mark)*.
d) The transpiration rate would not be as fast *(1 mark)* because with more water in the air, the water potential gradient between the air and the leaf would be lower *(1 mark)*.

4 a) i) Sieve plate *(1 mark)* — it allows sugars to pass from one sieve tube element to another / it connects cell cytoplasms *(1 mark)*.

ii) Cell B/the companion cell carries out the living functions for both itself and its sieve tube element *(1 mark)* because the sieve tube element can't survive on its own, e.g. it has no nucleus *(1 mark)*.

b) ATP is needed for the active loading of solutes/assimilates *(1 mark)*.

c) E.g. food storage organs *(1 mark)* / meristems/growth areas *(1 mark)*

d) *5-6 marks*
The answer identifies the pressure as being greater at the source end and explains the mechanism of translocation fully with correct reference to active loading, pressure gradients, water potential and osmosis.
The answer has a clear and logical structure. The information given is relevant and detailed.
3-4 marks
The answer identifies the pressure as being greater at the source end and partially explains the mechanism of translocation with some reference to active loading, pressure gradients, water potential and osmosis.
The answer has some structure. Most of the information given is relevant and there is some detail involved.
1-2 marks
The answer may identify the pressure as being greater at the source end and attempts to explain one aspect of the mechanism of translocation with partial reference to either active loading, pressure gradients, water potential or osmosis.
The answer has no clear structure. The information given is basic and lacking in detail. It may not all be relevant.
0 marks
No relevant information is given.
Here are some points your answer may include:
The pressure will be greatest at the source end. Active transport is used to actively load the solutes/assimilates into the sieve tubes of the phloem at the source end. Solutes/assimilates moving into the sieve tubes lowers the water potential inside the sieve tubes, so water enters the tubes from the xylem by osmosis. Water entering the sieve tubes creates a high pressure inside the sieve tubes at the source end of the phloem.
At the sink end, solutes/assimilates diffuse out of the phloem to be used up. The removal of solutes/assimilates increases the water potential inside the sieve tubes, so water leaves the tubes by osmosis. Water leaving the sieve tubes lowers the pressure inside the sieve tubes at the sink end. The result is a pressure gradient in the sieve tubes from the source to the sink end.

Module 4

Section 1 — Disease and the Immune System

1. Pathogens and Communicable Diseases
Page 218 — Application Questions
Q1 a) E.g. an infected plant touching a healthy, but damaged plant / an infected plant growing from an infected seed.
    b) E.g. by gardening tools / on a gardener's hands/gloves.
Q2 a) E.g. because they are closer together, so uninfected cattle are more likely to come into contact with an infected animal or spores.

b) indirect transmission
c) E.g. by washing hands and clothes after touching an infected cow or its environment / by wearing gloves while touching an infected cow or its environment.
Q3 Any two from: e.g. keep the person at home / increase ventilation in living spaces / person wears a mask (which will catch infected droplets) / monitor person's treatment (to make sure that the person is taking the antibiotics) / vaccinate people who are at increased risk of catching TB (as a longer term solution).
The spread of TB to the general public can also be controlled by isolating or quarantining people who are actively infected or suspected of being infected with the disease. It is usually enforced when the person is considered to be at high risk of spreading the disease and is only implemented in a minority of cases.

Page 218 — Fact Recall Questions
Q1 An organism that causes disease.
Q2 A disease that can spread between organisms.
Q3 banana plant
Q4 fungus
Q5 potato/tomato late blight / malaria
Q6 E.g. droplet infection / sexual intercourse / touching an infected organism.
Q7 An intermediate organism that helps to transmit a disease from one organism to another.
Q8 People are less likely to be diagnosed and treated for HIV, and the most effective anti-HIV drugs are less likely to be available.
Q9 Those countries have the ideal climate for the malarial vectors (mosquitoes) to breed.

2. Defence Against Pathogens
Page 221 — Application Questions
Q1 The mucous membranes in the lungs are coated in mucus, which traps the bacteria and contains antimicrobial enzymes that destroy the bacteria. These cells in the lung epithelium also have cilia that move the mucus up the trachea to the throat and mouth, so the bacteria are removed from the body.
Q2 The skin is a physical barrier against pathogens. When it is burnt, the barrier has been damaged, so bacteria that would not normally be able to enter the body are able to enter and cause disease.
Q3 To get to the sap, the aphids pierce the surface of the plant, which creates holes in its physical barriers against pathogens.

Page 221 — Fact Recall Questions
Q1 It produces antimicrobial chemicals that can inhibit the growth of pathogens.
Q2 a mesh of protein/fibrin fibres
Q3 Increased tissue fluid isolates any pathogens that may be present and increased blood flow brings white blood cells to kill them.
Q4 E.g. a cough / sneeze
Q5 Any two from: e.g. waxy cuticle / cell wall / callose deposition
Q6 a) E.g. if the plant cell is stressed / infected.
    b) Between the plasma membrane and cell wall, and at the plasmodesmata.
Q7 They inhibit the growth of pathogens.

3. The Immune System
Page 225 — Application Questions
Q1 a) A = neutrophil
          B = monocyte
          C = red blood cell
    b) Neutrophils carry out phagocytosis.
Q2 With fewer T lymphocytes, fewer pathogens are killed directly. Also, with fewer T lymphocytes in the blood there are fewer cells to be activated by pathogen antigens presented by phagocytes. This means that fewer B lymphocytes are activated, so fewer antibodies are produced against the pathogens. With fewer antibodies, pathogens can survive longer in the body so opportunistic infections can cause problems.
Q3 Antibodies will be generated against antigens on the surface of *S. pyogenes*. These will then bind to antigens on the surface of heart cells because the antigens are so similar in shape. The immune system would then attack the heart cells and cause rheumatic fever.
The command word in this question is 'suggest', so you're not expected to know the exact answer. You're expected to use what you know about the immune system to come up with a possible explanation.

Page 225 — Fact Recall Questions
Q1 The body's reaction to a foreign antigen.
Q2 Molecules found on the surface of cells.
Q3 Phagocytosis is the engulfment of pathogens.
Q4 A vesicle in the cytoplasm of a phagocyte (that contains engulfed pathogens).
Q5 It fuses with the phagosome and releases digestive enzymes that break down the (phagocytosed) pathogen.
Q6 cytokines
Q7 It presents the pathogen's antigens on its surface / becomes an antigen-presenting cell and the T lymphocytes that have complementary receptors to the presented antigens bind to them.
Q8 T helper cells release substances to activate B lymphocytes and T killer cells, T killer cells kill cells infected with a virus and T regulatory cells suppress the immune response from other white blood cells. Some activated T lymphocytes become memory cells. The function of plasma cells is to produce antibodies.
Q9

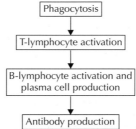

Q10 E.g. T helper cells release interleukins that bind to receptors on B lymphocytes. This activates the B lymphocytes — the T helper cells are signalling to the B lymphocytes that there's a pathogen in the body.

4. Antibodies
Page 227 — Application Question
Q1 The anti-toxins bind to the toxins in the poison. This prevents the toxins from affecting human cells, so the toxins are neutralised (inactivated). The toxin-antibody complexes are then phagocytosed and destroyed.

Page 227 — Fact Recall Questions
Q1 a) The variable region is complementary to a particular antigen and forms the antigen-binding site.
    b) The hinge region allows flexibility when an antibody binds to an antigen.
    c) The constant region allows the antibody to bind to receptors on immune system cells.
Q2 Antibodies have two antigen-binding sites. This is useful because it means that antibodies can bind to more than one pathogen at a time, so they can agglutinate the pathogens (clump them together).
Q3 Agglutinating groups of pathogens. Binding to and neutralising toxins produced by pathogens. Binding to receptors on pathogens and preventing them from entering host cells.

5. Primary and Secondary Immune Responses
Page 229 — Application Questions
Q1 Mouse A had 10 units, Mouse B had 10 000 units.
Q2 Mouse B was already immune. You can tell this because the immune response was much quicker and stronger than the immune response of Mouse A.
Q3 a) Day 20
    b) The mouse's memory B lymphocytes rapidly divided and produced the antibody needed to bind to the antigen. The mouse's memory T lymphocytes rapidly divided into the correct type of T lymphocytes to kill the cell carrying the antigen.

Page 229 — Fact Recall Questions
Q1 The primary response is slow because there aren't many T lymphocytes that can bind to the pathogen's antigens and there aren't many B lymphocytes that can make the right antibody to the antigens. The secondary response is faster because there are already memory T and B lymphocytes present that recognise the antigen and rapidly produce the right antibody to it.
Q2 Immunity doesn't always last forever because memory B and T lymphocytes have a limited lifespan. If the person is not exposed to the pathogen again, eventually all of the memory cells will die and the person will no longer be immune.
Q3 E.g. the primary response happens the first time a pathogen invades, the secondary response happens the second time a pathogen invades. / The primary response involves B and T lymphocytes, the secondary response involves memory cells. / There are symptoms with a primary response, but not with a secondary response.

6. Immunity and Vaccinations
Page 233 — Application Questions
Q1 B
A is an example of natural passive immunity, C is an example of natural active immunity and D is an example of artificial passive immunity.
Q2 a) 75% (accept answers in the range of 74-76%)
    b) 1000 cases
    c) The number of cases decreased in a fluctuating pattern from a peak of around 6000 cases in the early 1960s to a peak of nearly 2000 cases around 1975. This is because more people were directly protected by the vaccine, and some people were protected by herd immunity.

Page 233 — Fact Recall Questions

Q1 Active immunity is the type of immunity you get when your immune system makes its own antibodies after being stimulated by an antigen.
Passive immunity is the type of immunity you get from being given antibodies made by a different organism — your immune system doesn't produce any antibodies of its own.

Q2 a) A disease resulting from an abnormal immune response against the organism's own tissues.
b) The organism's immune system it isn't able to recognise certain self-antigens on the organism's cells / treats certain self-antigens on the cells as foreign antigens.

Q3 The immune system attacking cells in the connective tissues.

Q4 E.g. (rheumatoid) arthritis

Q5 Vaccines contain antigens that cause your body to produce memory cells against a particular pathogen. This makes you immune.

Q6 Herd immunity is where unvaccinated people are protected because the occurrence of the disease is reduced by the number of people who are vaccinated.

Q7 The influenza virus can change the antigens on its surface, so every year there are new strains of influenza circulating in the population.

7. Antibiotics and Other Medicines
Page 236 — Application Questions

Q1 D

Q2 They are more likely to become infected with antibiotic-resistant bacteria and there are fewer antibiotics that are able to treat these infections.

Q3 a) There was genetic variation in the *C. difficile* population that meant some of the bacteria had an allele that gave them resistance to fluoroquinolones. / A genetic mutation made some *C. difficile* more resistant to fluoroquinolones. This made them more likely to survive and reproduce in a host being treated with a fluoroquinolone. The bacteria passed the allele for fluoroquinolone resistance on to their offspring. Over time fluoroquinolone resistance became more common in the *C. difficile* population.
b) Patients who are already ill are more susceptible to infection because their immune systems are weakened. Hospitalised patients are also at risk because they are in an environment where lots of antibiotics are used, so *C. difficile* infections are more likely to be present.
Another factor here is that people who have recently been treated with antibiotics have lower amounts of harmless bacteria in their digestive systems, so there is more room for C. difficile to flourish.
c) Doctors should reduce their use of antibiotics / not prescribe them for minor infections or to prevent infections.
Patients should take all of the antibiotics they're prescribed to make sure the infection is fully cleared / all the bacteria have been killed.

Page 236 — Fact Recall Questions

Q1 Chemicals that kill or inhibit the growth of bacteria.

Q2 penicillin

Q3 e.g. MRSA (meticillin-resistant *Staphylococcus aureus*)

Q4 a fungus

Q5 Medicines that are tailored to an individual's DNA.

Q6 The use of technology to design and make things such as artificial proteins, cells and even microorganisms.

Exam-style Questions — pages 238-239

1 D *(1 mark)*
Malaria and tomato late blight are caused by a protoctist and ring rot is caused by a bacterium.

2 a) a bacterium *(1 mark)*
b) i) The number of reported TB cases in the UK increased overall, from about 6750 cases in 2000 to about 9000 cases in 2009 *(1 mark)*.
ii) 9000 − 7250 = 1750
(1750 ÷ 7250) × 100 *(1 mark)* = **24.1%** *(1 mark)*
iii) E.g. although the number of TB cases has risen by about 33% between 2000 and 2009, it doesn't necessarily mean this trend will continue *(1 mark)*. The graph shows the number of reported cases of TB, but the newspaper refers to the number of cases of TB — it may be that the reason for the increasing trend is just because more cases of TB are being reported (i.e. there's not an increase in overall number of cases) *(1 mark)*. The graph shows the number of reported cases of TB in the UK but the newspaper refers to the number of cases of TB in England, so this prediction doesn't fit the data shown in the graph *(1 mark)*.
Always read questions carefully — the introduction mentions that the graph shows the number of reported cases of TB in the UK. You'll miss this if you skim over the introduction and look at the graph first.

3 a) i) **5-6 marks:**
All of the stages of phagocytosis are described thoroughly and in the correct order.
The answer has a clear and logical structure.
The information given is relevant and detailed.
3-4 marks:
Some of the stages of phagocytosis are described and most of them are in order, but the answer is incomplete.
The answer has some structure. Most of the information given is relevant and there is some detail involved.
1-2 marks:
A few stages of phagocytosis are described briefly and not necessarily in the correct order.
The answer has no clear structure. The information given is basic and lacking in detail. It may not all be relevant.
0 marks:
No relevant information is given.
Here are some points your answer may include:
When a phagocyte recognises the antigens on a pathogen, the cytoplasm of the phagocyte moves around the pathogen, engulfing it. This may be made easier by the presence of opsonins — molecules in the blood that attach to foreign antigens to aid phagocytosis. The engulfed pathogen is contained in a phagosome inside the phagocyte. A lysosome fuses with the phagosome and the lysosomal enzymes from the lysosome break down the pathogen.
The phagocyte acts as an antigen-presenting cell by presenting the pathogen's antigens on its surface, in order to activate other immune system cells.

ii) They aid phagocytosis by attaching to foreign antigens *(1 mark)*.

iii) Receptors on the surface of T lymphocytes bind to the antigens presented by phagocytes, activating the T lymphocytes *(1 mark)*. When B lymphocytes, which are covered in antibodies, meet an antigen with a complementary shape they bind to it *(1 mark)*. This, along with substances released from T lymphocytes/T helper cells, activates the B lymphocytes *(1 mark)*. The B lymphocytes then divide into plasma cells *(1 mark)*. The plasma cells then produce antibodies specific to the antigen *(1 mark)*.

b) After the first infection their B lymphocytes and T lymphocytes produced memory cells *(1 mark)*. When they were exposed for a second time these memory cells divided into plasma cells and the correct type of T lymphocytes to quickly destroy the virus *(1 mark)*.

c) The neuraminidase and haemagglutinin antigens on the Asian flu strain were different from the antigens on the Spanish flu strain *(1 mark)*, so any memory cells created against H1N1 would not detect H2N2 *(1 mark)*. So the immune system would have to start from scratch and carry out a primary immune response if exposed to Asian flu *(1 mark)*.

Make sure you use scientific terminology in your answer, e.g. 'antigens' and 'primary immune response'.

d) To make people immune to more than one strain of flu *(1 mark)*.

4 a) i) Vaccines contain antigens *(1 mark)* which activate T lymphocytes *(1 mark)*. The antigens and T lymphocytes activate B lymphocytes, some of which differentiate into memory B lymphocytes *(1 mark)*.

ii) They will benefit from herd immunity *(1 mark)*. If most people in a community are vaccinated the disease becomes extremely rare *(1 mark)*. This means people who haven't been vaccinated are less likely to get the disease because there's no one to catch it from *(1 mark)*.

b) i) Variable region — forms the antigen-binding site *(1 mark)*.
Hinge region — allows flexibility when the antibody binds an antigen *(1 mark)*.
Constant region — allows binding to receptors on immune system cells *(1 mark)*.

ii)

Agglutinating pathogens	✓
Killing pathogens directly	
Neutralising toxins	✓
Activating memory T lymphocytes	
Mutating pathogen DNA	
Stopping pathogens binding cells	✓

(1 mark for each correct answer, if more than three boxes are ticked remove 1 mark for each incorrect answer.)

Section 2 — Biodiversity

1. Investigating Biodiversity
Pages 244-245 — Application Questions
Q1 Any two from, e.g. she could sweep the net through the same depth of water. / She could make sure her net stays in the water for the same length of time for each sample. / She could take samples at the same time of day. / She could use the same net/type of net for each sample.
Standardise just means 'make the same' — so the question is asking for ways the environmental officer could collect each sample in the same way.

Q2 a) Pond A because the population sizes of the species are more similar than in pond B.

b) i) Pond A
$$D = 1 - \left(\left(\frac{3}{18}\right)^2 + \left(\frac{5}{18}\right)^2 + \left(\frac{2}{18}\right)^2 + \left(\frac{3}{18}\right)^2 \right.$$
$$\left. + \left(\frac{1}{18}\right)^2 + \left(\frac{4}{18}\right)^2 \right)$$
= **0.802** (3 s.f.)

ii) Pond B
$$D = 1 - \left(\left(\frac{13}{54}\right)^2 + \left(\frac{5}{54}\right)^2 + \left(\frac{7}{54}\right)^2 + \left(\frac{2}{54}\right)^2 \right.$$
$$\left. + \left(\frac{18}{54}\right)^2 + \left(\frac{9}{54}\right)^2 \right)$$
= **0.776** (3 s.f.)

If you have to calculate Simpson's Index of Diversity in the exam, always show your working out. You could pick up a mark for showing you understand the equation if nothing else.

c) Yes, because they both have a fairly high index of diversity. This means the populations are stable and capable of coping with change.

Page 245 — Fact Recall Questions
Q1 a) The variety of living organisms in an area.
b) The area inhabited by a species.
c) A group of similar organisms able to reproduce to give fertile offspring.

Q2 Habitat diversity — the number of different habitats in an area. Species diversity — the number of different species (species richness) and the abundance of each species (species evenness) in an area. Genetic diversity — the variation of alleles within a species (or a population of a species).

Q3 a) It avoids bias in the results and makes it more likely that the sample is representative of the population as a whole.
b) E.g. If there's a lot of variety in the distribution of species in the habitat, you might want to make sure all the different areas in the habitat are sampled/all the different species in the habitat are sampled.
c) Systematic sampling, opportunistic sampling and stratified sampling.

Q4 a) The number of different species in an area.
b) It's a measure of the relative abundance of each species in an area.

Q5 The total number of organisms in one species. The total number of all organisms.

Q6 That a habitat is highly diverse, making it stable and able to cope with change.

2. Genetic Diversity

Page 247 — Application Questions

Q1 a) proportion of polymorphic gene loci = number of polymorphic gene loci ÷ total number of loci
= 12 ÷ 80 = **0.15**
b) E.g. they could introduce gorillas from other zoos to breed with the existing population.
c) A population with a low genetic diversity might not be able to adapt to a change in the environment and the whole population could be wiped out by a single event (e.g. a disease).

Q2 a) proportion of polymorphic gene loci = number of polymorphic gene loci ÷ total number of loci
= 66 ÷ 90 = 0.73...
percentage of genes with alleles = 0.73... × 100
= **73%** (2 s.f.)
b) proportion of polymorphic gene loci = 42 ÷ 90 = 0.46...
percentage of genes with alleles = 0.46... × 100
= **47%** (2 s.f.)
c) Species A, because it has a greater genetic diversity.

Page 247 — Fact Recall Questions

Q1 A locus that has two or more alleles.
Q2 Take a sample of the genes in the population and work out what proportion or percentage of them are polymorphic.
Q3 proportion of polymorphic gene loci = number of polymorphic gene loci ÷ total number of loci

3. Factors Affecting Biodiversity

Page 250 — Application Question

Q1 a) Sea surface temperature fluctuated around the average between 1950 and approximately 1978, then there was a steady increase between 1978 and 2000, up to just over 0.3 °C greater than the average. Subtropical plankton species were found in the sea south of the UK in 1958-1981. By 2000-2002 their distribution had moved further north along the west coast of the UK and Ireland to the Arctic Ocean.
b) The change in plankton distribution is correlated with the increase in sea surface temperature during the same period.
c) E.g. there could have been factors other than temperature involved, e.g. overfishing could have removed plankton predator species.
Just because the difference in average temperature and the distribution of plankton have both changed over the same time period doesn't mean to say that one caused the other — there could be other factors involved. Remember, correlation and cause aren't the same thing (see page 23).
d) E.g. biodiversity may have increased in the areas where the plankton moved to, as the plankton could have provided a new food source to support more marine organisms in those areas.

Page 250 — Fact Recall Questions

Q1 E.g. the need to develop more land for housing and to produce food leads to the destruction of habitats, which reduces biodiversity. / There is a greater demand for resources (such as food, water and energy). This means a lot of resources are being used up faster than they can be replenished, which can reduce both habitat and species diversity. / Sprawling cities and major road developments can isolate species, meaning populations are unable to interbreed and genetic diversity is decreased. / The increase in waste and pollution can kill species or destroy habitats, both of which decrease biodiversity.

Q2 E.g. monoculture affects biodiversity because habitats are lost as land is cleared to make way for the large fields. There is also a loss of local and naturally occurring plants and animals as they are seen as weeds and pests, and so are destroyed with pesticides and herbicides, reducing species diversity. Heritage (traditional) varieties of crops are lost because they don't make enough money and so are not planted any more, which reduces species diversity.

4. Biodiversity and Conservation

Page 253 — Application Question

Q1 E.g. prairie dogs are a keystone species because they maintain the environment needed for the ecosystem. Their removal would disrupt food chains as several animals and birds of prey rely on them as a food source, and the numbers of these species may decline as a result. The numbers of burrowing owls may also decline as they wouldn't have a supply of burrows in which to nest and lay eggs to produce more young. Plant growth would also be affected as the soil quality wouldn't be maintained and this may affect other species who rely on the plants for food.

Page 256 — Application Question

Q1 a) i) Any one from, e.g. both the Northern Quoll and its habitat are conserved which means that larger populations can be protected than with *ex situ* conservation. / *In situ* conservation is less disruptive than removing Northern Quoll from their habitats. / The chances of the Northern Quoll population recovering are greater than with *ex situ* methods.
ii) Any one from, e.g. it can be used to protect individual Northern Quolls in a controlled environment — things like predation and hunting can be managed more easily than in *in situ* conservation. / It's possible to reduce competition between Northern Quoll and other animals in *ex situ* conservation but not in *in situ* conservation. / It's easier to check on the health of Northern Quoll and treat them for diseases in *ex situ* than *in situ* conservation. / It's easier to manipulate breeding e.g. through the use of reproductive hormones and IVF, in *ex situ* than *in situ* conservation.
b) *In situ* conservation would involve eradicating the cane toads. Without the cane toads to eat the sugarcane pests, the yield of the sugarcane crops could fall, lowering farmers' income from the crop / forcing the farmers to spend more money on pesticides.

Q1 It's important to maintain biodiversity to protect species. Organisms in an ecosystem are interdependent — they depend on each other to survive. This means that the loss of just one species can have pretty drastic effects on an ecosystem, such as the disruption of food chains and the disruption of nutrient cycles. Protecting keystone species is particularly important as they often keep populations of prey in check and can also maintain the environment needed for the ecosystem. It is also important to maintain biodiversity to maintain genetic resources. We need to maintain genetic resources as they provide us with a variety of everyday products, such as food, drink, drugs and fuels. These products are important to the global economy as they are traded on a local and global scale. Genetic resources also allow us to adapt to changes in the environment.

Q2 a) E.g. to reduce soil depletion, so that crop yields don't decrease and spending on fertilisers doesn't need to increase.
   b) E.g. to protect beautiful landscapes.

Q3 The protection and management of species and habitats.

Q4 a) Conservation on site. / Protecting a species in its natural habitat.
   b) Any two from: e.g. establishing protected areas such as national parks/wildlife reserves/marine conservation zones. / Controlling or preventing the introduction of species that threaten local biodiversity. / Protecting habitats. / Restoring damaged areas. / Promoting particular species. / Giving legal protection to endangered species.

Q5 a) Conservation off site. / Protecting a species by removing part of the population from a threatened habitat and placing it in a new location.
   b) Any two from: e.g. relocating an organism to a safer area. / Breeding organisms in captivity/in animal sanctuaries/in zoos. / Growing plants in botanic gardens. / Storing plant seeds in seed banks.
   c) Any one from e.g. usually only a small number of individuals can be cared for. / It can be difficult and expensive to create and sustain the right environment. / It is usually less successful than *in situ* methods as many species can't breed in captivity or don't adapt to their new environment when moved to a new location.

Q6 An international agreement that aims to develop international strategies on the conservation of biodiversity and how to use animal and plant resources in a sustainable way.

Q7 An agreement designed to increase international cooperation in regulating trade in wild animal and plant specimens.

Q8 Any two from, e.g. regenerating hedgerows / leaving grassy margins around the edges of fields where wildflowers could grow / grazing upland areas to keep down bracken.

Exam-style Questions — pages 258-259

1 B *(1 mark)*
2 a) The number of different species *(1 mark)* and the abundance of each species in an area *(1 mark)*.
   b) Any two from, e.g. the sample was biased/not collected at random/the sample was only collected from one area *(1 mark)*. All the samples were collected on the same day/at the same time *(1 mark)*. / The student's method only collected insects that live on the ground *(1 mark)*.
   c) Any one from, e.g. that one or two species dominate the habitat *(1 mark)*. / That insect diversity is low *(1 mark)*.
   d) E.g. use the same sampling method/set up the pitfall traps in the same way *(1 mark)*.

3 **5-6 marks:**
The answer gives a detailed explanation of how climate change may affect the population of polar bears and makes several suggestions as to how, due to their role as a keystone species, this will affect the Arctic ecosystem.
The answer has a clear and logical structure.
The information given is relevant and detailed.
3-4 marks:
The answer describes how climate change may affect the population of polar bears and makes one or two suggestions as to how this might have a knock on effect on the Arctic ecosystem.
Most of the information given is relevant and there is some detail involved.
1-2 marks:
The answer suggests how climate change may affect the polar bears. An effect this may have on other Arctic organisms may be mentioned.
The answer has no clear structure. The information given is basic and lacking in detail. It may not all be relevant.
0 marks:
No relevant information is given.
Here are some points your answer may include:
Climate change includes global warming (the increasing global average temperature), which could cause the ice sheets to melt. This could reduce the overall area of the ice sheets/break up the ice sheets, leaving the polar bears a smaller area in which to hunt. This could make it harder for the bears to find food as a result. The lack of food could lead to a decrease in the number of polar bears/a change in their distribution. A decrease in the number of polar bears could mean fewer seals are eaten, causing the seal population to increase. This could have knock-on effects for the populations of organisms eaten by the seals. A decrease in the population of polar bears may also reduce the amount of food available for scavengers such as the Arctic fox and Arctic birds. These scavenger populations may also decrease as a result.

4 a) Wood
$$D = 1 - \left(\left(\frac{15}{101}\right)^2 + \left(\frac{18}{101}\right)^2 + \left(\frac{17}{101}\right)^2 + \left(\frac{19}{101}\right)^2 + \left(\frac{9}{101}\right)^2 \right.$$
$$\left. + \left(\frac{8}{101}\right)^2 + \left(\frac{7}{101}\right)^2 + \left(\frac{8}{101}\right)^2 + \left(\frac{0}{101}\right)^2 \right)$$
= 0.857 (3 s.f.)
(2 marks for the correct answer, 1 mark for evidence of the correct calculation.)
Town
$$D = 1 - \left(\left(\frac{1}{41}\right)^2 + \left(\frac{3}{41}\right)^2 + \left(\frac{2}{41}\right)^2 + \left(\frac{1}{41}\right)^2 + \left(\frac{1}{41}\right)^2 \right.$$
$$\left. + \left(\frac{2}{41}\right)^2 + \left(\frac{20}{41}\right)^2 + \left(\frac{6}{41}\right)^2 + \left(\frac{5}{41}\right)^2 \right)$$
= 0.714 (3 s.f.)
(2 marks for the correct answer, 1 mark for evidence of the correct calculation.)
   b) Both areas have a relatively high index of diversity/an index of biodiversity close to 1 *(1 mark)*. This means that both areas have a relatively high biodiversity and so are likely to be fairly stable habitats that are able to withstand change *(1 mark)*.

c) Any two from: e.g. the red squirrels could be relocated to a safer area. / The red squirrels could be bred in captivity and reintroduced into the wild elsewhere. / The remaining woodland could be made a protected area. *(1 mark for each correct answer up to a maximum of 2 marks.)*

There are lots of possible right answers here — just apply your scientific knowledge to the situation and make two sensible suggestions.

Section 3 — Classification and Evolution

1. Classification Basics
Pages 262-263 — Application Questions
Q1 a) sharks
    b) salamanders
    c) (i) crocodiles
       (ii) lizards
Q2

Taxonomic Group	
Domain	Eukarya
Kingdom	Animalia
Phylum	**Chordata**
Class	Mammalia
Order	Perrisodactyla
Family	Equidae
Genus	**Equus**
Species	**asinus**

Page 263 — Fact Recall Questions
Q1 The act of arranging organisms into groups based on their similarities and differences.
Q2 Each species is given a two-part Latin name. The first part is the genus name and the second part is the species name.
Q3 Any three from, e.g. eukaryotic / multicellular / cell walls made of cellulose / can photosynthesise / contain chlorophyll / autotrophic.
Q4 The smallest group of organisms that shares a common ancestor.

2. The Evolution of Classification Systems
Page 266 — Application Questions
Q1 Species A: TCGACGTGGGTAATCGAGC
    Species B: TCCACGTGTGTAATCGAGT
    Species C: ACGCCGAGTGTTATGGAGT
Q2 3
    Take your time with questions like this. Once you've got your answer, recount it to make sure it's right.
Q3 7
Q4 Species B. There are fewer base differences in the DNA when comparing A and B than A and C.
Q5 Species B. There are only 6 base differences between species C and B. This is fewer than for species C and A, so species C and B are more likely to be closely related.

Page 266 — Fact Recall Questions
Q1 You can compare the amino acid sequence of a particular protein that's shared between organisms. The more similar the amino acid sequence, the more closely related the species are likely to be.
Q2 In the three domain system, organisms with cells that contain a nucleus/eukaryotes are placed in the domain Eukarya. Organisms without a nucleus/prokaryotes are separated into two domains — Archaea and Bacteria.
Q3 Any one from, e.g. the RNA polymerase enzyme is different in Bacteria and Archaea. / Archaea have similar histones to Eukarya, but Bacteria don't. / The bonds of the lipids in the cell membranes of Bacteria and Archaea are different. / The development and composition of flagellae are different in Bacteria and Archaea.

3. Variation
Page 269 — Application Question
Q1 a) continuous
    Head circumference can take any value within a range, so it's continuous data. This indicates that head circumference is an example of continuous variation.
    b) The mean difference in head circumference is approximately 0.5 cm for identical twins, 3 cm for non-identical twins and 8.5 cm for unrelated individuals. So the mean difference in head circumference is much larger for unrelated individuals than for either identical twins or non-identical twins.
    c) The data suggests that genetic factors have a larger effect on head circumference, because the mean difference in head circumference is much larger for unrelated individuals than for either identical twins or non-identical twins. However, the mean difference for identical twins wasn't zero, so environmental factors appear to play some role.
    d) The mean difference in the number of steps taken is between 800 and 900 for all three sample groups. Identical twins and non-identical twins show the lowest difference and unrelated individuals the highest but the margins are very small. This suggests that environmental factors play a more important role than genetic factors in determining activity level when measured by the number of steps taken per day.

Page 269 — Fact Recall Questions
Q1 a) Variation within a species.
    b) Variation between different species.
Q2 Continuous variation is when the individuals in a population vary within a range — there are no distinct categories, e.g. height in humans. Discontinuous variation is when there are two or more distinct categories and each individual falls into only one of these categories — there are no intermediates, e.g. blood group in humans.
Q3 E.g. height in humans/plants / whether a microorganism grows a flagellum.

4. Investigating Variation
Page 273 — Application Questions
Q1 a) i) The mean wing span is approximately 27 cm for species A and 31 cm for species B. Both curves follow a normal distribution. Species A has a higher standard deviation than species B.
ii) Species A, because it has a higher standard deviation.
iii) E.g. genetics, because species A and species B live in the same environment, so the difference in wing span is probably a result of genetic factors.
b) $(31 - 27) \div 27 \times 100 = $ **14.8%**
Make sure you're confident at calculating percentages — they're a common mathsy-type question that examiners like to ask.

Q2 Work out the mean length of snakes:
$\bar{x} = (177 + 182 + 190 + 187 + 191) \div 5 = 185.4$ cm
Work out $(x - \bar{x})^2$ for each snake length:
A = $(177 - 185.4)^2 = (-8.4)^2 = 70.56$,
B = $(182 - 185.4)^2 = (-3.4)^2 = 11.56$,
C = $(190 - 185.4)^2 = (4.6)^2 = 21.16$,
D = $(187 - 185.4)^2 = (1.6)^2 = 2.56$,
E = $(191 - 185.4)^2 = (5.6)^2 = 31.36$
Work out $\Sigma = (x - \bar{x})^2$:
$70.56 + 11.56 + 21.16 + 2.56 + 31.36 = 137.2$
Divide it by the number of values, n, minus 1:
$137.2 \div 4 = 34.3$
Square root it:
$\sqrt{34.3} = $ **5.86 to 3 s.f.**

Page 275 — Application Question
Q1 a)

Space per cow (km²)	Rank	Average Daily Milk Yield (dm³)	Rank	Difference between ranks (d)	d²
0.004	8	32.1	8	0	0
0.005	7	36.2	5	2	4
0.006	6	37.4	3	3	9
0.007	5	34.3	6	1	1
0.008	4	36.7	4	0	0
0.009	3	38.9	1	2	4
0.010	2	37.6	2	0	0
0.011	1	33.4	7	6	36

$r_s = 1 - \dfrac{6\Sigma d^2}{n(n^2 - 1)}$

$r_s = 1 - \dfrac{6 \times (0 + 4 + 9 + 1 + 0 + 4 + 0 + 36)}{8 \times (8^2 - 1)}$

$r_s = 1 - \dfrac{6 \times 54}{8 \times 63}$

$r_s = 1 - \dfrac{324}{504}$

$= $ **0.357** (3 s.f.)

b) Accepted, because the result is lower than the critical value of 0.738.

Page 275 — Fact Recall Questions
Q1 Divide the total of all the values in your data by the number of values in your data.
Q2 Bell shaped
Q3 How much the values in a single sample vary / the spread of the values about the mean.

5. Adaptations
Page 277 — Application Question
Q1 a) Light flexible wings = anatomical. Male bats make mating calls to attract females = behavioural. Bats lower their metabolism to hibernate over winter = physiological.
b) E.g. light, flexible wings — allow the bat to fly after insects, increasing its chances of catching prey and so surviving. Mating calls — increase the bat's chance of finding a mate and reproducing successfully. Hibernation — saves the bat's energy when food is scarce and so increases the bat's chances of surviving.

Page 278 — Application Question
Q1 a) Anatomical
b) Both animals have evolved in similar environments to fill a similar ecological niche. Having opposable thumbs is beneficial for both types of animal because they both need to grip trees/branches. This means that individuals with opposable thumbs are more likely to survive and successfully reproduce, so the alleles responsible for the adaptation becomes widespread over generations.

Page 278 — Fact Recall Questions
Q1 Because it increases the organism's chances of survival and successful reproduction
Q2 A process inside of an organism's body that increases its chance of survival.
Q3 Any five from: e.g. small or nonexistent eyes — because they don't need to be able to see underground. / No external ears — to keep the head streamlined for burrowing. / Scoop-shaped front paws — which are good for digging. / Powerful front paws — which are good for digging. / Specialised claws — which are specialised for digging. / Tube shaped body — which makes it easier to push through sand or soil. / Cone shaped head — which makes it easier to push through sand or soil.

6. The Theory of Evolution
Page 281 — Application Questions
Q1 E.g. scientists could compare the amino acid sequence of cytochrome C in different organisms. Cytochrome C is present in almost all living organisms, so it suggests that we all evolved from a common ancestor. The more similar the amino acid sequence of cytochrome C in different organisms, the more recently the organisms are likely to have diverged away from one another.
Q2 Some individuals in the population had an allele for darker colouring that helped them to blend into their environment (wooded areas) better. This was beneficial because it helped them to avoid predators and sneak up on prey. So these individuals were more likely to survive, reproduce and pass on the allele for darker colouring. After some time most organisms in the population carried the allele for darker colouring.
Whatever adaptation you're asked about in the exam, make sure you get the phrase, 'it helps the organism to survive, reproduce and pass on their alleles' into your answer.

Q1 Any two from, e.g. organisms produce more offspring than survive. / There's variation in the characteristics of members of the same species. / Some characteristics can be passed on from one generation to the next. / Individuals that are best adapted to their environment are more likely to survive.

Q2 Any environmental factor that creates a struggle for survival.

Q3 (Alfred Russel) Wallace

Q4 a) By arranging fossils in chronological (date) order, gradual changes in organisms can be observed that provide evidence of evolution.

b) Scientists can analyse DNA base sequences. The theory of evolution suggests that all living organisms evolved from a common ancestor, so organisms that diverged away from each other more recently should have more similar DNA than those that diverged less recently (as less time has passed for changes in the DNA sequence to occur).

7. More on Evolution

Page 283 — Application Question

Q1 a) There was variation in the *P. falciparum* population. Genetic mutations made some of the population naturally resistant to chloroquine. When the population was exposed to chloroquine, only the resistant *P. falciparum* survived to reproduce. The alleles for chloroquine resistance were then passed on to the next generation. Over many generations, the population evolved to become resistant to chloroquine.

b) i) E.g. it could take doctors longer to figure out which drugs will get rid of their malaria, during which time the patient could become very ill or die.

ii) E.g. it means that the drug companies have to keep developing more anti-malarial drugs, which takes time and costs money.

Exam-Style Questions — pages 285-286

1 a)

Domain	Archaea
Kingdom	Euryarchaeota
Phylum	Euryarchaeota
Class	Halobacteria
Order	Halobacteriales
Family	Halobacteriaceae
Genus	*Halobacterium*
Species	*salinarum*

(1 mark for each correct column)

b) i) Any two from, e.g. no nucleus *(1 mark)* / unicellular *(1 mark)* / less than 5 μm *(1 mark)*

ii) Under the three domain system, organisms that would be in the Prokaryotae kingdom are split into two separate domains/Archaea and Bacteria *(1 mark)*. This is because of new evidence/molecular evidence that showed large differences between the two domains/Archaea and Bacteria *(1 mark)*.

iii) Any one from, e.g. the Protoctista/Plantae/Fungi/Animalia kingdom is present in both systems *(1 mark)*. / Four out of five kingdoms are present in both systems *(1 mark)*. / The hierarchy below domain (e.g. kingdom, phylum, class, order, family, genus, species) stays the same *(1 mark)*.

2 a) E.g. he/she could analyse the DNA base sequences of the genes *(1 mark)*. The more similar the base sequences, the more closely related the plant species are likely to be *(1 mark)*.

b) It is present in all plants, so any two species of plant can be compared by looking at RuBisCO *(1 mark)*.

c) The amino acid sequences of the RuBisCO enzyme can be compared *(1 mark)*. The more similar the amino acid sequences are, the more closely related the plant species are likely to be *(1 mark)*.

d) E.g. scientists don't always agree on the relative importance of different features *(1 mark)*. Groups based solely on physical features may not show how closely related organisms are *(1 mark)*.

3 a) i) At first, as the use of the pesticide increases, the number of aphids falls *(1 mark)*. After a period of time, the number of aphids plateaus and pesticide use increases less steeply *(1 mark)*. The number of aphids then begins to increase *(1 mark)*.

ii) E.g. the number of aphids fell as they were being killed by the pesticide *(1 mark)*. Random mutations may have occurred in the aphid DNA, resulting in pesticide resistance *(1 mark)*. Any aphids resistant to the pesticide were more likely to survive and pass on their alleles *(1 mark)*. Over many generations, the number of aphids increased as those carrying pesticide-resistant alleles became more common *(1 mark)*.

b) E.g. if the aphids are resistant to lots of other pesticides as well as this one, it might take the farmer a long time to find one that works *(1 mark)* — in that time the entire crop could be destroyed *(1 mark)*. / If the insects are resistant to specific pesticides, farmers might need to use broader pesticides *(1 mark)*, which might kill beneficial insects *(1 mark)*.

4 a) i) A feature of an organism that increases its chances of survival and reproduction *(1 mark)* and also the chances of its offspring reproducing successfully *(1 mark)*.

ii) behavioural *(1 mark)*, physiological *(1 mark)*

b) Individuals within the *Anoura fistulata* population showed variation in their phenotypes due to differences in their alleles *(1 mark)*. The bats with longer tongues were more likely to survive, reproduce and pass on their alleles *(1 mark)*. Over time the number of individuals with a longer tongue increased *(1 mark)*. Over generations this led to evolution as the alleles that caused the longer tongue became more common in the population *(1 mark)*.

Always try to use the correct scientific language in your answers — here you should be talking about organisms passing on 'alleles', not 'features' or 'characteristics'.

c) *Anoura fistulata*'s DNA base sequence could be compared with the other species' DNA base sequence *(1 mark)*. Species that diverged away from each other more recently should have more similar DNA than those that diverged less recently *(1 mark)*. Also, *Anoura fistulata*'s other molecules, such as proteins/antibodies, could be compared with the other species' proteins/antibodies *(1 mark)*. Species that diverged away from each other more recently should also have more similar proteins/antibodies than those that diverged less recently *(1 mark)*.

Glossary

A

Accurate result
A result that is really close to the true answer.

Activation energy
The energy that needs to be supplied before a chemical reaction will start.

Active immunity
The type of immunity you get when your immune system makes its own antibodies after being stimulated by an antigen.

Active loading
A process that happens at a source in a plant, in which assimilates are moved against their concentration gradient from surrounding tissues into the phloem. It requires energy.

Active site
The part of an enzyme where a substrate molecule binds.

Active transport
Movement of molecules and ions across plasma membranes, against a concentration gradient. Requires energy.

Adaptation
A feature of an organism that increases its chances of survival and reproduction, and also the chances of its offspring reproducing successfully.

ADP (adenosine diphosphate)
A molecule made up of adenine, a ribose sugar and two phosphate groups. ATP is synthesised from ADP and a phosphate group.

Affinity for oxygen
The tendency a molecule has to bind with oxygen.

Agglutinin
A substance (e.g. an antibody) that causes particles to clump together.

Allele
An alternative version of a gene.

Alveolus
A microscopic air sac in the lungs where gas exchange occurs.

Alzheimer's disease
A disease where nerve cells in the brain die in increasing numbers, which results in symptoms such as severe memory loss.

Amino acid
A monomer of proteins.

Anomalous result
A measurement that falls outside the range of values you'd expect or any pattern you already have.

Anti-toxin
An antibody that binds to a toxin produced by a pathogen and inactivates it.

Antibiotic
A chemical that kills or inhibits the growth of bacteria.

Antibiotic resistance
When bacteria are able to survive in the presence of antibiotics.

Antibody
A protein produced by B lymphocytes in response to the presence of a pathogen.

Antigen
A molecule found on the surface of a cell. A foreign antigen triggers an immune response.

Antigen-presenting cell
An immune system cell that processes and presents antigens on its surface to activate other immune system cells.

Apoplast pathway
A route that water takes through a plant root to the xylem, through cell walls.

Asexual reproduction
A form of reproduction where the parent cell divides into two daughter cells (by mitosis). The daughter cells are genetically identical to the parent cell.

Assimilate (in a plant)
A substance that becomes incorporated into the plant tissue, e.g. sucrose.

ATP (adenosine triphosphate)
A molecule made up of adenine, a ribose sugar and three phosphate groups. It is the immediate source of energy in a cell.

Atrioventricular node (AVN)
A group of cells in the heart wall that are responsible for passing waves of electrical activity from the SAN on to the bundle of His.

Atrioventricular (AV) valve
A valve in the heart linking the atria to the ventricles.

Autoimmune disease
A disease resulting from the immune system launching an immune response against the organism's own tissues.

B

B lymphocyte
A type of white blood cell involved in the immune response. It produces antibodies.

Benedict's test
A biochemical test for the presence of sugars.

Binomial system
The nomenclature (naming system) used for classification, in which each organism is given a two-part scientific (Latin) name.

Biodiversity
The variety of living organisms in an area.

Biuret test
A biochemical test for the presence of polypeptides and proteins.

Bohr effect
An effect by which an increase of carbon dioxide in the blood results in a reduction of haemoglobin's affinity for oxygen.

Breathing rate
How many breaths are taken per unit time.

Buccal cavity
The space inside the mouth of a fish.

Bundle of His
A group of muscle fibres in the heart, responsible for conducting waves of electrical activity from the AVN to the Purkyne tissue.

Callose
A plant polysaccharide.

Cardiac cycle
An ongoing sequence of contraction and relaxation of the atria and ventricles that keeps blood continuously circulating around the body.

Carrier protein
A protein that carries molecules across a plasma membrane.

Casparian strip
A waxy strip in the cell wall of an endodermis cell.

Catalyst
A substance that speeds up a chemical reaction without being used up itself.

Causal relationship
Where a change in one variable causes a change in the other.

Cell cycle
The process that all body cells in multicellular organisms use to grow and divide.

Cell signalling
The process by which cells communicate with each other.

Cell wall
A rigid structure that surrounds the plasma membrane of some cells, e.g. plant cells. Supports the cell.

Cellulose
A polysaccharide made of long, unbranched chains of β-glucose.

Centriole
A small, hollow cylinder, containing a ring of microtubules. Involved with the separation of chromosomes during cell division.

Centromere
The point at which two strands of a chromosome are joined together.

Channel protein
A membrane protein that forms a pore through which ions or small, polar molecules move.

Chloride shift
The process in which chloride ions diffuse from the plasma into red blood cells to compensate for the loss of hydrogencarbonate ions from red blood cells. It helps to maintain the pH of the blood.

Chloroplast
A small, flattened organelle present in plant cells. The site of photosynthesis.

Cholesterol
A lipid (fat) containing a hydrocarbon tail attached to a hydrocarbon ring and a hydroxyl group.

Chromatid
One 'arm' of a double stranded chromosome.

Ciliated epithelium
A layer of cells covered in cilia, found in animals (e.g. in the trachea or the bronchi).

Cilium
A small, hair-like structure found on the surface membrane of some animal cells. Used to move substances along the cell surface.

Cladistics
A method of classifying organisms based on their evolutionary relationships (phylogeny).

Classification
The act of arranging organisms into groups based on their similarities and differences.

Climate change
A significant long-term change in an area's climate.

Closed circulatory system
A circulatory system where the blood is enclosed inside blood vessels.

Coenzyme
An organic cofactor.

Cofactor
A non-protein substance that binds to an enzyme and activates it. It can be organic or inorganic.

Collagen
A fibrous protein that forms supportive tissue in animals.

Communicable disease
A disease that can be passed between individuals and is caused by infection with a pathogen.

Companion cell
A type of plant cell located next to a sieve tube element in phloem tissue, which carries out living functions for itself and the sieve cell.

Competitive inhibitor
A molecule with a similar shape to that of a substrate, so it competes with the substrate to bind to the enzyme's active site.

Complementary base pairing
Hydrogen bonds between specific pairs of bases on opposing polynucleotide strands, e.g. A always pairs with T and C always pairs with G.

Concentration gradient
The path from an area of higher concentration to an area of lower concentration.

Condensation reaction
A reaction that releases a water molecule when it links molecules together.

Conjugated protein
A protein with a non-protein group attached.

Conservation
The protection and management of species and habitats.

Continuous variation
When the individuals in a population vary within a range — there are no distinct categories.

Control group
A group in a study that is treated in exactly the same way as the experimental group, apart from the factor you're investigating.

Control variable
A variable you keep constant throughout an experiment.

Convergent evolution
When two species evolve similar characteristics independently of one another because they've adapted to live in similar environments.

Correlation
A relationship between two variables.

Counter-current system
The system in which blood flows in one direction and water flows in the opposite direction across the gills of a fish.

Cytokine
A protein that acts as a messenger molecule.

Cytokinesis
The process by which the cytoplasm divides in eukaryotic cells.

Cytoplasm
A gel-like substance where most of the chemical reactions in a cell happen.

Cytoskeleton
The network of protein threads contained in a cell.

Denatured
The point at which an enzyme no longer functions as a catalyst.

Dependent variable
The variable you measure in an experiment.

Differentiation
The process by which a cell becomes specialised.

Diffusion
The net movement of particles from an area of higher concentration to an area of lower concentration.

Dipeptide
A molecule formed from two amino acids.

Diploid
When a cell contains two copies of each chromosome.

Direct transmission
When a disease is transmitted directly from one organism to another.

Disaccharide
A molecule formed from two monosaccharides.

Discontinuous variation
When there are two or more distinct categories in a population — each individual falls into only one of these categories and there are no intermediates.

Disease
A condition that impairs the normal functioning of an organism.

Disulfide bond
A bond formed between two sulfur atoms, which links together two cysteine amino acids in a polypeptide chain.

DNA (deoxyribonucleic acid)
A nucleic acid containing the pentose sugar deoxyribose. Stores genetic information in cells.

DNA helicase
An enzyme that breaks the hydrogen bonds between the two polynucleotide DNA strands during DNA replication.

DNA polymerase
An enzyme that joins together the nucleotides on a new strand of DNA during DNA replication.

Double circulatory system
A circulatory system where blood passes through the heart twice for each complete circuit of the body.

Emulsion test
A biochemical test for the presence of lipids.

End-product inhibition
When the final product in a metabolic pathway inhibits an enzyme that acts earlier on in the pathway.

Endangered species
A species whose population is so low that they could become extinct.

Endocytosis
The process by which a cell surrounds substances with a section of its plasma membrane and takes them into the cell.

Enzyme
A globular protein that speeds up the rate of chemical reactions.

Enzyme-product complex
The intermediate formed when a substrate has been converted into its products, but they've not yet been released from the active site of an enzyme.

Enzyme-substrate complex
The intermediate formed when a substrate molecule binds to the active site of an enzyme.

Erythrocyte
A red blood cell.

Esterification
The process in which triglycerides are synthesised.

Eukaryote
Organism made up of a cell (or cells) containing a nucleus, e.g. animals and plants.

Evolution
The slow and continual change of organisms from one generation to the next.

***Ex situ* conservation**
Protecting a species by removing part of the population from a threatened habitat and placing it in a new location.

Exchange organ
An organ (e.g. the lungs) specialised to exchange substances.

Exocytosis
The process by which a cell secretes substances using vesicles.

Expulsive reflex
An attempt to expel foreign objects, including pathogens, from the body automatically, e.g. a cough or sneeze.

Extracellular
Outside cells.

Eyepiece graticule
A transparent disc with a scale on it present inside the eyepiece of a microscope.

Facilitated diffusion
The diffusion of particles through carrier proteins or channel proteins in the plasma membrane.

Fibrous protein
An insoluble, rope-shaped protein.

Flaccid plant cell
A plant cell which is limp due to lack of water.

Flagellum
Like a cilium, but longer, it sticks out from the cell surface and is surrounded by the plasma membrane. Used to move the cell.

Fluid mosaic model
Model describing the arrangement of molecules in a cell membrane.

Gas exchange
The process of taking in gases that are needed for life processes and getting rid of waste gases.

Gas exchange surface
A boundary between the outside environment and the internal environment of an organism, over which gas exchange occurs.

Gene
A sequence of DNA nucleotides that codes for a polypeptide.

Genetic code
The sequence of base triplets (codons) in mRNA which codes for specific amino acids.

Genetic diversity
The variation of alleles within a species (or a population of a species).

Genetic resource
Material from plants, animals or microorganisms, containing genes, that we find valuable.

Genotype
All the alleles an organism has.

Gill filament
A thin plate, many of which make up a fish gill.

Gill plate
A tiny structure, which covers the gill filaments in a fish gill.

Globular protein
A soluble, round and compact protein.

Glycogen
A polysaccharide made from a long, very branched chain of α-glucose.

Glycolipid
A lipid which has a carbohydrate chain attached.

Glycoprotein
A protein which has a carbohydrate chain attached.

Glycosidic bond
A bond formed between monosaccharides.

Golgi apparatus
A group of fluid-filled flattened sacs. Involved with processing and packaging lipids and proteins, and making lysosomes.

Habitat
The area inhabited by a species.

Habitat diversity
The number of different habitats in an area.

Haploid
When a cell contains one copy of each chromosome.

Herd immunity
Where unvaccinated people are protected because the occurrence of the disease is reduced by the number of people who are vaccinated.

Homologous chromosomes
Pairs of matching chromosomes — each chromosome in the pair contains the same genes but different alleles.

Hydrogen bond
A weak bond between a slightly positively charged hydrogen atom in one molecule and a slightly negatively charged atom in another molecule.

Hydrolysis
A chemical reaction that uses a water molecule when it breaks bonds between molecules.

Hydrophilic
Attracts water.

Hydrophobic
Repels water.

Hydrophytic plant
A plant that is adapted to live in aquatic habitats.

Hydrostatic pressure
The pressure exerted by a liquid.

Hypothesis
A specific testable statement, based on a theory, about what will happen in a test situation.

Immune response
The body's reaction to a foreign antigen.

Immunity
The ability to respond quickly to an infection.

***In situ* conservation**
Protecting species in their natural habitat.

Inactive precursor
An inactive form of an enzyme.

Independent variable
The variable you change in an experiment.

Indirect transmission
When a disease is transmitted from one organism to another via an intermediate.

Inorganic ion
An ion (charged particle) that doesn't contain carbon.

Interdependence (of organisms)
The dependence of organisms in an ecosystem on each other for survival.

Interphase
A period of cell growth, consisting of G1, S and G2 phases, during which the cell's genetic material is copied and checked for DNA damage

Interspecific variation
Variation between species.

Intracellular
Inside cells.

Intraspecific variation
Variation within a species.

Iodine test
A biochemical test for the presence of starch.

Ionic bond (in a protein)
An attraction between a negatively charged R group and a positively charged R group on different parts of the molecule.

Keystone species
A species that many of the other species in an ecosystem depend on and without which the ecosystem would change dramatically.

Latent heat of evaporation
The heat energy required to change a liquid to a gas.

Locus
The position on a chromosome where a particular allele is found.

Lymph
Excess tissue fluid that has drained into lymph vessels.

Lysosome
A round organelle that contains digestive enzymes.

Macromolecule
A complex molecule with a relatively large molecular mass, e.g. a protein or lipid.

Magnification
How much bigger an image from a microscope is compared to the specimen.

Margin of error
The range in which the true value of a measurement lies.

Mass flow hypothesis
The best supported theory for how translocation works.

Mean
The average of the values collected in a sample, obtained by adding all the values together and dividing by the total number of values in the sample.

Meiosis
A type of cell division where a parent cell divides to create four genetically different haploid cells.

Membrane-bound receptor
A molecule (often a glycoprotein or glycolipid) that acts as a specific, complementary receptor for a messenger molecule in cell signalling.

Memory cell
A B or T lymphocyte which remains in the body for a long time and initiates a secondary immune response if a pathogen is re-encountered.

Meristem
Mitotically active tissue found in the growing parts of plants (e.g. the roots and shoots).

Microfilament
A very thin protein strand in the cytoplasm of a cell.

Microtubule
A tiny protein cylinder in the cytoplasm of a cell.

Mitochondrion
An oval-shaped organelle with a double membrane. The site of aerobic respiration.

Mitosis
A type of cell division where a parent cell divides to produce two genetically identical daughter cells.

Model (scientific)
A simplified picture of what's physically going on.

Monoculture
The growing of a single variety of crop on a large area of land.

Monomer
A small, basic molecular unit, e.g. amino acids and monosaccharides.

Monosaccharide
A monomer of carbohydrates.

mRNA (messenger RNA)
A type of RNA that is the template for protein synthesis. It carries the genetic code from the DNA in the nucleus into the cytoplasm.

Mucous membrane
A membrane which protects body openings that are exposed to the environment (e.g. the mouth).

Mucus
A sticky substance that traps pathogens and contains antimicrobial enzymes.

Myogenic
Produced by muscle cells without receiving a nerve's signal.

Natural selection
The process whereby an allele becomes more common in a population because it codes for an adaptation that makes an organism more likely to survive, reproduce and pass on its alleles to the next generation.

Neutrophil
A type of phagocyte.

Non-competitive inhibitor
A molecule that binds to an enzyme away from its active site. This changes the shape of the active site so the substrate can no longer bind.

Non-specific defence
A defence that works the same against all pathogens.

Nuclear envelope
A double membrane found around the nucleus of a cell, which contains many pores.

Nucleolus
A structure inside the nucleus of a cell, which makes ribosomes.

Nucleotide
The monomer that makes up polynucleotides — consists of a pentose sugar, a phosphate group and a nitrogenous base.

Nucleus
A large organelle surrounded by a nuclear envelope. Contains DNA which controls the cell's activities.

Oncotic pressure
The pressure which is generated by plasma proteins in a capillary.

Open circulatory system
A circulatory system where the blood isn't enclosed in blood vessels all the time — it flows freely through the body cavity.

Operculum
A bony flap that covers and protects a fish gill.

Opsonin
A molecule in the blood that attaches to foreign antigens to aid phagocytosis.

Optimum pH
The pH at which the rate of an enzyme-controlled reaction is at its fastest.

Optimum temperature
The temperature at which the rate of an enzyme-controlled reaction is at its fastest.

Organ
A group of different tissues that work together to perform a particular function.

Organ system
A group of organs that work together to perform a particular function.

Organelle
A part of a cell, e.g. the nucleus.

Osmosis
The diffusion of water molecules across a partially permeable membrane, from an area of higher water potential to an area of lower water potential.

Oxygen dissociation curve
A curve on a graph that shows how saturated with oxygen haemoglobin is at any given partial pressure.

Oxygen uptake (consumption)
The rate at which a person uses up oxygen.

pCO$_2$
Partial pressure of carbon dioxide — a measure of carbon dioxide concentration.

pO₂
Partial pressure of oxygen — a measure of oxygen concentration.

Parasite
An organism that lives on or in another organism (the host) and causes damage to that organism.

Parkinson's disease
A disease which causes the loss of a particular type of nerve cell found in the brain, leading to uncontrollable tremors.

Partially permeable membrane
A membrane that lets some molecules through it, but not others.

Passive immunity
The type of immunity you get from being given antibodies made by a different organism.

Pathogen
An organism that can cause damage to the organism it infects (the host).

Peer review
Where a scientific report is sent out to peers (other scientists) who examine the data and results, and if they think that the conclusion is reasonable it's published.

Pentose sugar
A sugar with five carbon atoms.

Peptide bond
A bond formed between the amino group of one amino acid and the carboxyl group of another amino acid.

Pesticide resistance
When pests, e.g. insects, are able to survive in the presence of pesticides.

Phagocyte
A type of white blood cell that carries out phagocytosis, e.g. a neutrophil.

Phagocytosis
The engulfment of pathogens.

Phagosome
A type of vesicle in a cell that contains a phagocytosed pathogen.

Phenotype
The characteristics displayed by an organism.

Phloem
A tissue in plants that transports sugars (e.g. sucrose) from their source to their sink.

Phospholipid
A lipid containing one molecule of glycerol attached to two fatty acids and a phosphate group. Main component of the cell membrane.

Photomicrograph
A photo of a microscopic object taken through a type of microscope.

Phylogeny
The study of the evolutionary history of groups of organisms.

Placebo
A dummy pill or injection that looks exactly like the real drug, but doesn't contain the drug.

Plasma cell
A type of B lymphocyte that produces antibodies.

Plasma membrane
The membrane found on the surface of animal cells and just inside the cell wall of plant cells and prokaryotic cells. Regulates the movement of substances into and out of the cell.

Plasmodesmata
Channels in plant cell walls for exchanging substances between neighbouring cells.

Plasmolysis (plant cells)
The pulling away of the cytoplasm and plasma membrane from the cell wall due to lack of water.

Polar molecule
A molecule with a slight negative charge on one side and a slight positive charge on the other.

Polymer
A large, complex molecule composed of long chains of monomers, e.g. proteins and carbohydrates.

Polymorphic gene locus
A point on a chromosome that can have more than one allele.

Polynucleotide
A molecule made up of lots of nucleotides joined together in a long chain.

Polypeptide
A molecule formed from more than two amino acids.

Polysaccharide
A molecule formed from more than two monosaccharides.

Precise result
A result that is really close to the mean.

Prediction
See hypothesis.

Pressure filtration
The process by which substances move out of capillaries into the tissue fluid, at the arteriole end of a capillary bed.

Primary immune response
The immune response triggered when a foreign antigen enters the body for the first time.

Product inhibition
When an enzyme is inhibited by the product of the reaction it catalyses.

Prokaryote
Single-celled organism without a nucleus or membrane-bound organelles, e.g. bacteria.

Prosthetic group
A cofactor that is tightly bound to an enzyme.

Purine
A type of nucleotide base that contains two carbon-nitrogen rings joined together, e.g. adenine and guanine.

Purkyne tissue
Fine muscle fibres in the heart that carry waves of electrical activity into the muscular walls of the right and left ventricles.

Pyrimidine
A type of nucleotide base that contains one carbon-nitrogen ring joined together, e.g. cytosine, thymine and uracil.

Qualitative result
Non-numerical result.

Quantitative result
Numerical result.

Random error
A difference in a measurement caused by an unpredictable factor, e.g. human error.

Repeatable result
A result that can be repeated by the same person using the same method and equipment.

Reproducible result
A result that can be consistently reproduced in an independent experiment.

Resolution
How well a microscope distinguishes between two points close together.

Ribosome
A small organelle that makes proteins.

RNA (ribonucleic acid)
A type of nucleic acid, similar to DNA but containing the pentose sugar ribose instead of deoxyribose and uracil instead of thymine.

Rough endoplasmic reticulum (RER)
A system of ribosome-covered membranes enclosing a fluid-filled space. Involved in protein synthesis.

rRNA (ribosomal RNA)
A type of RNA that forms the two subunits in a ribosome. It helps to catalyse the formation of peptide bonds between the amino acids.

S

Sample size
The number of samples in the investigation, e.g. the number of people in a drug trial.

Secondary immune response
The immune response triggered when a foreign antigen enters the body for the second time.

Selection pressure
Anything that affects an organism's chance of survival and reproduction.

Selective breeding
A process that involves humans selecting which strains of plants or animals to reproduce together in order to increase productivity.

Semi-conservative replication
The process by which DNA molecules replicate. The two strands of a DNA double helix separate, each acting as a template for the formation of a new strand.

Semi-lunar (SL) valve
A valve in the heart linking the ventricles to the aorta and pulmonary artery.

Sexual reproduction
A form of reproduction where two gametes join together at fertilisation to form a zygote, which divides and develops into a new organism.

Sieve tube element
Living plant cells that form the tube for transporting assimilates through a plant.

Single circulatory system
A circulatory system where blood only passes through the heart once for each complete circuit of the body.

Sink (in a plant)
Where assimilates (e.g. sucrose) are used up.

Sino-atrial node (SAN)
A group of cells in the wall of the right atrium that set the rhythm of the heartbeat by sending regular waves of electrical activity over the atrial walls.

Smooth endoplasmic reticulum (SER)
Similar to rough endoplasmic reticulum, but with no ribosomes. Involved in lipid synthesis.

Source (in a plant)
Where assimilates (e.g. sucrose) are produced.

Specialised cell
A cell adapted to carry out specific functions.

Species
A group of similar organisms able to reproduce to give fertile offspring.

Species diversity
The number of different species and the abundance of each species in an area.

Species evenness
A measure of the relative abundance of each species in an area.

Species richness
The number of different species in an area.

Specific heat capacity
The energy needed to raise the temperature of 1 gram of substance by 1 °C.

Spiracle
A pore on the surface of an insect.

Squamous epithelium
A single layer of flat cells lining a surface found in animals (e.g. in the alveoli).

Stage micrometer
A microscope slide with an accurate scale that's used to work out the value of the divisions on the eyepiece graticule at a particular magnification.

Standard deviation
A measure of the spread of values about the mean.

Starch
A carbohydrate molecule made up of two polysaccharides — amylose and amylopectin.

Stem cell
An unspecialised cell that can differentiate into different types of cell.

Substrate
A substance that interacts with an enzyme.

Surface area to volume ratio
An organism's or structure's surface area in relation to its volume.

Symplast pathway
A route that water takes through a plant root to the xylem, through the cytoplasm of cells.

T helper cell
A differentiated form of a T lymphocyte which releases substances that activate B lymphocytes.

T killer cell
A differentiated form of a T lymphocyte which attaches to an antigen on a pathogen and kills the cell.

T regulatory cell
A differentiated form of a T lymphocyte which suppresses the immune response from other white blood cells to stop immune system cells from mistakenly attacking the host's body cells.

T lymphocyte
A type of white blood cell involved in the immune response. Some types activate B lymphocytes, some kill pathogens directly and some suppress the immune response.

Taxonomy
The study of classification.

Temperature coefficient (Q_{10})
A value for a reaction that shows how much the rate of that reaction changes when the temperature is raised by 10 °C.

Theory
A possible explanation for something.

Tidal volume
The volume of air in each breath.

Tissue
A group of cells (plus any extracellular material secreted by them) that are specialised to work together to carry out a particular function.

Tissue fluid
The fluid that surrounds cells in tissues.

Trachea (insects)
A pipe that carries air between the external environment and the inside of an insect's body.

Tracheole
A small pipe that branches off the trachea in an insect and is used for gas exchange.

Transcription
The first stage of protein synthesis in which an mRNA copy of a gene is made from DNA in the nucleus.

Translation
The second stage of protein synthesis in which amino acids are joined together by ribosomes to make a polypeptide chain (protein).

Translocation
The movement of assimilates to where they're needed in a plant.

Transpiration
The evaporation of water from a plant's surface.

Triglyceride
A lipid containing one molecule of glycerol attached to three fatty acids.

tRNA (transfer RNA)
A type of RNA involved in translation. It carries the amino acids used to make proteins to the ribosomes.

Turgid plant cell
A cell which is swollen with water.

Ultrastructure (of a cell)
The details of a cell's internal structure and organelles that can be seen under an electron microscope.

Uncertainty (of data)
The amount of error measurements might have.

Vaccination
The administering of a vaccine containing antigens to give immunity.

Vacuole
An organelle that contains cell sap (a weak solution of sugar and salts).

Valid conclusion
A conclusion that answers the original question.

Variable
A quantity that has the potential to change, e.g. weight, temperature, concentration.

Variation
The differences that exist between individuals.

Vector (in disease)
An organism that transmits a disease from one organism to another.

Vesicle
A small fluid-filled sac in the cytoplasm. Transports substances in and out of the cell and between organelles.

Vital capacity
The maximum volume of air that can be breathed in or out.

Water potential
The likelihood of water molecules to diffuse into or out of solution.

Xerophytic plant
A plant that is adapted to live in dry climates.

Xylem
A tissue in plants that transports water and mineral ions.

Acknowledgements

OCR Specification reference points are reproduced with the permission of OCR.

Data acknowledgements

Data for graph showing glucose concentration vs absorbance on page 72 was obtained using a Mystrica colorimeter © Mystrica Ltd www.mystrica.com

Graph of whooping cough and vaccine uptake on page 233 from Health in Scotland 2000, CMO Annual Report, September 2001. This information is licensed under the terms of the Open Government Licence http://www.nationalarchives.gov.uk/doc/open-government-licence/version/3/ (www.department.gov.uk/ document, accessed November 2011).

With thanks to the HPA for permission to use the graph on page 238, adapted from Tuberculosis in the UK: Annual report on tuberculosis surveillance in the UK, 2010. London: Health Protection Agency Centre for Infections, October 2010

Data used to construct the graph of global sea temperature on page 250 © NASA/GISS.

Diagram showing the distribution of subtropical plankton on page 250 reproduced with kind permission from Plankton distribution changes, due to climate changes - North Sea. (February 2008). Hugo Ahlenius, UNEP/ GRID-Arendal Maps and Graphics Library. http://maps.grida.no/go/graphic/plankton-distribution-changes-due-to-climate-changes-north-sea.

Critical values for the Spearman's rank test on page 275 abridged from Significance Testing of the Spearman Rank Correlation Coefficient by Jerrold H. Zar from the Journal of the American Statistical Association © 1972 Taylor & Francis, reprinted by the publisher Taylor & Francis Ltd, http://www.tandfonline.com

Photograph acknowledgements

p 1 **Dr Jeremy Burgess**/Science Photo Library, p 4 © **stevanovicigor**/iStockphoto.com, p 7 (top) **Andrew Lambert Photography**/Science Photo Library, p 7 (bottom) **Tek Image**/Science Photo Library, p 31 **Omikron**/ Science Photo Library, p 32 (top) **Biophoto Associates**/Science Photo Library, p 32 (bottom) **Martin M. Rotker**/ Science Photo Library, p 33 (top) **Science Photo Library**, p 33 (middle) **Don W. Fawcett**/Science Photo Library, p 33 (bottom) **Biology Pics**/Science Photo Library, p 34 (top) **Don W. Fawcett**/Science Photo Library, p 34 (bottom left) **Dr David Furness, Keele University**/Science Photo Library, p 34 (bottom right) **Science Photo Library**, p 35 (left) **Dr Kari Lounatmaa**/Science Photo Library, p 35 (right) **Prof. P. Motta/Dept. of Anatomy/ University "La Sapienza", Rome**/Science Photo Library, p 36 **Dr Torsten Wittmann**/Science Photo Library, p 37 **Juergen Berger**/Science Photo Library, p 38 **Ami Images**/Science Photo Library, p 40 (top) **Steve Gschmeissner**/Science Photo Library, p 40 (middle) **NIAID/CDC**/Science Photo Library, p 40 (bottom) **CNRI**/ Science Photo Library, p 41 (Fig. 1 top) **Dr. Michael Gabridge, Visuals Unlimited**/Science Photo Library, p 41 (Fig. 1 bottom) **Heiti Paves**/Science Photo Library, p 41 (middle) **Andrew Brookes, National Physical Laboratory**/Science Photo Library, p 41 (Fig. 3 top) **Science Photo Library**, p 41 (Fig. 3 bottom) **Alfred Pasieka**/ Science Photo Library, p 42 (left) **K. R. Porter**/Science Photo Library, p 42 (right) **Professors P. Motta & T. Naguro**/Science Photo Library, p 44 (Fig. 1) **Jack Bostrack, Visuals Unlimited**/Science Photo Library, p 44 (Fig. 2) **Eric Grave**/Science Photo Library, p 44 (bottom) **M. I. Walker**/Science Photo Library, p 46 **Martin Shields**/Science Photo Library, p 50 **CNRI**/Science Photo Library, p 53 (left and right) **Clive Freeman/Biosym Technologies**/Science Photo Library, p 57 **Biophoto Associates**/Science Photo Library, p 64 (Fig. 8) **animante4. com**/Science Photo Library, p 64 (Fig. 10-12) **Laguna Design**/Science Photo Library, p 65 (top) **Susumu Nishinaga**/Science Photo Library, p 65 (bottom) **Biophoto Associates**/Science Photo Library, p 67 **Nigel Cattlin**/Science Photo Library, p 68 **Andrew Lambert Photography**/Science Photo Library, p 69 (top and bottom) **Andrew Lambert Photography**/Science Photo Library, p 70 (Fig. 8) **Andrew Lambert Photography**/ Science Photo Library, p 70 (bottom) **Saturn Stills**/Science Photo Library, p 71 **Martyn F. Chillmaid**/Science Photo Library, p 73 **Jim Varney**/Science Photo Library, p 74 **Sinclair Stammers**/Science Photo Library, p 82 **ISM**/Science Photo Library, p 84 **Science Photo Library**, p 85 **Philippe Psaila**/Science Photo Library, p 92 **Ramon Andrade 3Dciencia**/Science Photo Library, p 98 **Clive Freeman, The Royal Institution**/Science Photo Library, p 108 **Jeff Daly, Visuals Unlimited**/Science Photo Library, p 117 **Russell Kightley**/Science Photo Library, p 126 **Andrew Lambert Photography**/Science Photo Library, p 127 (top and bottom) **J. C. Revy, ISM**/

Science Photo Library, p 128 **Charles D. Winters**/Science Photo Library, p 132 **Science Picture Co**/Science Photo Library, p 133 **Don Fawcett**/Science Photo Library, p 137 (left and right) **J. C. Revy, ISM**/Science Photo Library, p 140 (all) **Pr. G Gimenez-Martin**/Science Photo Library, p 141 (top) **Pr. G Gimenez-Martin**/Science Photo Library, p 141 (bottom) **Herve Conge, ISM**/Science Photo Library, p 142 **Steve Gschmeissner**/Science Photo Library, p 143 **Eye of Science**/Science Photo Library, p 144 **Science Pictures Ltd**/Science Photo Library, p 145 (top) **Pr. G Gimenez-Martin**/Science Photo Library, p 145 (bottom) **Adrian T Sumner**/Science Photo Library, p 147 (left) **Science Photo Library**, p 147 (right) **Dr. Tony Brain**/Science Photo Library, p 149 (top) **Steve Gschmeissner**/Science Photo Library, p 149 (middle) **Eye of Science**/Science Photo Library, p 149 (bottom) **Steve Gschmeissner**/Science Photo Library, p 150 (top) **Dr Keith Wheeler**/Science Photo Library, p 150 (middle) **Microfield Scientific Ltd**/Science Photo Library, p 150 (bottom) **Dr Jeremy Burgess**/Science Photo Library, p 151 **Steve Gschmeissner**/Science Photo Library, p 152 **Martin Oeggerli**/Science Photo Library, p 153 (top) **Steve Gschmeissner**/Science Photo Library, p 153 (bottom) **Eye of Science**/Science Photo Library, p 154 **Biophoto Associates**/Science Photo Library, p 157 **Power And Syred**/Science Photo Library, p 158 © **alptraum**/iStockphoto.com, p 160 **Steve Gschmeissner**/Science Photo Library, p 161 **Science Vu, Visuals Unlimited**/Science Photo Library, p 162 (top) **Dr Keith Wheeler**/Science Photo Library, p 162 (bottom) **Manfred Kage**/Science Photo Library, p 163 **Dr. Richard Kessel & Dr. Gene Shih, Visuals Unlimited**/Science Photo Library, p 164 (top) **Science Photo Library**, p 164 (bottom) **Sinclair Stammers**/Science Photo Library, p 165 **Microscape**/Science Photo Library, p 167 **John Thys/Reporters**/Science Photo Library, p 169 **Power And Syred**/Science Photo Library, p 170 (top) © **2lbgil**/iStockphoto.com, p 170 (bottom) **Microfield Scientific Ltd**/Science Photo Library, p 172 (top) **Science Photo Library**, p 172 (bottom) **Herve Conge, ISM**/Science Photo Library, p 173 **Dr Keith Wheeler**/Science Photo Library, p 176 (top left) **Eye of Science**/Science Photo Library, p 176 (top right) **Dr. Fred Hossler, Visuals Unlimited**/Science Photo Library, p 176 (bottom) **Dr. Richard Kessel & Dr. Gene Shih, Visuals Unlimited**/Science Photo Library, p 180 (top) **Biophoto Associates**/Science Photo Library, p 180 (bottom) **Ralph Hutchings, Visuals Unlimited**/Science Photo Library, p 182 **Astrid & Hanns-Frieder Michler**/Science Photo Library, p 184 (top) **Science Picture Co**/Science Photo Library, p 184 (bottom) © **Alexandra Thompson**/iStockphoto.com, p 187 **Simon Fraser/Coronary Care Unit/Hexham General Hospital**/Science Photo Library, p 188 **D. Varty, ISM**/Science Photo Library, p 190 **Dr P. Marazzi**/Science Photo Library, p 199 **Dr David Furness, Keele University**/Science Photo Library, p 200 (top) **Dr Keith Wheeler**/Science Photo Library, p 200 (bottom) **Herve Conge, ISM**/Science Photo Library, p 201 (Fig. 10) **Biophoto Associates**/Science Photo Library, p 201 (Fig. 11) **Dr Keith Wheeler**/Science Photo Library, p 201 (Q1 photo) **Dr Keith Wheeler**/Science Photo Library, p 201 (Figure A) **J. C. Revy, ISM**/Science Photo Library, p 201(Figure B) **Power And Syred**/Science Photo Library, p 203 **Microfield Scientific Ltd**/Science Photo Library, p 208 **Dr Keith Wheeler**/Science Photo Library, p 209 (left) **Eye of Science**/Science Photo Library, p 209 (right) **Power And Syred**/Science Photo Library, p 214 (both) **Dr Keith Wheeler**/Science Photo Library, p 217 (top) © **idrisesen**/iStockphoto.com, p 217 (middle) © **WebSubstance**/iStockphoto.com, p 217 (bottom) **A. Dowsett, Public Health England**/Science Photo Library, p 218 (top) **Dr Jeremy Burgess**/Science Photo Library, p 218 (bottom) **Norm Thomas**/Science Photo Library, p 219 (top) **Steve Gschmeissner**/Science Photo Library, p 219 (bottom) **Eye of Science**/Science Photo Library, p 220 (top) **Dr P. Marazzi**/Science Photo Library, p 220 (middle) © **gangliu10**/iStockphoto.com, p 220 (bottom) **Nigel Cattlin**/Science Photo Library, p 221 **Scimat**/Science Photo Library, p 223 **Dr Olivier Schwartz, Institute Pasteur**/Science Photo Library, p 224 **Biophoto Associates**/Science Photo Library, p 225 **Biophoto Associates**/Science Photo Library, p 226 (top) **Phantatomix**/Science Photo Library, p 226 (bottom) **Science Photo Library**, p 227 **NIBSC**/Science Photo Library, p 231 (top) **Dr P. Marazzi**/Science Photo Library, p 231 (bottom) **Simon Fraser**/Science Photo Library, p 232 **CNRI**/Science Photo Library, p 235 (top) **D. Phillips**/Science Photo Library, p 235 (bottom) **Dr Jeremy Burgess**/Science Photo Library, p 242 **Nigel Cattlin**/Science Photo Library, p 248 **Dr Morley Read**/Science Photo Library, p 249 © **WhitcombeRD**/iStockphoto.com, p 253 **Simon Little**, p 254 (top) **Dr P. Marazzi**/Science Photo Library, p 254 (bottom) **Paul Shoesmith**/Science Photo Library, p 255 **John Reader**/Science Photo Library, p 256 **B. G. Thomson**/Science Photo Library, p 261 (bacterium) **A. Dowsett, Public Health England**/Science Photo Library, p 261 (protoctista) **Michael Abbey**/Science Photo Library, p 265 (both) **Eye of Science**/Science Photo Library, p 268 **Wally Eberhart, Visuals Unlimited**/Science Photo Library, p 276 (top) **David M Schleser/Nature's Images**/Science Photo Library, p 276 (bottom) **Duncan Shaw**/Science Photo Library, p 278 (top) © **Auscape International Pty Ltd**/Alamy, p 278 (bottom) © **Tramper2**/iStockphoto.com, p 279 **Michael W. Tweedie**/Science Photo Library, p 281 **John Serrao**/Science Photo Library.

Index

A

accuracy 5, 7
activation energy 98
active immunity 230
active loading 211, 212
active sites 97-103
active transport 132, 211
adaptations 276
adhesion (in plant water transport) 205
ADP 81, 82
affinity for oxygen 191
agglutinins 226
alleles 246, 268
alveoli 161, 163, 164
Alzheimer's 148
amino acids 61, 88
ammonium ions 66
amylase 64, 97, 108
amylopectin 56
amylose 56
anaphase 140, 144
anatomical adaptations 276
animal cells 30
Animalia 261
animal tissues 152
anions 67
anomalous results 10
antibiotic resistance 234, 235
antibiotics 234
antibodies 223-227
  structure of 226
anticodons 89, 92
antigen-presenting cells 222, 223
antigens 222-232
anti-toxins 227
aorta 183-185
apoplast pathway 204
arteries 180
arterioles 180
artificial immunity 230
asexual reproduction 140, 141
assimilates 210
athlete's foot 216
ATP 81, 82, 132, 212
atria 183-185
atrioventricular node (AVN) 187

atrioventricular valves 184, 185
autoimmune diseases 230
averages 11, 12

B

bacteria 38, 216
bacterial meningitis 216
bases (nucleotides) 80, 81
behavioural adaptations 276
Benedict's test 69-72
  quantitative testing 71
bias 27
binomial system 260
biochemical tests for molecules 68-73
biodiversity 240-255
  collecting data on 240-242
  factors affecting 248-250
  maintenance of 251-255
biosensors 73
biuret test 68
black sigatoka 216
blood 182
  clotting 219
  smears 224
blood vessels 180
B lymphocytes 223
Bohr effect 193
bone marrow 147
bradycardia 189
breathing rate 167
bronchi 163, 164
bronchioles 163, 164
buccal cavity 170
bundle of His 187

C

cacti 207
calcium ions 66
calibration curves 72
callose deposition 220
capillaries 180, 181
carbohydrates 55-57
carbonic acid 193, 194
carbonic anhydrase 108, 193, 194

cardiac cycle 185
cardiac output 186
carrier proteins 131
cartilage 152, 164
Casparian strip 204
catalase 97, 104
cations 66
causal relationships 23
cell cycle 139-141
cell membranes 31, 116-123
  function of 116, 117
  investigating permeability of 120
  permeability of 119
  receptors 122, 123
  structure of 117, 118
cells 30-34
cell signalling 122, 123, 224
cellulose 57
cell ultrastructure 30
cell walls 31
centrioles 34
centromeres 140
channel proteins 131
chloride ions 67, 108, 194
chloride shift 194
chloroplasts 33
cholesterol 59, 60, 118
chromatids 140, 145
chromatography 74-76
chromosomes 140
cilia 34, 163
ciliated epithelia 152, 163
circulatory systems 177-179
CITES agreement 255
cladistics 262
classes 260
classification 260, 261
classification systems 264-266
  evidence for 264
  five kingdom system 261, 265
  three domain system 265
climate change 249
clonal expansion 223
clonal selection 223
closed circulatory systems 178
Clostridium difficile 235

codons 88, 89
coenzymes 108
cofactors 108
cohesion (of water molecules) 52
  in plant water transport 205
collagen 64
colorimetry 71, 120
communicable diseases 216-218
companion cells 200, 211, 212
competitive inhibitors 109
complementary base pairing 83
conclusions 23, 26
condensation reactions 54
conjugated proteins 64
conservation 251-255
constant regions (of antibodies) 226
continuous data 18
continuous variation 267
controls 6
convergent evolution 277
correlations 23
co-transport proteins 211
counter-current systems 169
Countryside Stewardship Scheme (CSS) 255
crossing over (of chromatids) 145
cytokines 222
cytokinesis 139, 141
cytoplasm 30, 31
cytoskeletons 36

D

Darwin, Charles 279
data
  presenting 17-19
  processing 11-16
  recording 9, 10
  uncertainty in 24
data loggers 7, 167
decision making 4
dependent variables 5
diaphragm 163, 166
differentiation (of cells) 147, 148
diffusion 124, 125
  investigating 125
dipeptides 61
diploid cells 143
direct transmission (of disease) 217
disaccharides 56
discontinuous variation 268
discrete data 17

dissection
  of gaseous exchange systems 172, 173
  of hearts 184
  of plant stems 201
disulfide bonds 63
DNA (deoxyribonucleic acid) 80, 83-87
  purification of 84, 85
  replication 86, 87
DNA helicase 86
DNA polymerase 86
domains 260
double circulatory systems 178
drug resistance 234, 235, 283

E

ectopic heartbeat 189
elastic fibres (in the airways) 164
elastin 65
electrocardiograms (ECGs) 187-190
electron micrographs 42
electron microscopes 41
emulsion test 69
endocytosis 132
environmental variation 268
enzymes 97-112
  action of 98
  denaturing 101
  factors affecting activity 101-103
  inhibition of 109-112
  investigating activity of 104, 105
  models of action 99
  structure of 97, 98
enzyme-substrate complex 97, 98
epidemics 231
epithelial cells 149
erythrocytes 147, 149
ester bonds 58
ethical issues 7
eukaryotic cells 30, 38
evaluations 25, 26
evidence 3
evolution 279-283
  evidence for 280, 281
  of antibiotic resistance 234
  of drug resistance 283
  of pesticide resistance 282

exams 287, 288
exchange surfaces 158-161
exocytosis 133
experimental design 5-7
expiration 166
expulsive reflexes 220
ex situ conservation 254
extracellular enzymes 97
eyepiece graticules 46

F

facilitated diffusion 131, 132
families (in classification) 260
fatty acids 58, 59
fetal haemoglobin 192, 193
fibrillation 190
fibrous proteins 64, 65
five kingdoms classification system 261
flaccid cells 127
flagella 34
fluid mosaic model 117
fossil record 280
frequency tables 10
fungi 216
Fungi (kingdom) 261

G

gametes 143
gaseous exchange (in plants) 206
gaseous exchange systems
  dissections 172, 173
  in bony fish 169
  in insects 170
  in mammals 163, 164
genes 88
genetic code 88-90
genetic diversity 240, 246
genetic resources 251, 252
genetic variation 145
genera 260
gill filaments 169
gill plates 169
gills 161, 169, 170, 172
  dissection of 172
globular proteins 64
glucose 55
  test for 69, 70
glycogen 57
glycolipids 117, 118
glycoproteins 117, 118

glycosidic bonds 55, 56
goblet cells 163
Golgi apparatus 33, 36
graphs 17-22
    correlations 23
    finding the initial rate from 106
    finding the rate from 20-22
guard cells 150

H

habitat diversity 240
haemoglobin 191-194
    structure 64
haemoglobinic acid 194
haploid cells 143
heart 183-190
    dissection of 184
    electrical activity of 187
    problems 189, 190
    rate 188
    structure of 183
    valves 184
heartbeat 187-191
herd immunity 231
hinge region (of antibodies) 226
histograms 18
HIV 216
homologous chromosomes 143
hormones (as messenger
        molecules) 122, 123
human population growth 248
hydrogen bonding 52, 63, 83
hydrogencarbonate ions
        67, 193, 194
hydrogen ions
        66, 193, 194, 212
hydrolysis reactions 54
hydrophobic and hydrophilic
        interactions 63
hydrophytes 208
hydrostatic pressure 181
hydroxide ions 67
hypertonic solutions 127
hypotheses 1
hypotonic solutions 127

I

immune response
        222-224, 228, 229
immune system 222-224

immunity 228
inactive precursors 112
independent assortment
        (of chromosomes) 146
independent variables 5
indirect transmission (of disease)
        217
induced fit model 99
inflammation 220
influenza 216, 232
initial rates of reaction 106
inorganic ions 66, 67
in situ conservation 253
inspiration 166
insulin 64
intercostal muscles 163, 166
interdependent organisms 251
interleukins 224
interphase 139, 144
interspecific variation 267
intracellular enzymes 97
intraspecific variation 267
iodine test 69
ionic bonds 63
isotonic solutions 127

K

keratin 65
keystone species 251
kingdoms 260, 261

L

lactose 56
laser scanning confocal
        microscopes 41
latent heat of evaporation 52
leaves 153, 204
light microscopes 41, 46
lignin 199
line graphs 18
lipids 58-60
    test for 69
loci 246
lock and key model 99
lungs 153, 163
lupus 230
lymph 181, 182
lymphocytes 223, 224
lymph vessels 181, 182
lysosomes 32, 222

M

macromolecules 54
magnification 39, 42
malaria 216
maltose 56
margins of error 24
marram grass 208
marsupial moles 278
mass flow hypothesis 210, 211
mean 11, 270
median 12
medicines
    personalised 236
    sources of 235
meiosis 143-146
membrane-bound receptors
        122, 123
memory cells 228, 231
meningitis C vaccine 231
meristems 148, 210
messenger molecules 122
metabolic pathways 111
metabolic poisons 111
metabolic rates 177
metaphase 140, 144
microfibrils 57
microfilaments 36
microscopes 39
    how to use light microscopes
        46
    types of 41, 42
microscope slides 45
microtubules 34, 36
migrations 250
mitochondria 33
mitosis 139-141
    investigating 141
MMR 231
models (scientific) 1
mode 12
monoculture 249, 252
monocytes 224
monomers 54
monosaccharides 55
mRNA (messenger RNA)
        88, 91-93
MRSA 235
mucous membranes 219
muscle tissue 152
mutations 87

N

natural immunity 230
natural selection 279
negative controls 6
neutrophils 147, 149, 222, 224
nitrate ions 67
non-competitive inhibitors 109
non-random sampling 241
non-reducing sugars 70
non-specific immune response 222
normal distribution 270
nuclear envelope 32
nuclei 32
nucleic acids 80, 81
nucleotides 80-82
null hypotheses 16, 274

O

oncotic pressure 181
open circulatory systems 179
operculum 170
opportunistic sampling 241
opsonins 222
orders (in classification) 260
organelles 30-34
organs 153
organ systems 154
osmosis 126, 129
oxygen dissociation curves 192, 193
oxygen uptake 167
oxyhaemoglobin 191

P

palisade mesophyll cells 150
Parkinson's 148
partial pressure
    of carbon dioxide (pCO$_2$) 193
    of oxygen (pO$_2$) 191
passive immunity 230
pathogens 216
peer reviews 2
penicillin 234
pentose sugars (monosaccharides) 55, 80
peptide bonds 61
percentage error 24, 25
percentages 13
personalised medicines 236
pesticide resistance 282

phagocytosis 222, 226, 227
phagosomes 222
phloem 148, 153, 198-200
phosphate bonds 82
phosphate ions 67
phosphodiester bonds 83
phospholipids 59, 60, 117
phyla 260
phylogeny 262
physiological adaptations 276
phytoalexins 221
placebos 6
placental moles 278
planning experiments 5-7
Plantae 261
plant cells 31
plant defences 220, 221
plant dissection 201
plant tissues 153
    examination of 200
plasma cells 224
plasma membranes 31, 116
plasmodesmata 31, 203, 220
plasmolysis 127
polar molecules 51
polymers 54
polymorphism 246
polynucleotides 83-85
polypeptides 61
polysaccharides 55-57
positive controls 6
potassium ions 66
potato/tomato late blight 216
potometers 207
practical context questions 287
precision 5
predictions 1
pressure filtration 181
primary defences 219
primary immune response 228, 229
product inhibition 111
Prokaryotae 261
prokaryotic cells 30, 38
prophase 140, 144
prosthetic groups 108
proteins 61-65
    structure 62, 63
    test for 68
protein synthesis 88-93
Protoctista 216, 261
pulmonary artery 183-185
pulmonary vein 183, 185
purines 81

Purkyne tissue 187
pyrimidines 81

Q

Q$_{10}$ (temperature coefficient) 101, 102
qualitative data 17

R

random sampling 241
range 11
rate of diffusion 124
rates 20-22
ratios 13
receptors 122, 123
recording data 9
reducing sugars 69
repeatable results 5, 6, 25
reproducible results 5, 25
resolution 40, 42
respiratory system 154
R$_f$ values 75
rheumatoid arthritis 231
ribcage 163, 166
ribose 55, 81
ribosomes 32, 89, 92, 93
ring rot 216
ringworm 216
Rio Convention on Biological Diversity (CBD) 255
risk assessments 7
RNA (ribonucleic acid) 81, 88, 89
RNA polymerase 91
root hair cells 150, 160
rough endoplasmic reticulum (RER) 32, 36
routine vaccines 231
rRNA (ribosomal RNA) 89, 93

S

sample sizes 6
sampling 241
saponins 221
scanning electron microscopes (SEMs) 41
scattergrams 19
scientific journals 2
secondary immune response 228, 229
selection pressures 279

self-antigens 230
semi-conservative replication 86
semi-lunar valves 184, 185
serial dilutions 71
sexual reproduction 143-146
sieve tube elements
       199, 200, 211, 212
significant figures 14
Simpson's Index of Diversity
       243, 244
single circulatory systems 177
sinks (in translocation) 210, 211
sino-atrial node (SAN) 187
skin 219
smooth endoplasmic reticulum
       (SER) 32
smooth muscle (in the airways)
       164
sodium ions 66
soil depletion 252
sources (in translocation) 210
sources of medicines 235
Spearman's rank correlation
       coefficient 273-275
specialised cells 149, 150
species 260, 262
    diversity 240
    evenness 243
    richness 243
specific heat capacity 52
sperm cells 149
spindle fibres 140, 141, 144
spiracles 170
spirometers 167, 168
spores 217
squamous epithelia 152
stage micrometers 46
staining microscope samples 44
standard deviation 12, 271, 272
standard form 15
starch 56
    test for 69
statistical tests 16
stem cells 147, 148
    differentiation 147
    potential in medicine 148
stomata 204, 206
stop codons 93
stratified sampling 241
studies 3
sucrose 56
sugars 55
    test for 69, 70
superbugs 235

superkingdoms 265
surface area calculations 159
surface area : volume ratios 158
symplast pathway 203
synthetic biology 236
systematic sampling 241

T

tachycardia 189
tangents 21, 22, 106
target cells 122
taxonomic hierarchies 260
taxonomy 260
telophase 141, 144
temperature coefficient (Q_{10})
       101, 102
tension (in plant water transport)
       205
test strips (for glucose) 70
T helper cells 223
theories 1, 2
theory of evolution 279
three domains classification
       system 265
tidal volume (TV) 167
time management (in exams) 288
tissue fluid 181
tissues 152, 153
T killer cells 223
T lymphocytes 223
tobacco mosaic virus 216
tracheae (in insects) 170, 173
trachea (windpipe) 163, 164
tracheoles 170
transcription 88, 91
translation 88, 92, 93
translocation 210-212
transmission electron microscopes
       (TEMs) 41
transmission (disease) 217, 218
transpiration 204, 206-208
    estimating rate of 207
    factors affecting 206
transpiration stream 205
transport systems
    in animals 177
    in plants 198
T regulatory cells 223
triglycerides 58-60
triplets (of bases) 88, 90
tRNA (transfer RNA) 89, 92, 93
trypsin 97
tuberculosis (TB) 216

turgid cells 127

U

uncertainty (of measurements) 24
unspecialised cells 147

V

vaccination 231, 232
vaccination programmes 232
vacuoles 31
validity 5, 25
variable regions (antibodies) 226
variables 3, 5
variation 267-271, 273
    causes 268
vascular system (in plants) 198
vectors (in disease) 217
veins 180
vena cava 183, 185
ventilation
    in bony fish 170
    in insects 170
    in mammals 166
ventricles 183-185
venules 180
vesicles 33
viruses 216
vital capacity 167
volume calculations 159

W

Wallace, Alfred Russel 280
water 51-53
    transport in plants 203-205
water lilies 208
water potential 126-129
    investigating effect on
       animal cells 129
    investigating effect on
       plant cells 128, 129
wound repair 220

X

xerophytes 207, 208
xylem 148, 153, 198-201

Z

zinc ions 108
zygotes 143

BRATB52